# Histones
# and
# Other Nuclear Proteins

# HISTONES AND OTHER NUCLEAR PROTEINS

By

HARRIS BUSCH

DEPARTMENT OF PHARMACOLOGY
BAYLOR UNIVERSITY COLLEGE OF MEDICINE
HOUSTON, TEXAS

1965

ACADEMIC PRESS NEW YORK • LONDON

ACADEMIC PRESS INC.
111 Fifth Avenue, New York, New York 10003

*United Kingdom Edition published by*
ACADEMIC PRESS INC. (LONDON) LTD.
Berkeley Square House, London W.1

LIBRARY OF CONGRESS CATALOG CARD NUMBER: 65-15770

PRINTED IN THE UNITED STATES OF AMERICA.

*This book is affectionately dedicated to Rose.*

# Preface

The nucleus represents that organelle which contains the total genetic potential of the cell. In ways that are not yet clear, it must respond to extracellular changes and stimuli for cell specialization, including those for neoplastic transformation, in such a way that the cell successfully adapts to the new external and internal environment. In recent years, the remarkable advancements in molecular biology have been highlighted by the clarification of the primary role of DNA for biosynthesis of messenger-RNA and ribosomal-RNA of the polysomes. Now that the mechanisms of gene action have been clarified, important questions have been raised regarding the mechanisms of gene control. At present, varieties of substances with low and high molecular weights have been suggested as likely candidates for the functions of gene repressors and derepressors.

Recently, the histones and possibly other nuclear proteins have been implicated as gene repressors inasmuch as evidence has been obtained that they inhibit the activity of DNA as a primer for RNA synthesis. In addition, the histones have been reported to have a role in the maintenance of the coiled state of the deoxyribonucleoproteins.

In the first monograph on the histones by Kossel, relatively little was understood of their structure and function. The broad advances in this field have recently been highlighted in a World Conference on Nucleohistones. As will be evident to the reader, however, there is still a very great opportunity for research on the histones because satisfactory definition of the number, the types, and the functions of the histones is still to be achieved.

Although most attention of workers in the field of nuclear proteins has been centered on the histones, there are two other groups of nuclear proteins that are likely to be of great importance in the future. The first group is the acidic nuclear proteins, which have high rates of turnover and probably form the protein components of the ribosomes. Their function in the nucleus and their role in the cytoplasmic ribosomes await clarification. The second group is the nuclear enzymes, which constitute a subject of rapidly increasing interest. With the development of important techniques for the isolation of nuclei, a clearer picture is emerging as to which of these enzymes are limited in location to the nucleus and which are present both in the nucleus and cytoplasm.

The present volume was designed to be an introduction to the current status of research and knowledge in this field. The orientation has been to provide the student or research worker with a view of the subject that permits its ready comprehension and at the same time indicates the areas where new research is required. Because of the importance of the subject, it seems clear that rapid expansion in the study of the chemistry and function of nuclear proteins will take place within a few years.

*Houston, Texas* HARRIS BUSCH
*December, 1964*

# Acknowledgments

The author wishes to express his sincere appreciation for critical reading of the manuscript and most helpful suggestions to Dr. James Bonner, Professor of Biology, California Institute of Technology; Dr. J. Logan Irvin, Professor and Chairman of Biochemistry, University of North Carolina School of Medicine; Dr. Saul Kit, Professor and Head of Biochemical Virology, Baylor University College of Medicine; Dr. Geoffrey Zubay, Department of Biology, Brookhaven National Laboratory, Associated Universities, Inc.; Dr. Edward Bresnick, Assistant Professor of Pharmacology, Baylor University College of Medicine; Dr. Lubomir S. Hnilica, Assistant Biochemist, M. D. Anderson Hospital; Dr. Masami Muramatsu, Research Assistant Professor of Pharmacology, Baylor University College of Medicine; Dr. Arnold Schwartz, Assistant Professor of Pharmacology, Baylor University College of Medicine; Dr. Wesley C. Starbuck, Assistant Professor of Pharmacology, Baylor University College of Medicine; Dr. William J. Steele, Assistant Professor of Pharmacology, Baylor University College of Medicine; Dr. Raoul Desjardins, Post-doctoral Fellow in Pharmacology, Baylor University College of Medicine. I am also grateful to Dr. David Prescott, Professor and Chairman of Anatomy, University of Colorado, for helpful comments and to Dr. Gunther Siebert, Department of Physiological Chemistry, Johannes Gutenberg University, Mainz, for the opportunity to read his forthcoming review on nuclear enzymes.

The author wishes to acknowledge the aid of the following agencies which have made possible the original research of this laboratory that is presented in a number of sections of this volume: the U. S. Public Health Service, the American Cancer Society, the Jane Coffin Childs Fund, the Anna Fuller Fund, and the National Science Foundation.

The author would like to express his appreciation to the following for permission to reproduce figures and tables: Dr. James M. Neelin for Fig. 3-5; Dr. Edward Horn and the *Proceedings of the National Academy of Science* for Fig. 4-2; Dr. Arthur R. Sohval and the *American Journal of Medicine* for Fig. 4-3; Dr. Arthur Cole for Fig. 4-4; Dr. Dale Steffensen and the Brookhaven National Laboratories for Fig. 4-5; Dr. J. Herbert Taylor for Figs. 4-8a and 4-8b; Dr. G. Zubay and Holden-Day, Inc. for Figs. 4-10 and 4-11; Dr. James Bonner and the *Proceedings of the National Academy of Science* for Fig. 5-1; Dr. Vincent Allfrey and the National Academy of Sciences for Fig. 5-2; Dr. John Hindley for Fig. 5-3; Dr. David Bloch and the *Journal of Histochemistry and Cytochemistry* for Fig. 5-4; Dr. Maurice R. Hilleman and the Wistar Institute of Anatomy and Biology for Table 5-2; Dr. Wesley C. Starbuck and Mr. Charles W. Taylor for Figs. 6-4, 6-5, and 6-6; Dr. J. L. Sirlin for Fig. 7-1; Dr. David J. Holbrook for Fig. 7-5; Dr. Sam Sorof and Mr. Bohdan Bakay for Figs. 8-1 and 8-2; *Cancer Research* for Figs. 3-3, 4-1a, 5-5, 7-2, and 7-4; the *Journal of Biological Chemistry* for Figs. 2-2, 2-3, 3-1, and 3-2; and the Wistar Institute of Anatomy and Biology for Figs. 2-1, 6-1, and 6-2.

# Contents

# Introduction



## Classification of the Nuclear Proteins

The nuclear proteins are a complex group of proteins that may be classified in three groups: the basic nuclear proteins that include the protamines and the histones, the acidic nuclear proteins, and the nuclear enzymes. Evidence available at present shows that the histones are linked to deoxyribonucleic acid (DNA) in the chromatin of the interphase cell. The acidic proteins are distributed more widely throughout the nuclear components. The enzymes of the nucleus include those involved in biosynthesis of nucleic acids in most cells. In some nuclei, the enzymes present include a variety of hydrolytic enzymes and enzymes involved in glycolysis and oxidations. A simple classification of the nuclear proteins is presented in Table I.

Although much effort has been expended in the separation and identification of the nuclear proteins, the subject has become of great interest recently as investigations have been made on the mechanism of gene control. Recent evidence has shown that the nuclear enzymes DNA polymerase and ribonucleic acid (RNA) polymerase play key roles in the "duplicase" and the "transcriptase" activities of the cell.

TABLE I

CLASSIFICATION OF THE NUCLEAR PROTEINS

| Classification | |
|---|---|
| Basic nuclear proteins | |
| Protamines | |
| Histones | |
| Very lysine-rich histones | Lysine-rich histones |
| Slightly lysine-rich histones | Lysine-rich histones |
| *N*-Proline histone (of fraction 2b) | |
| *N*-Acetylalanine histone (of fraction 2a) | |
| "Arginine-rich" histones | |
| Acidic nuclear proteins | |
| Proteins of the nuclear sap | |
| "Soluble" proteins | |
| Ribosomal proteins | |
| Nuclear globulins | |
| Acidic proteins of the chromatin | |
| Acidic nucleolar proteins | |
| Glutamic acid-rich nuclear proteins | |
| Nuclear enzymes | |
| Enzymes of nucleic acid synthesis | |
| DNA polymerase | |
| RNA polymerase | |
| Glycolytic enzymes | |
| Oxidative enzymes | |
| Hydrolytic enzymes | |
| Enzymes of protein synthesis | |

Moreover, evidence has been presented that histones may serve as repressors of both these enzymatically catalyzed reaction sequences. Since the mechanisms of gene control are of such general interest, this subject will be considered first.

## The Role of Proteins in Control of the Genome

***The Biological Clock.*** The present time in the history of biochemistry is characterized by a great wave of progress in the comprehension of the function of the nucleic acids and their importance to the field of biochemical genetics. The rate of progress is sufficiently great that a number of splinter sciences have developed, such as "molecular biology" and "biochemical genetics." In bacteria and in viruses, the genome appears to be localized to single chromosomes composed largely of deoxyribonucleic acid or ribonucleic acid that functions in such a way that much of the total genetic potential of the genome becomes expressed. At least in viruses, expression of genetic potential is not simultaneous, but rather it is timed so that a sequence of events occurs. Thus, some of the genes function early and others function later in the life cycle of the organism. The controls are delicately balanced so as to provide for the needs of the organism in its maturation and replication. The requirements for function and reproduction occur in a logical and well-timed sequence, and the term "biological clock" has been applied to the progressive turning on and off of events in and by the genome (12, 40).

Another aspect of control of the genome involves the different extents of expression of particular genes. Ohtaka and Spiegelman (62) have pointed out that the cistron coding for coat proteins in viruses may be 1500 times as active as the cistron that codes for synthesis of other kinds of proteins. The mechanism for the differential rates of synthesis may be either that many more cistrons code for coat proteins, that the other cistrons are 1500 times more suppressed, or that one cistron is read frequently. The latter possibility would appear to be more likely from the point of view of genome efficiency.

At the present time, the mechanism of the biological clock is not clear. Why does the genome function in an ordered sequence? It has been assumed that there is continuity of the DNA throughout the bacterial or viral chromosome, and it is difficult to perceive a mechanism whereby DNA itself could block the function of either adjacent or distant DNA. Hence, any biochemical mechanism that would be invoked necessarily involves other substances. It is well known that the DNA "codes" for RNA and that RNA "codes" for proteins. Conceivably, then, a functional segment of the genome might code for both RNA and protein that represent its cellularly useful products, and also RNA or protein repressors that would serve to repress other genomic loci (39).

*Specialization of Mammalian Cells.* In mammalian cells, the relationships between the nucleic acids and the remainder of the cell are much more complex than in microorganisms. Most mammalian cells have more than twenty chromosomes, and man has 46 in each somatic cell. There is evidence from studies on many types of nuclear activities, such as nucleolar functions (14), that several or many chromosomes are functioning simultaneously to produce similar products. Mammalian cells are multipotential in terms of their specialization, and, as a result, there are many varieties of cells in animals. These vary in secretory, electrical, contractile, supportive, and metabolic activities and also differ very much in size and in shape. For example, there is a wide variety of cells in the central nervous system that have remarkably different structures and function despite the fact that they have the same genome.

*Structure of Mammalian Cell Nuclei.* Mammalian cells have structural features related to the genome that differ from those of microorganisms. They have a refractile nuclear membrane with a highly ordered structure (90) that separates the deoxyribonucleoprotein from the remainder of the cell. In addition, nuclei of mammalian cells contain one or more nucleoli that are rich in ribonucleoproteins. Among the proteins of nuclei of mammalian cells are the histones, a group of basic proteins that are either absent from bacterial cells or present in very small amounts. In addition to the histones, there are at least two groups of acidic nuclear proteins and a number of special enzymes for biosynthesis of nucleic acids. The nuclei of some cells are apparently capable of oxidative, glycolytic, and a variety of hydrolytic reactions, as well as biosynthesis of proteins (see Chapter IX).

## Repressor Substances

*RNA.* In the specialized cells of mammalian species many types of functions that would be permitted by the genome are obviously suppressed. In such cells, the two major functional units may be limited to two groups of operons or polyoperons, i.e., one fundamental to cell physiology which provides for basic cellular metabolism and the other which provides for phenotypic specification of the specialized cell function. The mechanism(s) of repression of other operon groups is of great importance to biochemists interested in function of mammalian cells. At present there is no clear evidence that would permit one to do more than suggest possible mechanisms of repression in mammalian systems. The suggestions that have been made are (i) RNA controls gene expression (39); (ii) histones or other proteins control gene expression (78); or (iii) molecules of low molecular weight may be involved. Although there is little evidence that RNA is a means of gene control, Yanagisawa (94) showed that in bacterial systems there was an accumulation of RNA along with the accumulation of repressor substances. Such a finding would be more meaningful if the RNA that accumulated could be demonstrated to have repressor activity. In addition, there is little if any histone in bacteria (see pages 12, 54).

One report that suggests a relationship of proteins to the biological clock in viruses is that of Ebisuzaki (29), who found that late synthesis of structural proteins by phage was inhibited when there was defective formation of the "early" proteins. The defects in these proteins were introduced by addition of either 7-azatryptophan, 5 methyltryptophan, or *p*-fluorophenylalanine to the medium. 5-Fluorodeoxyuridine inhibited the synthesis of the normal phage but did not prevent the appearance of the structural proteins. These results were interpreted as suggesting that the timing mechanism is inhibited when synthesis of normal "early" proteins is blocked.[1]

In the mammalian nucleus, a possible role of RNA in suppression of the activity of DNA would be difficult to visualize at the moment. Conceivably, the types of hybrids described by Spiegelman and his colleagues (77) would be formed, and these would be decomposed into the DNA and RNA strands when appropriate competitors for the DNA template were introduced into the system. However, there is relatively little RNA associated with the nucleoproteins of mammalian cells, i.e., less than 20% of the dry weight of the nucleoproteins is composed of RNA. Included in this RNA is a significant amount of the rapidly turning over RNA, some of which is messenger-RNA. It is difficult to visualize that this small amount of RNA serves as a gene suppressor, but one cannot rule out the possibility that RNA exerts a role in the suppression of the genome solely on the basis of the quantity of RNA present in the chromatin.

*The Nuclear Proteins.* On the other hand, there is such a very large amount of protein in the deoxyribonucleoprotein complex that the protein comprises 60–70% of the dry weight of the chromatin. On the basis of virtual equality of weight of histone to DNA, histones would seem to be a candidate for control of gene function. In nucleohistones, the purified derivative of chromatin that contains largely DNA and histone, there is approximately an equal amount of DNA and histone. The results reported by Bonner and his colleagues (10, 38) and later results of Allfrey *et al.* (1) have supported the concept

[1] Recently, Gallant and Stapleton (34b) have reported that a repressor of alkaline phosphatase synthesis in *E. coli* is a protein rich in arginine.

that histones are regulators of gene function by demonstrating that DNA-primed RNA synthesis could be partially to completely suppressed by addition of histones to the appropriate cell-free systems. This evidence, coupled with studies on the biosynthesis of histones by means of radioactive tracers, has provided support for a possible role of nuclear proteins in regulation of the genome.

As might be anticipated in cell reproduction, a high rate of biosynthesis of histones has been demonstrated in dividing cells such as neoplastic cells and those of the regenerating liver. On the other hand, there is a slow, *but definite,* turnover of histones in cells in which virtually no synthesis of DNA occurs (15, 17, 35). Along with the *in vitro* studies, such findings suggest that histones could exert a suppressive role in DNA function. If so, there would be a degree of flexibility in the system to provide for environmental adaptability of the cells. For example, partial hepatectomy seems to derepress the operon groups or polyoperons for cell growth and cell division in adult liver cells. The fact that only liver cells are produced as a result of hepatectomy indicates a persistent restriction on the totipotency of these dividing cells.

The acidic nuclear proteins, on the other hand, seem to be more closely associated with ribonucleic acids than with DNA. In each of the ribonucleic acid components of the nucleus, such as the nucleolus, nuclear ribosomes, and the ribonucleoprotein of the chromatin that was extracted with 1 *M* NaCl, there was a high concentration of these acidic proteins. Recently, a glutamic acid-rich protein fraction was found in histone preparations; this fraction possibly represents a strongly acidic soluble nuclear protein fraction (see page 53).

*Special Cases of Nuclear Function.* If the nuclear proteins were to function as controls for gene action they would be expected to vary in different types of cells, and a lack of variation has been found (16, 25–27, 35, 65). The most extreme case occurs in certain cells in which the genome is apparently totally nonfunctional. In the chicken erythrocyte, the cell is nucleated but no longer has the capacity for division. This nucleus, which may contain a special histone, is apparently nonfunctional according to Cameron and Prescott (20), who showed that the mature nucleated red cells neither incorporated labeled pyrimidines into RNA nor incorporated labeled amino acids into protein. Another totally nonfunctional nucleus is in a virus-infected fibroblast, in which a basic protein produced by Mengo virus (34a) totally shuts off the function of the genome of the infected cell.

In some lower species the histones vary with stages of development and cell specialization (8, 9). In the mature sperm, in which the genome is apparently totally repressed, the protamines replace the histones as the basic proteins linked to DNA.

Markert and Ursprung (52, 85) have reported that both histones and albumin fractions caused a cessation of cell division and arrest of development of the embryo in the late blastula stage. They injected a variety of proteins into nuclei of frog eggs. Transplanted nuclei from arrested blastula did not recover, as indicated by their failure to support embryonic growth beyond the late blastula stage after they were transplanted into new ova. The suggestion is that this inability to promote differentiation is a manifestation of a chromosomal change, particularly in view of the production of abnormal chromosomes.

The possible relationships of histones and other repressors to carcinogenesis have been reviewed (13). Although specific evidence that neoplasia results from a derepression of a "cancer operon group" has not been obtained, this possibility would eliminate the necessity for either mutational alteration of DNA or lysogeny of the genome by viral components. It remains to be established whether this "permanent derepression" occurs without a mutation.

In summary, various types of evidence suggest that the nuclear proteins may be important in some circumstances in control of the genome in mammalian and plant cells. Definitive experiments to establish this point have not yet been reported, and the arguments presented thus far are largely inferential (see Chapter V). Before conclusive experiments can be performed, nuclear proteins and specifically controlled genetic systems must be isolated in highly purified states.

## History of the Nuclear Proteins

*The Protamines.* Miescher reported his findings on "nucleins" in 1869 (55). He had originally studied cells in pus and had found a protein-containing nuclear fraction that had a high concentration of phosphorus. This phosphorus-rich protein fraction was derived from the nuclei of the cells and hence was referred to as "nuclein." However, this fraction was found to have two parts: the nucleic acid fraction and the protein fraction. Because of the limitations of studies on pus, Miescher turned to the study of sperm of the Rhine salmon; these sperm had the biochemical advantage of being very rich in nucleic acids and in the special proteins that he named "protamines."

The Rhine salmon has a very interesting natural history. Like the

Alaska and Columbia river salmon, Rhine salmon are born in fresh water, far upstream and hundreds of miles from the ocean. They enter the ocean, where they feed and mature for periods of two to three years. At the end of this period the salmon move back to fresh water, where they reproduce. When the Rhine salmon moves upstream it weighs approximately 10 kg, and the weight of the testes is less than 1% of the body weight. After the male salmon has been in the Rhine for 5–15 months, its testes are "ripe" and have increased to almost 6% of the body weight. Since the fish does not consume any food during this entire period of sexual maturation, the increase in testicular mass must come from other body substance. Kossel (47) found that the protein content of the fish muscle dropped from 18 to 13%, and he suggested that the protein in the testis was derived largely from the muscle mass. These fish are composed largely of muscle, i.e., about 68% of the body weight is muscle; hence, there could hardly be any other source of the protein. The loss of protein in the male fish approximates 20–30% of the muscle mass; in the female the loss of protein approximates 55% of the body weight. The protein products of the female fish are not so clearly established as in the male, in which both nucleic acids and protamines are produced in the course of maturation of the testes (see page 27).

At least the Rhine salmon can survive this remarkable attrition that is associated with sexual maturation. In the Columbia River, the Chinook salmon loses much more weight, possibly because of the enormously long run it must make, which in the aggregate totals 700–1000 miles. After this salmon has spawned, it dies. The Rhine salmon survives several spawning periods.

*Composition of Spermatozoa.* Sperm heads were studied by Kossel (46, 47) and later workers (32, 33) after a method had been developed for their purification from testis extracts by means of treatment with distilled water. Felix *et al.* (32, 33) calculated that a single sperm nucleus contained approximately 7 picograms (pg) of DNA. On the basis of molecular volume of the nucleoprotamine and the volume of 7 $\mu^3$ of the sperm nucleus, they calculated that the maximum number of molecules of nucleoprotamine that could be present was $4.7 \times 10^6$. This was essentially the same as the value derived from the chemical determination. Felix *et al.* (32, 33) concluded that the molecules of nucleoprotamine in a fish sperm must lie together in a packed three-dimensional semicrystalline structure. X-ray studies confirmed this impression. On the basis of X-ray diffraction patterns, Wilkins and his colleagues (34, 92, 93) suggested that the protamines are specifically linked to DNA across the small groove of the double helix of the DNA. This regular arrangement of protamines with respect to DNA differs considerably from that of the histones (see Chapter IV).

Miescher (55) suggested that the protamines, the basic part of the "nuclein," functioned to neutralize the phosphoric acid groups of the nucleic acid. He also suggested that protamine was a simple organic base. Two groups of studies established that the protamines were in reality a group of small proteins, namely, the experiments of Kossel (46, 47) and the supporting experiments of Waldschmidt-Leitz (86–89). Kossel developed a series of methods, in collaboration with Kutscher (48), for the quantitative isolation of arginine, histidine, and lysine. These methods, based upon selective precipitation of silver and barium salts of the basic amino acids as well as formation of specific derivatives, such as the flavianate of arginine, and the picrolonate of histidine, provided a highly accurate determination of the concentration of the basic amino acids in the protamines.

*Structure of the Protamines.* The development of methods for the determination of the basic amino acids in proteins enabled Kossel and his colleagues (46–48) to establish that the protamines were the most "arginine-rich" proteins. In some of the protamines, arginine accounts for more than 80% of the total amino acid residues in the peptide chain (Chapter I). Their studies and those of Waldschmidt-Leitz *et al.* (86–89) established that the protamines were simple proteins, composed only of amino acids. Later studies showed that the molecular weight of these proteins was small, approximating 4000–12,000 (19, 32), and that proline was the $NH_2$-terminal amino acid (33, 53). Structural studies on the protamines have employed conventional analytical procedures (30, 31, 67, 68), but thus far a satisfactory structure has not been presented (4, 5, 33).

*The Function of the Protamines.* It has been assumed that protamines function as a binding material for DNA so that it would be kept both compact and stable in the sperm. Although protamine has been assumed to be the main co-constituent of DNA in sperm of various species (7), recently other proteins have been found in bovine sperm (11). Protamines have been used commercially because of their ability to combine with other proteins, particularly insulin. Moreover, protamines have been used to protect nucleic acids and viruses in experiments on uptake of labeled nucleic acids and viruses in tissue culture (3, 51, 54, 75, 76, 91).

## The Histones

In 1884, Kossel (47) undertook a series of studies on goose blood. He gave no explanation for initiation of studies on fowl, but presumably he selected the goose because it was readily available. It was quite simple to obtain satisfactory nuclear preparations from fowl blood. The red cells were placed in water and the cell membranes were ruptured to leave behind an insoluble mass of nuclei. The nuclei were placed in dilute hydrochloric acid, and all the histones were dissolved as the hydrochlorides. To purify the histones it was necessary only to salt out the hydrochlorides with NaCl, dialyze the preparation against water to solubilize the histones, and then precipitate the proteins with alcohol. Treatment of an aqueous solution of the histones with ammonia resulted in precipitation of a protein mass that was no longer readily soluble since it was, in part, denatured. Kossel suggested that 58% of the nucleus of the erythrocytes was composed of protein and that 42% was composed of nucleic acids; these values are not dissimilar to those recently reported (81) (see Chapter III). There were no other nitrogen-containing substances of significance in these nuclei.

The name "histone," the origin of which is not available, suggests that Kossel regarded these proteins as tissue components (hist-) that were partial breakdown products analogous to the peptones (-ones).

***Composition of the Histones.*** From studies carried out in the period 1884–1910, Kossel (47) concluded that the histones were more complex than protamines and were also larger molecules. He put forward the general concept that the histones were a stage more complex than the protamines, and he gave the impression that protamines form a "core" of the histones. The high isoelectric point of the histones and their ability to combine with acids suggested that they were probably basic substances similar to the protamines. Since the protamines contained so much arginine, it was not surprising that an early search was made for this amino acid in the histones. Based upon nitrogen content, the amount of arginine was high: arginine contained about 19–30% of the total nitrogen in Kossel's histones. This finding led him to the conclusion that these proteins were relatively rich in arginine, despite the fact that, in his histones, arginine averaged only 8–10% of the total amino acid residues. This value is markedly lower than that obtained for the protamines, yet the concept existed for years that the histones were "arginine-rich" (16). Certainly, the high content of arginine is not a major characteristic of the histones as compared to their content of lysine and alanine.

Kossel (47) was aware that the histones were a complex of proteins. For example, some of the histones were precipitated from solution by the addition of ammonia to the dialyzed preparation. On the other hand, others were not, and on the basis of solubility alone it was possible to divide the histones into two categories. Among their differences from the protamines was the fact that they were hydrolyzed by pepsin with the formation of "peptones," polypeptides of a higher molecular weight. Moreover, they were precipitated from neutral or feebly alkaline solutions by alkaloidal reagents. In addition, the histones contained all the amino acids, including tyrosine, phenylalanine, and glutamic acid.

***Localization of the Histones.*** Kossel (47) made the point that the histones were always found in combination with nucleic acids and hence were one type of protein constituent of the nucleoproteins. Histones were prepared from a variety of species of fish, including the cod, from frogs, and later from calf thymus. In the fish, histones were obtained from the unripe gonads whereas protamines were obtained from the ripe testes. In the various species, there were varying concentrations of the basic amino acids in the histones. The values for the lysine contents in the histones of the species studied ranged from 4 to 17%. As in the case of the protamines, there were similarities in the products obtained from a single species, but there were marked differences when the products of different species were compared. Kossel (47) was aware of the probability that there were variations in the contaminants as well as in the histones themselves, and his conclusions regarding the types and the number of histones were very limited.

One of the points of some interest that was approached at about the time that Kossel was developing information on the nucleohistones was that these proteins might be parts of some cytoplasmic or extracellular proteins. In particular, globin was thought to be a histone (6) because of the fact that 10.3% of the total amino acid residues were arginine residues, 7% were histidine residues, and 4.9% were lysine residues. The high histidine content is one of the main features of the globins. Like the histones, the globins were precipitated by alkaloidal reagents at neutral pH and they were also readily precipitated by nitric acid and potassium ferrocyanide. Although the histones were reported to be very toxic on injection intravenously into animals, the globins were not toxic at all.

*Thymus Histones.* Lilienfeld (50) was the first to isolate nucleohistones and histones from calf thymus. The isolation of these products represented an important advance in the field of histone chemistry because it made possible studies on histones from mammalian species on a regular basis, since calves are slaughtered routinely and many pounds of thymus can be obtained. Thymocytes are cells that have a very large ratio of nucleus to cytoplasm in volume or in diameter, and the yield of histones is high. The initial procedure employed by Lilienfeld was simple (50): the aqueous extract of the thymus was treated with dilute acetic acid until a precipitate had formed. The "nucleohistone" was separated by centrifugation or by filtration and was treated again with dilute acetic acid to remove contaminants. To extract the histones, either HCl or $H_2SO_4$ was added. Lilienfeld (50) objected to the use of ammonia for purification of the histones since denatured and insoluble histones were reported to result from this treatment. Even the use of aqueous solutions of ethanol was regarded as damaging to the products formed by these isolation procedures. The product obtained contained virtually all the amino acids, was precipitated by alkaloids, and had an alkaline isoelectric point, i.e., about 8.5. Evidence was provided that the product contained considerable arginine and was probably composed mainly of the "arginine-rich" histones. This term is still used although most current studies agree that the concentration of arginine is only about 12–14% of the total amino acid residues in the "arginine-rich" histones. Later, Cruft *et al.* (26, 27) made extensive studies on the electrophoretic behavior, solubility, and other physical characteristics of these proteins.

*Other Sources of Histones.* It is generally assumed that histones are widely distributed in nature (65), and on the basis of histochemical evidence histones have been reported in many plant and animal tissues (38a, 46, 47, 69). Conflicting evidence has been reported regarding the presence of histones in bacteria (24, 64, 95). In many of these studies, the proteins have not been isolated in sufficient quantity to provide adequate analytical information regarding the amino acid composition or other characteristics (see Chapter II).

It is noteworthy that cellular fractions other than the nucleus contain basic proteins. Many experiments (63, 84) have shown that cytochrome c is an extremely basic protein with an isoelectric point of pH

10.5. Approximately 20% of the total amino acid residues of this protein are lysine residues. Recently, the entire structure of cytochrome c was elucidated. The globins are also basic proteins (6). Proteins have been found in microsomal preparations that are basic[2] electrophoretically and in greater number than the histones (18, 21, 69). Studies on the amino acid composition of such proteins have shown that the ratio of basic to acidic proteins was approximately 1 and that the $NH_2$ terminal amino acids were similar in type to those of the histones (21). The amount of these proteins is small compared to the total acid-insoluble microsomal proteins (18).

*The Lysine-Rich Histones.* These were described long after the initial studies were made on the histones. In 1928, Kossel and Schenk (49) described a protamine from the carp in which lysine accounted for about 25% of the total amino acids. However, until the studies of Daly and Mirsky (28) there was little evidence that there were lysine-rich components in mammalian histones. Daly and Mirsky extracted calf thymus, liver, and turtle red cells with $H_2SO_4$ and precipitated the "arginine-rich" histones at pH 10.6. The supernatant solution, that had previously been discarded by Kossel and later workers, was reexamined by Daly and Mirsky (28) and was found to contain 35.9 gm of lysine per 100 gm of protein. The fraction obtained by precipitation with ammonia contained 12.7 gm of lysine and 15.1 gm of arginine per 100 gm of protein. Thus, lysine comprised 11.5 and 33.7% of the amino acid residues in the "arginine-rich" and lysine-rich fractions, respectively. In their "arginine-rich" fraction, arginine comprised only 11.3% of the total amino acid residues. The lysine-rich fraction was interesting because it contained *no* histidine or cystine. Previously, Mirsky and Pollister (56, 57) had pointed out that there was no tryptophan in the histones.

One of the important aspects of the study of Daly and Mirsky (28) on the lysine-rich histones was their suggestion that the histones were a heterogeneous mixture of various basic proteins. They suggested that proteins with intermediate concentrations of lysine and arginine would be found and expressed the belief that they had found a number of "arginine-rich" histones.

The *slightly lysine-rich* histones have been the subject of a number of recent publications and discussions. In view of the fact that products obtained could simply be mixtures of the lysine-rich and "arginine-

---

[2] Among other basic proteins are ribonucleases, lysozymes, interferons (p. 143), portions of the globulins, and some mucoproteins (p. 96).

rich" histones in varying proportions, it was difficult to provide clear-cut evidence for the existence of these proteins. For example, in 1955 Crampton *et al.* (22, 23) obtained evidence for an intermediate fraction by chromatographic separation of the proteins. Cruft *et al.* (25) presented similar evidence in 1957, based on electrophoretic fractionation of the histones. However, in neither case was the possibility of formation of mixtures ruled out. Cruft *et al.* (27) showed the existence of several γ-histones, or slightly lysine-rich histones, of which one was referred to as a 1.6 S γ-histone. In this protein, lysine and arginine, respectively, accounted for 11 and 9% of the total moles of amino acids.

The utilization of modified extraction methods, salt precipitations, and gel electrophoresis enabled Johns and his colleagues (41–43) to develop reasonable evidence for the existence of two fractions that could be included in the category of the "slightly lysine-rich" histones. In these two fractions, referred to as fractions 2a and 2b, lysine accounted for 11.4 and 15.8% of the total amino acid residues.

## The Acidic Nuclear Proteins

The general impression seems to have existed up to 1944 that histones constituted most, if not all, of the nuclear proteins. This concept arose in part from the early findings of Felix and others on the virtual equality of the mass of the sperm head with the mass of the nucleoprotamines present (32, 33). However, in 1944, Stedman and Stedman (79) reported that, after extraction of nuclei with acid, another protein fraction could be obtained that was soluble in dilute NaOH. They named the alkali-soluble fraction "chromosomin" and reported that it contained acidic and basic amino acids as well as tryptophan (80). Initially they reported that this fraction comprised approximately 60–70% of the total nuclear mass; and further, they suggested, in 1944, that "chromosomin" was the chief agent of genetic transmission.

Actually, previous workers were not completely unaware of the existence of proteins that were not histones in the nucleus of such tissues as thymus. In 1893, Lilienfeld (50) noted that there were proteins in the thymocytes that were not extracted with acids. Lilienfeld showed that the nucleoproteins could be subdivided as shown in the scheme on the opposite page. The extraction with alcoholic base removed the nucleic acid from the protein that later was discovered by Stedman and Stedman (79) or perhaps more specifically by Mirsky and Pollister (56, 57). However, the early workers were cautious in their conclusions regarding the acidic nuclear proteins, possibly because of their crude and impure nuclear preparations.

LILIENFELD'S EXTRACTION PROCEDURE

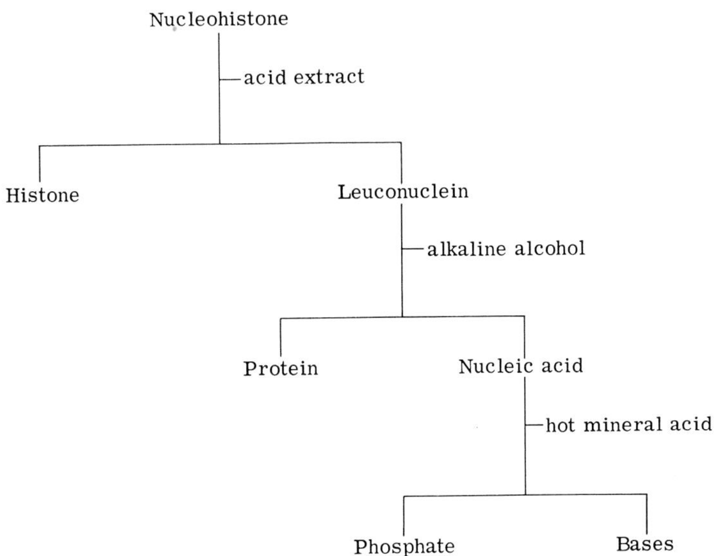


The peculiar designation, "Tr.Pr.," or "tryptophan protein," was applied to the protein residue of the chromatin extracted from nuclei with 2 *M* NaCl (66) and subsequently treated with HCl to remove the histones (55, 56). Mirsky and his associates referred to the nuclear chromatin extracted with 2 *M* NaCl by the interesting name "chromosin." This name was rather confusing, since it appeared at about the same time as the term "chromosomin" coined by the Stedmans. However, Mirsky and Pollister (56, 57) believed that "chromosin" contained all the chromosomes, and on treating the mass extracted with 2 *M* NaCl by blending, Mirsky and Ris (58–61) isolated structures suggested to be interphase chromosomes.

Tr.Pr., or the "residual protein," was reported to comprise only about 8–10% of the chromosomal mass. Its content of tryptophan was actually quite low, about 1.36% of the total amino acid residues. However, a most important role was assigned to this protein by Mirsky and Ris (58–61), namely, the formation of the elementary or basic structure of the chromosome. This role has not been confirmed, but on the other hand, there is still no clear evidence against this role for these proteins.

It is only recently that endeavors have been made to characterize these proteins in definitive chemical terms (see Chapter VIII) with regard to amino acid composition or to $NH_2$-terminal amino acids (81). At present, it would appear that there are a number of these acidic nuclear proteins and that they are distributed in a number of sites in the nucleus and cytoplasm.

## Enzymes of the Nucleus

The wave of interest in enzymes that began in the early 1930's included intensive studies on the glycolytic enzymes and substrates. Logically, these studies were extended to the nucleus by Hogeboom and Schneider (36, 37), Allfrey *et al.* (2), and Siebert *et al.* (70–72). There is now general agreement that some enzymes of glycolysis are present in the nucleus, and in the opinion of some (70–72) the evidence is virtually conclusive for the existence of all glycolytic enzymes and substrates in the nucleus.

One important question relates to the role of these enzymes in the nucleus. So far as is known, the cytoplasm of many cells possesses enormous potential not only for glycolysis, but also for oxidation of substrates of both glycolysis and of the citric acid cycle. There are, of course, some variations in cells, and those of the thymus are quite peculiar in their very large nuclear mass as compared to their cytoplasmic mass. Presumably in these cells, the nucleus would have to have its own energy supply. In cells such as those of the liver, where there is an enormous concentration of mitochondria in the cytoplasm, a nuclear requirement for energy could presumably be readily met by the oxidative activity of the cytoplasm. Beginning with the studies of Stern *et al.* (82, 83) and Allfrey *et al.* (1) and those of Siebert and his colleagues (70–72), there has been a convincing demonstration that there are nuclear enzymes that possess the capacities for glycolytic activity. Whether, in fact, *in vivo* these enzymes have activities commensurate with these capacities is not at all clear. There is little evidence that intracellularly the nuclei carry out oxidative reactions or that they have an active glycolysis. While there is no evidence that glycolytic or oxidative enzymes are concentrated in the nucleus, there is conclusive evidence that the glycolytic and oxidative enzymes are concentrated in cytoplasmic structures of many cells. Such findings, however, do not establish whether the nuclear enzymes of glycolysis and oxidation are important to the function of the nucleus in most cells.

One enzyme that was definitely shown to be localized to the nucleus is the enzyme diphosphopyridine nucleotide (DPN) synthetase (36). If there is little glycolytic or oxidative activity in the nucleus, this enzyme would be of little use to the nucleus since it catalyzes the synthesis of DPN and/or its reduction product, DPNH, from nicotinamide mononucleotide and adenosine triphosphate (ATP) for reactions that occur in the course of glycolysis and oxidations. In any event, the largest requirement for DPN as a cofactor occurs in the cytoplasm. On this account, Hogeboom and Schneider (36, 37) suggested that it might be through the activity of this enzyme that the nucleus exerts some control on the oxidative activity of the cell.

The one biochemical phenomenon that has been established with certainty as a nucleus-specific function is the biosynthesis of nucleoprotein, including the biosynthesis of RNA, DNA, and the histones. When the initial studies were made on the intracellular localization of DNA polymerase or DNA-nucleotidyl transferase, there was considerable surprise at the reports that this enzyme was present primarily, if not exclusively, in the cytoplasm of regenerating liver cells (44, 45, 73, 74). The localization and the number of types of this enzyme intracellularly are not yet completely clear, but present evidence indicates that the initial conclusions on localization in the cytoplasm were made on the basis of the technique of isolation of nuclei in aqueous media, which perhaps leached out the nuclear enzyme. Many nuclear enzymes are readily soluble in the aqueous media and are leached out in the course of procedures for isolation of nuclei. This subject, which is one of great importance to the study of the nuclear proteins, will be considered in Chapter III. At present, there is little doubt that synthesis of RNA is exclusively a nuclear function; the same appears to be true for the synthesis of the histones.

## References


1. Allfrey, V. G., Littau, V. C., and Mirsky, A. E.: On the role of histones in regulating ribonucleic acid synthesis in the cell nucleus. *Proc. Natl. Acad. Sci. U.S.* **49**: 414-421 (1963).
2. Allfrey, V. G., Mirsky, A. E., and Stern, H.: The chemistry of the cell nucleus. *Advan. Enzymol.* **16**: 411-500 (1955).
3. Amos, H., and Kearns, K. E.: Influence of bacterial ribonucleic acid on animal cells in culture. II. Protamine enhancement of RNA uptake. *Exptl. Cell Res.* **32**: 14-25 (1963).

4. Ando, T., Ishii, S., and Yamasaki, M.: Peptides obtained by tryptic digestion of clupeine. *Biochim. Biophys. Acta* **34**: 600-601 (1959).
5. Ando, T., Iwai, K., Yamasaki, M., Hashimoto, C., Kimura, M., Ishii, S., and Tamura, T.: Protamines. *Bull. Chem. Soc. Japan* **26**: 406-407 (1953).
6. Bang, I.: Studies on histones. *Z. Physiol. Chem.* **27**: 463-486 (1899).
7. Berry, R. E., and Mayer, D. T.: The histone-like basic protein of bovine spermatozoa. *Exptl. Cell Res.* **20**: 116-126 (1960).
8. Bloch, D. P.: On the derivation of histone specificity. *Proc. Natl. Acad. Sci. U.S.* **48**: 324-326 (1962).
9. Bloch, D. P.: Synthetic processes in the cell nucleus. I. Histone synthesis in non-replicating chromosomes. *J. Histochem. Cytochem.* **10**: 137-143 (1962).
10. Bonner, J., and Huang, R. C.: Properties of chromosomal nucleohistone. *J. Mol. Biol.* **6**: 169-174 (1963).
11. Bril-Petersen, E., and Westenbrink, H. G. K.: A structural basic protein as a counterpart of deoxyribonucleic acid in mammalian spermatozoa. *Biochim. Biophys. Acta* **76**: 152-154 (1963).
12. Bunning, E.: Biological clocks. *Cold Spring Harbor Symp. Quant. Biol.* **25**: 1-9 (1960).
13. Busch, H.: "An Introduction to the Biochemistry of the Cancer Cell." Academic Press, New York, 1962.
14. Busch, H., Byvoet, P., and Smetana, K.: The nucleolus of the cancer cell: A review. *Cancer Res.* **23**: 313-339 (1963).
15. Busch, H., Davis, J. R., and Anderson, D. C.: Labeling of histones and other nuclear proteins with L-lysine-U-$C^{14}$ in tissues of tumor-bearing rats. *Cancer Res.* **18**: 916-926 (1958).
16. Busch, H., and Davis, J. R.: Nuclear proteins of tumors and other tissues. *Cancer Res.* **19**: 1241-1256 (1958).
17. Busch, H., Davis, J. R., Honig, G. R., Anderson, D. C., Nair, P. V., and Nyhan, W. L.: The uptake of a variety of amino acids into nuclear proteins of tumor and other tissues. *Cancer Res.* **19**: 1030-1039 (1959).
18. Busch, H., and Steele, W. J.: Nuclear proteins of neoplastic cells. *Advan. Cancer Res.* **8**: 41-120 (1964).
19. Callanan, M. J., Carroll, W. R., and Mitchell, E. R.: Physical and chemical properties of protamine from the sperm of salmon (*Oncorhynchus tschawytacha*). I. Preparation and characterization. *J. Biol. Chem.* **229**: 279-287 (1957).
20. Cameron, I. L., and Prescott, D. M.: RNA and protein metabolism in the maturation of the nucleated chick erythrocyte. *Exptl. Cell Res.* **30**: 609-612 (1963).
21. Cohn, P., and Simson, P.: Basic and other proteins in microsomes of rat liver. *Biochem. J.* **88**: 206-212 (1963).
22. Crampton, C. F., Moore, S., and Stein, W. H.: Chromatographic fractionation of calf thymus histones. *J. Biol. Chem.* **215**: 787-801 (1955).
23. Crampton, C. F., Stein, W. H., and Moore, S.: Comparative studies on chromatographically purified histones. *J. Biol. Chem.* **225**: 363-386 (1957).
24. Cruft, H. J., and Leaver, J. L.: Isolation of histones from *Staphylococcus aureus*. *Nature* **192**: 556-557 (1961).

25. Cruft, H. J., Mauritzen, C. M., and Stedman, E.: The nature and physicochemical properties of histones. *Phil. Trans. Roy. Soc. London* **B241**: 93-145 (1957).
26. Cruft, H. J., Mauritzen, C. M., and Stedman, E.: The isolation of β-histone from calf thymocytes and the factors affecting its aggregation. *Proc. Roy. Soc.* **B149**: 21-41 (1958).
27. Cruft, H. J., Mauritzen, C. M., and Stedman, E.: The isolation and properties of 1.6 S γ-histone from calf thymocytes. *Proc. Roy. Soc.* **B149**: 36-41 (1958).
28. Daly, M. M., and Mirsky, A. E.: Histones with high lysine content. *J. Gen. Physiol.* **38**: 405-413 (1954-1955).
29. Ebisuzaki, K.: On the regulation of the morphogenesis of bacteriophage T4. *J. Mol. Biol.* **7**: 379-387 (1963).
30. Edman, P.: Method for determination of the amino acid sequence in peptides. *Acta Chem. Scand.* **4**: 283-293 (1950).
31. Edman, P.: Note on the stepwise degradation of peptides via phenylthiohydantoins. *Acta Chem. Scand.* **7**: 700-701 (1953).
32. Felix, K., Fischer, H., and Krekels, A.: Nucleoprotamin. III Mitteilung. *Z. Physiol. Chem.* **289**: 127-131 (1952).
33. Felix, K., Fischer, H., and Krekels, A.: Protamines and nucleoprotamines. *Progr. Biophys. Biophys. Chem.* **6**: 1-23 (1956).
34. Feughelman, M., Langridge, R., Seeds, W. E., Stokes, A. R., Wilson, H. R., Hooper, C. W., Wilkins, M. H. F., Barclay, R. K., and Hamilton, L. D.: Molecular structure of deoxyribonucleic acid and nucleoproteins. *Nature* **175**: 834-838 (1955).
34a. Franklin, R. M.: Personal communication.
34b. Gallant, J., and Stapleton, R.: Derepression of alkaline phosphatase synthesis by chloramphenicol and canavanine inhibition. *J. Mol. Biol.* **8**, 442-451 (1964).
35. Hnilica, L. S., and Busch, H.: Fractionation of the histones of the Walker 256 carcinosarcoma by combined chemical and chromatographic techniques. *J. Biol. Chem.* **238**: 918-924 (1963).
36. Hogeboom, G. H., and Schneider, W. C.: Cytochemical studies. VI. The synthesis of DPN by liver cell nuclei. *J. Biol. Chem.* **197**: 611-620 (1952).
37. Hogeboom, G. H., and Schneider, W. C.: The cytoplasm. *In* "The Nucleic Acids" (E. Chargaff and J. N. Davidson, eds.), Vol. 2, pp. 199-246. Academic Press, New York, 1955.
38. Huang, R. C., and Bonner, J.: Histone, a suppressor of chromosomal RNA synthesis. *Proc. Natl. Acad. Sci. U.S.* **48**: 1216-1222 (1962).
38a. Iwai, K.: Histones of mice embryos and of chlorella. *In* "The Nucleohistones" (J. Bonner and P. Ts'o, eds.), pp. 59-65. Holden-Day, San Francisco, California, 1964.
39. Jacob, F., and Monod, J.: Genetic regulatory mechanisms in the synthesis of proteins. *J. Mol. Biol.* **3**: 318-356 (1961).
40. Jacob, F., and Wollman, E. L.: "Sexuality and the Genetics of Bacteria," p. 300. Academic Press, New York, 1961.
41. Johns, E. W., and Butler, J. A. V.: Further fractionation of histones from calf thymus. *Biochem. J.* **82**: 15-18 (1962).

42. Johns, E. W., Phillips, D. M. P., Simson, P., and Butler, J. A. V.: Improved fractionation of arginine-rich histones from calf thymus. *Biochem. J.* **77**: 631-636 (1960).
43. Johns, E. W., Phillips, D. M. P., Simson, P., and Butler, J. A. V.: The electrophoresis of histones and histone fractions on starch gel. *Biochem. J.* **80**: 189-193 (1961).
44. Keir, H. M., Smellie, R. M. S., and Siebert, G.: Intracellular location of DNA nucleotidyl transferase. *Nature* **196**: 752-754 (1962).
45. Keir, H. M., and Smith, M. J.: Characteristics of the DNA nucleotidyltransferase activity in non-aqueous type calfthymus nuclei. *Biochim. Biophys. Acta* **68**: 589-598 (1963).
46. Kossel, A.: Ueber einen peptonartigen Bestandtheil des Zellkerns. *Z. Physiol. Chem.* **8**: 511-515 (1884).
47. Kossel, A.: "The Protamines and Histones." Longmans, Green, London, 1921.
48. Kossel, A., and Kutscher, F.: Beiträge zur Kenntnis der Eiweisskörper. *Z. Physiol. Chem.* **31**: 165-214 (1900).
49. Kossel, A., and Schenk, E. G.: Untersuchungen über die basischen Eiweissstoffe, ein Beitrag zu ihrer Entwicklungsgeschichte. *Z Physiol. Chem.* **173**: 278-308 (1928).
50. Lilienfeld, L.: Zur Chemie der Leukocyten. *Z. Physiol. Chem.* **18**: 472-486 (1893).
51. Ludwig, E. H., and Smull, C. E.: Infectivity of histone-poliovirus ribonucleic acid preparations. *J. Bacteriol.* **85**: 1334-1338 (1963).
52. Markert, C. L., and Ursprung, H.: Production of replicable persistent changes in zygote chromosomes of *Rana pipiens* by injected proteins from adult liver nuclei. *Develop. Biol.* **7**: 560-577 (1963).
53. Mason, H. S., and Peterson, E. W.: The reaction of quinones with protamine and nucleoprotamine: N-terminal proline. *J. Biol. Chem.* **212**: 485-493 (1955).
54. Mendecki, J., and Wilczok, T.: The interaction of basic proteins during the donor DNA incorporation into neoplastic cells. *Neoplasma* **10**: 561-564 (1963).
55. Miescher, F.: "Die histochemischen und physiologischen Arbeiten." Vogel, Leipzig, 1897.
56. Mirsky, A. E., and Pollister, A. W.: Nucleoproteins of cell nuclei. *Proc. Natl. Acad. Sci. U.S.* **28**: 344-352 (1942).
57. Mirsky, A. E., and Pollister, A. W.: Chromosomin, a deoxyribonucleoprotein complex of the cell nucleus. *J. Gen. Physiol.* **30**: 117-147 (1946).
58. Mirsky, A. E., and Ris, H.: Isolated chromosomes. *J. Gen. Physiol.* **31**: 1-6 (1947).
59. Mirsky, A. E., and Ris, H.: The chemical composition of isolated chromosomes. *J. Gen. Physiol.* **31**: 7-18 (1947).
60. Mirsky, A. E., and Ris, H.: Variable and constant components of chromosomes. *Nature* **163**: 666-667 (1949).
61. Mirsky, A. E., and Ris, H.: The composition and structure of isolated chromosomes. *J. Gen. Physiol.* **34**: 475-492 (1950).
62. Ohtaka, Y., and Spiegelman, S.: Translational control of protein synthesis in a cell-free system directed by a polycistronic viral RNA. *Science* **142**: 493-497 (1963).

63. Paleus, S., and Paul, K. G.: Mammalian cytochrome C. *In* "The Enzymes" (P. D. Boyer, H. Lardy, and K. Myrbäck, eds.), Vol. 8 pp. 97-112. Academic Press, New York, 1963.

64. Palmade, C., Chevallier, M-R., Knobloch, A., and Vendrely, R.: Isolement d'une déoxyribonucléohistone à partir d'*Escherichia coli. Compt. Rend. Acad. Sci.* **246**: 2534-2537 (1958).

65. Phillips, D. M. P.: The Histones. *Progr. Biophys. Biophys. Chem.* **12**: 211-280 (1961).

66. Pollister, A. W., and Mirsky, A. E.: The nucleoprotamine of trout sperm. *J. Gen. Physiol.* **30**: 101-115 (1946).

67. Ryle, A. P., Sanger, F., Smith, L. F., and Kital, R.: The disulphide bonds of insulin. *Biochem. J.* **60**: 541-565 (1955).

68. Sanger, F.: The free amino groups of insulin. *Biochem. J.* **39**: 507-515 (1945).

69. Setterfield, G., Neelin, J. M., Neelin, E. M., and Bayley, S. T.: Studies on basic proteins from ribosomes of buds of pea seedlings. *J. Mol. Biol.* **2**: 416-424 (1960).

70. Siebert, G.: Enzymes of cancer nuclei. *Exptl. Cell Res. Suppl.* **9**: 389-418 (1963).

71. Siebert, G., and Smellie, R. M. S.: Enzymatic and metabolic studies on isolated nuclei. *Intern. Rev. Cytol.* **6**: 383-424 (1957).

72. Siebert, G., Lang, K., Muller, L., Lucius, S., Muller, E., and Kuhle, E.: Metabolic processes in isolated cell nuclei. VII. Enzymes of amino acid and peptide metabolism in nuclei. *Biochem. Z.* **323**: 532-545 (1953).

73. Smellie, R. M. S.: Some studies on the enzymes of the DNA biosynthesis. *Exptl. Cell Res. Suppl.* **9**: 245-259 (1963).

74. Smellie, R. M. S., and Eason, R.: Studies on the intracellular location of deoxyribonucleic acid "Polymerase." *Biochem. J.* **80**: 39P (1961).

75. Smull, C. E., and Ludwig, E. H.: Enhancement of the plaque-forming capacity of poliovirus ribonucleic acid with basic proteins. *J. Bacteriol.* **84**: 1035-1040 (1962).

76. Smull, C. E., Mallette, M. F., and Ludwig, E. H.: The use of basic proteins to increase infectivity of enterovirus ribonucleic acid. *Biochem. Biophys. Res. Commun.* **5**: 247-249 (1961).

77. Spiegelman, S.: Genetic mechanisms. Information transfer from the genome. *Federation Proc.* **22**: 36-54 (1963).

78. Stedman, E., and Stedman, E.: Probable function of histone as a regulator of mitosis. *Nature* **152**: 556 (1943).

79. Stedman, E., and Stedman, E.: "Chromosomin" and nucleic acids. *Nature* **153**: 500-502 (1944).

80. Stedman, E., and Stedman, E.: Function of deoxyribose nucleic acids in the cell nucleus. *Symp. Soc. Exptl. Biol.* **1**: 232-251 (1947).

81. Steele, W. J., and Busch, H.: Studies on the acidic nuclear proteins of the Walker tumor and the liver. *Cancer Res.* **23**: 1153-1163 (1963).

82. Stern, H., Allfrey, V. G., Mirsky, A. E., and Saetren, H.: Some enzymes of isolated nuclei. *J. Gen. Physiol.* **35**: 559-578 (1952).

83. Stern, H., and Timonen, S.: Position of the cell nucleus in pathways of hydrogen transfer: Cytochrome C, flavoproteins, glutathione, and ascorbic acid. *J. Gen. Physiol.* **38**: 41-52 (1954).

84. Takemori, S., Wada, K., Sekuzu, I., and Okunuki, K.: Reaction of cytochrome A with chemically modified cytochrome C and basic proteins. *Nature* **195**: 456-457 (1962).
85. Ursprung, H., and Markert, C. L.: Chromosome complements of *Rana pipiens* embryos developing from eggs injected with protein from adult liver cells. *Develop. Biol.* **8**: 309-321 (1963).
86. Waldschmidt-Leitz, E., and Gutermann, H.: Über die Struktur der Protamine. VI. Vergleich der Protamine aus Salmonidenarten. *Z. Physiol. Chem.* **323**: 98-104 (1961).
87. Waldschmidt-Leitz, E., and Pflanz, L.: Über die Struktur der Protamine. III. Dinitrophenyl Clupein und seine enzymatische Spaltung. *Z. Physiol. Chem.* **292**: 150-156 (1953).
88. Waldschmidt-Leitz, E., and Voh, R.: Über die Struktur der Protamine. IV. Fraktionierung von Clupein. *Z. Physiol. Chem.* **298**: 257-267 (1954).
89. Waldschmidt-Leitz, E., Ziegler, F., Schäffner, A., and Weil, L.: Über die Struktur der Protamine. I. Protaminase und die Produkte ihrer Einwirkung auf Clupein und Salmin. *Z. Physiol. Chem.* **197**: 219-236 (1931).
90. Watson, M. L.: Pores in the mammalian nuclear membrane. *Biochim. Biophys. Acta* **15**: 475-479 (1954).
91. Wilczok, T., and Mendecki, J.: The effect of protamines and histones on incorporation of donor DNA into neoplastic cells. *Neoplasma* **10**: 113-119 (1963).
92. Wilkins, M. H. F.: Physical studies of the molecular structure of deoxyribose nucleic acid and nucleoprotein. *Cold Spring Harbor Symp. Quant. Biol.* **21**: 75-90 (1956).
93. Wilkins, M. H. F., and Zubay, G.: X-ray diffraction study of the structure of nucleohistone and nucleoprotamines. *J. Mol. Biol.* **7**: 756-757 (1963).
94. Yanagisawa, K.: The simultaneous accumulation of RNA and a repressor of β-galactosidase synthesis. *Biochem. Biophys. Res. Commun.* **9**: 88-93 (1962).
95. Zubay, G., and Watson, M. R.: The absence of histone in the bacterium *Escherichia coli*. I. Preparation and analysis of nucleoprotein extract. *J. Biophys. Biochem. Cytol.* **5**: 51-54 (1959).

# PART I

# The Basic Nuclear Proteins

# CHAPTER I

# The Protamines



## General Discussion

Although the protamines were the first of the nuclear proteins to be studied, interest in their structure and function has waned partly because of the difficulty in obtaining suitable starting materials and partly because they have been found mainly in spermatozoa of fish. With respect to biochemical analysis of the primary structure of the protamines, the existing methods for the selective hydrolysis of proteins are not satisfactory for sequential analysis of proteins that contain so much arginine (13, 14, 18, 19, 35, 36, 40). Because of their historical interest as well as the fact that concepts arose from analysis of the protamines, they represent a background for discussion of the histones and other nuclear proteins.

*Nucleoprotamines.* Protamines are naturally present in spermatozoa of fish and some other species as nucleoprotamines, which are complexes of these small basic proteins with DNA. Nucleoprotamines have been isolated by repeated washing of milt from fish with dilute saline solutions to extract most of the nonnucleoprotein constituents (15, 16,

49) or by extraction of the deoxyribonucleoprotamine with concentrated saline solutions (34). Although the deoxyribonucleoprotamine is a gel, repeated treatment with salt solutions results in the formation of a water-soluble whitish precipitate that probably differs in physical properties from the intracellular deoxyribonucleoprotamine.

Beginning with the report of Feughelman *et al.* (17), it was suggested by the group working with Wilkins (9, 10, 17, 48, 49) that the protamines lie in the shallow groove of the DNA helix. Studies with X-ray diffraction (49) and polarized infrared light (9, 23–25) show that the protamines are not aggregated in the deoxyribonucleoprotamine and may be present as random coils rather than in the α-helical or β-sheet form. It was also suggested that the polypeptide chain is wrapped around the DNA helix in such a way that some folds are present in the protein. Luzatti and Nicolaieff (27, 28) have taken exception to these interpretations of the structure of deoxyribonucleoprotamine and have suggested that the protein serves to bind together a number of molecules of DNA. In their model, a single protamine or histone would link several DNA molecules in complex associations.

The relative amounts of protamine and DNA in deoxyribonucleoprotamine preparations have been analyzed by Vendrely *et al.* (42) and others (16). Although they found precise equivalence in the amounts of histone and DNA in some deoxyribonucleohistone preparations, they did not find equivalent amounts of protamine and DNA in deoxyribonucleoprotamines. They suggested that intracellularly, however, the amounts of protein and DNA are equivalent and that some of the more soluble protein is lost in the isolation of the nucleoprotein. They also calculated that the total number of molecules of arginine, lysine, and histidine should be equal to the total number of phosphorus atoms in DNA of the deoxyribonucleoprotamine. However, in the recovered deoxyribonucleohistone and deoxyribonucleoprotamine, the basic amino acid residues approximated only 59–75% of the total phosphorus atoms in DNA. They reported that a protein was present in their extracts that might account for the missing protamine. In their preparations, Felix *et al.* (16) found that the ratio of the weight of DNA to protamine was 1:0.94.

*Extraction of Protamines from Deoxyribonucleoprotamines.* A number of procedures have been used to isolate purified protamines. Most are modifications of the original procedure of Kossel (20–22) in which 1% $H_2SO_4$ was used to extract the protamines from sperm heads that had been treated with dilute acetic acid. The protamine sulfate formed was precipitated with ethanol. In the procedure developed by Pollister and Mirsky (34), the deoxyribonucleoprotamines were extracted with 10% NaCl and the protamine was salted out by decreasing the concentration of the salt.

*Nomenclature and Composition of the Protamines.* The protamines have been named on the basis of their origin so that, for example, the protamine of salmon is salmine, the protein of herring roe is clupeine, and the protamine of the trout is truttine (Table 1-I). Perhaps the major characteristic of these proteins is their extremely high content of arginine, which makes them the most "arginine-rich" proteins. In a number of these proteins, arginine accounts for more than 70% of the total amino acids and in some, arginine accounts for more than 80% of the total amino acids. To Kossel (20), the chief implication of this fact was the possibility that the fish could simplify its proteins through the following sequence:

tissue protein ⟶ histones ⟶ protamines

Because protamines had a low molecular weight and also had a very high concentration of arginine, it seemed logical that they might be breakdown products of the "higher proteins" of the fish. Since they seemed to form at the expense of the muscle protein, this possibility seemed to be even more plausible.

Although virtually all the protamines had high concentrations of arginine, one fraction obtained from the protamine cyprinine had a high concentration of lysine, i.e., more than 70% of the total nitrogen in the protamine was accountable for as lysine nitrogen (16, 22). Even in this protamine there was another fraction that was "arginine-rich," as in the case of most fish protamines. In contrast to the protamines, the basic proteins of lower marine animals (Table 1-II) have varying concentrations of lysine and arginine, as well as alanine.

*Properties of the Protamines.* From the amino acid analysis it would be expected that the properties of the protamines would be those of very basic polypeptides. These properties are (16):

1. alkaline reaction in aqueous solution;
2. high isoelectric point;
3. strong reactions with Sakaguchi's reagent for arginine;
4. ready hydrolysis by trypsin;
5. formation of colloids in aqueous solution;

## TABLE 1-I

AMINO ACID COMPOSITION OF THE PROTAMINES[a, b]

| Protamine | Species | Arginine | Lysine | Histidine | Glycine | Alanine | Serine | Threonine | Proline | Valine | Isoleucine | Aspartic acid | Glutamic acid | Tyrosine | Total |
|---|---|---|---|---|---|---|---|---|---|---|---|---|---|---|---|
| Clupeine | *Clupeus harengus* | 65 (71) | — | — | — | 7 | 4 | 2 | 9 | 4 | 1 | — | — | — | 92 |
| | | 53 (71) | — | — | — | 4 | 6 | 2 | 5 | 4 | 1 | — | — | — | 75 |
| | | 60 (82) | — | — | — | 5 | 1 | 1 | 4 | 1 | 1 | — | — | — | 73 |
| Salmine | *Salmo salar* | 51 (70) | — | — | — | 4 | 6 | — | 7 | 4 | 1 | — | — | — | 73 |
| | | 55 (74) | — | — | 3 | 2 | 5 | — | 5 | 4 | — | — | — | — | 74 |
| | | 41 (70) | — | — | 3 | 1 | 7 | — | 4 | 2 | 1 | — | — | — | 59 |
| | | 75 (70) | — | — | 7 | 1 | 8 | — | 6 | 5 | 2 | — | — | — | 104 |
| | | 34 (69) | — | — | 3 | 1 | 4 | — | 4 | 3 | ? | — | — | — | 49 |
| | | 50 (70) | — | — | 4 | 1 | 7 | — | 6 | 3 | 1 | — | — | — | 72 |
| | | 78 (85) | — | — | 4 | 1 | 4 | — | 3 | 1 | 1 | — | — | — | 92 |
| Scombrine | *Scombre scombrus* | 112 (81) | — | — | — | 9 | 4 | 2 | 7 | 3 | 1 | — | — | — | 138 |
| Spheroidine | *Spheroides rubripes* | 71 (78) | — | — | — | 9 | 7 | 1 | 1 | 1 | 1 | — | — | — | 91 |
| Iridine | *Salmo irideus* | 50 (73) | 2 | — | 2 | 2 | 3 | — | 5 | 4 | 1 | — | — | — | 69 |
| Truttine | *Salmo trutta* | 50 (75) | — | — | 2 | 2 | 3 | — | 5 | 5 | — | — | — | — | 67 |
| Fontinine | *Salmo fontinalis* | 50 (75) | — | — | 2 | 2 | 3 | — | 5 | 5 | — | — | — | — | 67 |
| Lacustrine | *Salmo lacustris* | 50 (66) | — | 5–15 | 2 | 2 | 2 | — | 5 | 2 | 1 | 1 | 1 | — | 76 |
| Sturine | *Acipenser sturio* | 35 (54) | 9 | 7 | 2 | 5 | 3 | 1 | — | — | 2 | — | 1 | — | 65 |
| | *Gallus domesticus* | 75 (60) | — | 2 | 10 | 2 | 14 | 3 | 7 | 2 | 1 | 1 | 2 | 6 | 125 |
| Galline | | 44 (66) | — | — | 1 | 5 | 5 | 2 | 5 | 3 | 1 | — | 1 | — | 67 |

[a] Based on data from Felix *et al.* (16).

[b] The values represent the number of residues of the amino acids in the protamines; the amino acid in lowest concentration was assigned the value of 1. The numbers in parentheses after the values for arginine are the percentages of the total moles of amino acids in the protamine accounted for by arginine.

TABLE 1-II

AMINO ACID COMPOSITION OF BASIC PROTEINS OF LOWER MARINE ANIMALS[a,b]

| Species | Arginine | Lysine | Histi-dine | Gly-cine | Ala-nine | Ser-ine | Threo-nine | Pro-line | Val-ine | Leu-cine | Iso-leucine | Total resi-dues |
|---|---|---|---|---|---|---|---|---|---|---|---|---|
| *Patella vulgata* | 40 (25) | 32 | 1 | 15 | 20 | 15 | 7 | 15 | 7 | 6 | 2 | 160 |
| *Patella coerulea* | 80 (46) | 14 | — | 14 | 9 | 21 | 3 | 21 | 6 | 6 | 1 | 175 |
| *Arbacia lixula* | 14 (10.6) | 30 | 1 | 22 | 30 | 9 | 3 | 12 | 3 | 5 | 4 | 133 |

[a] Based on data from Felix *et al.* (16).

[b] The values represent the number of residues of the amino acids in the proteins; the amino acid in lowest concentration was assigned the value of 1. The numbers in parentheses after the values for arginine are the percentages of the total moles of amino acids in the protein accounted for by arginine.

6. precipitability by protein precipitants such as picric acid and phosphotungstic acid;
7. formation of compounds with salts of heavy metals;
8. ready staining with the dye, Fast Green (1–4), like the histones.

The molecular weight of the protamines has not been fully established, but values cited by Felix *et al.* (15, 16) range from 2000 to 12,000, an indication that these polypeptides are relatively small substances (12).

*Characterization of the Protamines.* These proteins would seem to be relatively simple in overall composition because of the large numbers of arginine residues (Table 1-I). Hence, it is not surprising that an effort was made by Felix and his colleagues (15) to determine the structure of these substances. The initial step in the characterization of the protamines was undertaken and completed by Kossel (20–22) and Waldschmidt-Leitz (43–46) and their co-workers, who showed that the only components of the protamines were amino acids and thus placed these molecules in the class of simple proteins. Moreover, they showed that the protamines were largely devoid of the aromatic amino acids such as tryptophan, tyrosine, and phenylalanine. In some of the protamines, such as salmine and clupeine, arginine is the only basic amino acid, Table 1-I); these protamines were referred to as the *simple* or *monoprotamines.* Those that contained arginine and either lysine or histidine were referred to as the *diprotamines;* iridine is an example of this class of protamines. Those that, like sturine, contained all three basic amino acids were referred to as *triprotamines.*

*Number of Protamines in a Given Species.* When the *elementary amino acid* composition of the protamines was established, endeavors were made to determine the number of the protamines in a given species. One of the reasons for the uncertainty that still exists as to the number of protamines in a species is that protamines are reported to have some proteinase activity that may either reside in the polypeptides themselves or be present as contaminants in the preparations. As a result, the reports of two species of clupeine or the varied electrophoretic mobility of fractions obtained from protamine preparations (15) may reflect either the breakdown of some of the molecules or the heterogeneity of the protamines as isolated. None of the chemical methods employed, however, have proved that there is marked heterogeneity of the protamines in a given species although both lysine-rich and arginine-rich protamines exist in spermatozoa of the carp (22). The variability in the amino acid analysis of protamines from a single species (Table 1-I) suggests that either the individual samples differ in amino acid composition or there are differing amounts of individual protamines in the total protamine fraction. Support for the latter possibility was obtained by Scanes and Tozer (37), who separated clupeine into three fractions by countercurrent distribution and elution from basic alumina. One fraction contained only arginine, alanine, proline, serine, and valine; the second contained threonine but no glycine, leucine, or isoleucine; and the third contained threonine, leucine or isoleucine, and glycine.

*The $NH_2$-Terminal Amino Acids.* These acids are remarkably constant in the protamines, as Table 1-III shows. For virtually all the mono- and

TABLE 1-III

$NH_2$-TERMINAL AMINO ACIDS OF SOME PROTAMINES[a]

| Protamine | $NH_2$-terminal |
|---|---|
| Clupeine (*Clupea harengus*) | Proline |
| Iridine (*Salmo irideus*) | Proline |
| Truttine (*Salmo trutta*) | Proline |
| Fontinine (*Salmo fontinalis*) | Proline |
| Salmine (*Salmo salar*) | Proline |
| Sturine (*Acipenser sturio*) | Alanine, glutamic acid |

[a] Data from Felix *et al.* (16).

diprotamines, proline was found to be the $NH_2$-terminal amino acid (16, 17, 30). Only sturine, of the group of protamines studied, had alanine and/or glutamic acid as the $NH_2$-terminal acid. The $NH_2$-terminal amino acids were determined both by the Sanger procedure (35, 36) and by the Edman procedure (13, 14). Although the results were very similar, Felix *et al.* (15, 16) noted that, in the Edman procedure, the $NH_2$-terminals were contaminated from time to time with a second amino acid. They ascribed the presence of the second amino acid to the formation of phenylthiohydantoins of both the first and the second amino acid. It seemed possible, then, to determine the second amino acid in each of the protamines studied. Alanine was the amino acid adjacent to the $NH_2$-terminal in clupeine, but in salmine, iridine, truttine, and fontinine, valine was found to be the second amino acid. Determination of the C-terminal amino acid was achieved initially by chemical analysis for guanidinium groups and later by short-time hydrolysis with carboxypeptidase (Table 1-IV). In clupeine, iridine, salmine, and sturine, arginine was found to be the C-terminal. Alanine and valine appeared later in the hydrolysis and hence were assumed to be adjacent to arginine in the case of clupeine, iridine, salmine, and

TABLE 1-IV
C-TERMINAL AMINO ACIDS OF PROTAMINES[a]

| Protamine | C-terminal |
|---|---|
| Clupeine | Arginine, alanine, valine, proline |
| Iridine | Arginine, alanine, valine |
| Truttine | Alanine, valine, proline |
| Fontinine | Alanine, valine, serine |
| Salmine | Arginine, alanine, valine, proline |
| Sturine | Arginine, alanine, valine |

[a] Data from Felix *et al.* (16).

sturine. In truttine and fontinine, the C-terminal amino acid was alanine and valine was found to be the adjacent amino acid.

## Primary Structure of Protamines

***Peptides of Protamines.*** Peptides were isolated following hydrolysis of protamines with a variety of proteinases by Kossel (20) and Ando *et al.* (6, 7). Following tryptic hydrolysis, both small and large peptides were found; the latter were called "protones," a term that has now become obsolete. Hydrolysis of the protamines did not occur when pepsin was added to the solutions containing protamines. The lack of hydrolysis was suggested as a differential point to distinguish this group of proteins from the histones that were hydrolyzed by pepsin. Kossel (20) suggested that the arginine residues in the protamines might be linked in a regular sort of peptide sequence with some alteration in the long chain with monoamino acids. He also raised the question whether there might be piperidines or piperazines in the protamines, but apparently was not convinced they were present. Unfortunately, the biochemical techniques available to him were insufficient to permit satisfactory structural analysis of the protamines.

Felix and his colleagues (16) made a number of studies on partial hydrolyzates of the protamines. Mainly, they isolated and characterized peptides present in clupeine. Among the dipeptides isolated were:

1. arginyl arginine;
2. arginine, serine;
3. arginine, alanine;

4. arginine, valine;
5. serine, alanine (seryl-alanine);
6. isoleucine, alanine (isoleucyl-alanine);
7. valine, alanine (valyl-alanine);
8. DNP-prolyl-alanine.

Among the tripeptides isolated were:

1. alanyl-arginyl-arginine;
2. seryl-arginyl-arginine;
3. DNP-prolyl-alanyl-arginine.

A series of tetrapeptides was also found after hydrolysis of clupeine, and this included:

1. a tetrapeptide of arginine;
2. prolyl-valyl-arginyl-arginine;
3. valyl-alanyl-arginyl-arginine.

Two longer peptides were isolated and the following sequences were determined:

1. DNP-prolyl-alanyl-(arginyl)$_4$-threonyl-serine;
2. all the above, but linked to the carboxyl of serine were -(arginyl)$_4$-valyl-isoleucine.

From these facts and the associated experiments, a general formula for clupeine was suggested to be:

pro-ala-arg$_4$(monoamino acid$_2$·arg$_4$)$_n$ monoamino acid$_2$·arg$_2$

Although it could not be established with certainty, a formula for a clupeine that would have a molecular weight of 12,000 was suggested as follows:

pro-ala-arg$_4$-pro-val-arg$_4$·ileu-ala-arg$_4$-val-ser-arg$_4$-ser-prol-arg$_4$-ser-threo-arg$_4$-ser-ala-arg$_4$-prol-ser-arg$_4$-ser-val-arg$_4$-threo-prol-arg$_4$-val-ala-arg$_2$

Although the formula presented by Felix *et al.* (16) had the merit of being an initial framework for the development of a structure of a protamine, it had two major defects. The first of these is the lack of an accurate molecular weight for the protamines. The formula presumes a molecular weight of 12,000 but this value disagrees with the molecular weight of 4000 reported by Callanan *et al.* (12). Secondly, the presence of tetrapeptides of arginine in the molecule is reasonable, but there is no certainty of a regular sequence of amino acids, as the formula suggests. Indeed, all the information now available on the primary amino acid sequences in proteins shows that there is a marked *lack of regularity* rather than a high order of regularity in the structure of most proteins. It is also peculiar that the overall formula proposed did not include the longer peptides actually characterized.

## Functions of the Protamines

It is generally accepted that the primary function of spermatozoa is to serve as simple carriers for deoxyribonucleic acids. On the basis of their simplicity and equivalence in amount to DNA, the function of the protamines has been assumed to be that of maintaining the DNA in a stable, compact, and transportable form (16, 32). Most of the studies on protamines have been carried out on a variety of fish sperm and testes. Attempts to demonstrate similar proteins in mammalian sperm have met with only limited success. Bril-Petersen and Westenbrink (11) have extracted bovine spermatozoa with 0.3 *N* HCl and reported that the proteins extracted were not histones and probably originated from the perinuclear cytoplasmic layer and the tails. To remove deoxyribonucleoprotein from the heads, 1 *N* NaOH was required, since neither 0.3 *N* HCl nor 0.1 *N* NaOH extracted any of the protein or DNA. Initially, the DNA was extracted and the protein emerged more slowly. The protein extracted contained a large amount of arginine, i.e., arginine residues accounted for 36% of the weight of the total protein in the extract. What was particularly interesting in view of the virtual absence of cystine from histones and protamines was the fact that 6.3% of the weight of their protein was accounted for by cystine. In the sperm, the ratio of arginine to DNA-phosphoric acid residues was 0.9 and the ratio of total basic amino acids to DNA phosphoric acid residues was 1.0. Bril-Petersen and Westenbrink (11) suggest that the DNA is loculated in a sponge-like matrix of keratinoid threads composed of this arginine-rich protein. Presumably, the function of the matrix would be to transport the DNA in a highly protected state.

In earlier studies, Berry and Mayer (8) treated bovine spermatozoa with 1 *M* NaCl and 0.1 *N* HCl after they had been shaken with glass beads. The protein extracted with the acid was precipitated with ammonia and ethanol. In this protein, basic amino acids accounted for 20% of the total amino acid residues. Although a direct amino acid analysis was not made, these authors suggested that protein in the bovine spermatozoa was histone-like.

**Other Effects of Protamines.** Some interesting side effects of protamines have recently been found, but it is not certain whether these are characteristic of protamines or simply polybasic molecules (41). Amos and Kearns (5) showed that addition of RNA to cultures containing chick embryo fibroblasts resulted in a diminution of the initial lag in protein synthesis. The stimulatory RNA, which was similar to messenger-RNA, was rapidly broken down in the medium by RNases. Polybasic substances such as spermine, spermidine, and streptomycin as well as protamines and histones blocked the breakdown of the RNA. In addition, the protamines and histones enhanced the uptake of the $P^{32}$-labeled RNA by a factor of almost 10. Trypsin destroyed this enhancement by the basic polypeptides. Similarly, Smull and Ludwig (26, 38, 39) have reported that the plaque-forming capacity and infectivity of poliovirus was remarkably increased by addition of protamines and histones to the virus RNA. Histones were slightly more effective than the protamines. When increasing concentrations of NaCl were added to the medium, there was a loss of infectivity of the histone-RNA preparation, presumably due to dissociation of the nucleoprotein complexes. They suggested that the enhancing effect was related to viral penetration of the cells or increased activity of the virus.

Wilczok and Mendecki (31, 47) have found a similar protective effect of polybasic substances on DNA; they reported that basic proteins as well as spermine enhanced uptake of labeled DNA onto cell surfaces or into cells in tissue culture. The polybasic substances protected DNA against DNase. Since the most effective basic substance was spermine, the effects of histones and protamines are probably nonspecific.

Protamines have been reported to have a number of *inhibitory effects* in biological systems. McIlwain (29) has reported that protamines as well as other polybasic substances have inhibitory effects on excitability of cerebral cortex slices which were reversed by addition of acidic substances to the system. It has also been found (33) that protamines in relatively high doses inhibit the growth of some tumors in mice.

## References

1. Alfert, M.: Chemical differentiation of nuclear proteins during spermatogenesis in the salmon. *J. Biophys. Biochem. Cytol.* **2**: 109-114 (1956).
2. Alfert, M.: Some cytochemical contributions to genetic chemistry. *In* "The Chemical Basis of Heredity" (W. D. McElroy and B. Glass, eds.), pp. 186-194. Johns Hopkins Press, Baltimore, Maryland, 1957.

3. Alfert, M.: Variations in cytochemical properties of cell nuclei. *Exptl. Cell Res. Suppl.* **6**: 227-235 (1958).
4. Alfert, M., and Geschwind, I. I.: A selective staining method for the basic proteins of cell nuclei. *Proc. Natl. Acad. Sci. U.S.* **39**: 991-999 (1953).
5. Amos, H., and Kearns, K. E.: Influence of bacterial ribonucleic acid on animal cells in culture. II. Protamine enhancement of RNA uptake. *Exptl. Cell Res.* **32**: 14-25 (1963).
6. Ando, T., Ishii, S., and Yamasaki, M.: Peptides obtained by tryptic digestion of clupeine. *Biochim. Biophys. Acta* **34**: 600-601 (1959).
7. Ando, T., Iwai, K., Yamasaki, M., Hashimoto, C., Kimura, M., Ishii, S., and Tamura, T.: Protamines. *Bull. Chem. Soc. Japan* **26**: 406-407 (1953).
8. Berry, R. E., and Mayer, D. T.: The histone-like basic protein of bovine spermatozoa. *Exptl. Cell Res.* **20**: 116-126 (1960).
9. Bradbury, E. M., Price, W. C., and Wilkinson, G. R.: Polarized infrared studies on nucleoproteins. I. Nucleoprotamine. *J. Mol. Biol.* **4**: 39-49 (1962).
10. Bradbury, E. M., Price, W. C., Wilkinson, G. R., and Zubay, G.: Polarized infrared studies of nucleoproteins. II. Nucleohistone. *J. Mol. Biol.* **4**: 50-60 (1962).
11. Bril-Petersen, E., and Westenbrink, H. G. K.: A structural basic protein as a counterpart of deoxyribonucleic acid in mammalian spermatozoa. *Biochim. Biophys. Acta* **76**: 152-154 (1963).
12. Callanan, M. J., Carroll, W. R., and Mitchell, E. R.: Physical and chemical properties of protamine from the sperm of salmon (*Oncorhynchus tschanytscha*). I. Preparation and characterization. *J. Biol. Chem.* **229**: 279-287 (1957).
13. Edman, P.: Method for determination of the amino acid sequence in peptides. *Acta Chem. Scand.* **4**: 283-293 (1950).
14. Edman, P.: Note on the stepwise degradation of peptides via phenylthiohydantoins. *Acta Chem. Scand.* **7**: 700-701 (1953).
15. Felix, K., Fischer, H., and Krekels, A.: Nucleoprotamin. III. Mitteilung. *Z. Physiol. Chem.* **289**: 127-131 (1952).
16. Felix, K., Fischer, H., and Krekels, A.: Protamines and nucleoprotamines. *Progr. Biophys. Biophys. Chem.* **6**: 1-23 (1956).
17. Feughelman, M., Langridge, R., Seeds, W. E., Stokes, A. R., Wilson, H. R., Hooper, C. W., Wilkins, M. H. F., Barclay, R. K., and Hamilton, L. D.: Molecular structure of deoxyribose nucleic acid and nucleoprotein. *Nature* **175**: 834-838 (1955).
18. Hirs, C. H. W., Stein, W. H., and Moore, S.: The amino acid composition of ribonuclease. *J. Biol. Chem.* **211**: 941-950 (1954).
19. Hirs, C. H. W., Stein, W. H., and Moore, S.: Peptides obtained by chymotryptic hydrolysis of performic acid-oxidized ribonuclease. A. Partial structural formula for the oxidized protein. *J. Biol. Chem.* **221**: 151-169 (1956).
20. Kossel, A.: "The Protamines and Histones." Longmans, Green, London, 1921.
21. Kossel, A., and Kutscher, F.: Beiträge zur Kenntnis der Eiweisskörper. *Z. Physiol. Chem.* **31**: 165-214 (1900).

22. Kossel, A., and Schenk, E. G.: Untersuchungen über die basischen Eiweissstoffe, ein Beitrag zu ihrer Entwicklungsgeschichte. *Z. Physiol. Chem.* **173**: 278-308 (1928).

23. de Loze, C.: Infrared spectra and structure of deoxyribonucleoproteins and their components. *Ann. Chim. (Paris)* [13] **3**: 145-203 (1958).

24. de Loze, C.: Spectre infrarouge et structure de l'histone. *Compt. Rend. Acad. Sci.* **246**: 417-418, 599 (1958).

25. de Loze, C., and Lenormant, H.: Effet des fixateurs sur la nucléohistone de thymus. *Bull. Soc. Chim. Biol.* **41**: 337-343 (1959).

26. Ludwig, E. H., and Smull, C. E.: Infectivity of histone-poliovirus ribonucleic acid preparations. *J. Bacteriol.* **85**: 1334-1338 (1963).

27. Luzzati, V.: The structure of nucleohistones and nucleoprotamines. *J. Mol. Biol.* **7**: 758-759 (1963).

28. Luzzati, V., and Nicolaieff, A.: The structure of nucleohistones and nucleoprotamines. *J. Mol. Biol.* **7**: 142-163 (1963).

29. McIlwain, H.: Polybasic and polyacidic substances or aggregates and the excitability of cerebral tissues, electrically stimulated *in vitro*. *Biochem. J.* **90**: 442-448 (1963).

30. Mason, H. S., and Peterson, E. W.: The reaction of quinones with protamine and nucleoprotamine: N-terminal proline. *J. Biol. Chem.* **212**: 485-493 (1955).

31. Mendecki, J., and Wilczok, T.: The interaction of basic proteins during the donor DNA incorporation into neoplastic cells. *Neoplasma* **10**: 561-564 (1963).

32. Miescher, F.: "Die histochemischen und physiologischen Arbeiten." Vogel, Leipzig, 1897.

33. Muggleton, P. W., MacLaren, J. G., and Dyke, W. J. C.: Effect of protamine sulfate on experimental tumours in mice. *Lancet* **i**: 409-410 (1964).

34. Pollister, A. W., and Mirsky, A. E.: The nucleoprotamine of trout sperm. *J. Gen. Physiol.* **30**: 101-115 (1946-1947).

35. Ryle, A. P., Sanger, F., Smith, L. F., and Kital, R.: The disulphide bonds of insulin. *Biochem. J.* **60**: 541-556 (1955).

36. Sanger, F.: The free amino groups of insulin. *Biochem. J.* **39**: 507-515 (1945).

37. Scanes, F. S., and Tozer, B. T.: Fractionation of basic proteins and polypeptides: Clupeine and salmine. *Biochem. J.* **63**: 565-576 (1956).

38. Smull, C. E., and Ludwig, E. H.: Enhancement of the plaque-forming capacity of poliovirus ribonucleic acid with basic proteins. *J. Bacteriol.* **84**: 1035-1040 (1962).

39. Smull, C. E., Mallette, M. F., and Ludwig, E. H.: The use of basic proteins to increase infectivity of enterovirus ribonucleic acid. *Biochem. Biophys. Res. Commun.* **5**: 247-249 (1961).

40. Stein, W. H.: Structure-activity relationships in ribonuclease. *Federation Proc.* **23**: 599-608 (1964).

41. Tabor, H., Tabor, C. W., and Rosenthal, S. M.: The biochemistry of the polyamines: spermidine and spermine. *Ann. Rev. Biochem.* **30**: 579-604 (1961).

42. Vendrely, R., Knobloch-Mazen, A., and Vendrely, C.: A comparative biochemical study of nucleohistones and nucleoprotamines in the cell. *In* "The Cell Nucleus" (J. S. Mitchell, ed.), pp. 200-205. Butterworths, London and Washington, D. C., 1960.

43. Waldschmidt-Leitz, E., and Gutermann, H. Ueber die Struktur der Protamine. VI. Vergleich der Protamin des Salmonidenarten. *Z. Physiol. Chem.* **323**: 98-104 (1961).

44. Waldschmidt-Leitz, E., and Pflanz, L.: Ueber die Struktur der Protamine. III. Dinitrophenylclupein und seine enzymatische Spaltung. *Z. Physiol. Chem.* **292**: 150-156 (1953).

45. Waldschmidt-Leitz, E., and Voh, R.: Ueber die Struktur der Protamine. IV. Fraktionierung von Clupein. *Z. Physiol. Chem.* **298**: 257-267 (1954).

46. Waldschmidt-Leitz, E., Ziegler, F., Schäffner, A., and Weil, L.: Ueber die Struktur der Protamine. I. Protaminase und die Produkte ihrer Einwirkung auf Clupein und Salmin. *Z. Physiol. Chem.* **197**: 219-236 (1931).

47. Wilczok, T., and Mendecki, J.: The effect of protamines and histones on incorporation of donor DNA into neoplastic cells. *Neoplasma* **10**: 113-119 (1963).

48. Wilkins, M. H. F., and Zubay, G.: X-ray diffraction study of the structure of nucleohistone and nucleoprotamines. *J. Mol. Biol.* **7**: 756-757 (1963).

49. Zubay, G., and Wilkins, M. H. F.: An X-ray diffraction study of histone and protamine in isolation and in combination with DNA. *J. Mol. Biol.* **4**: 444-450 (1962).

# CHAPTER II

# Types, Composition, and Number of Histones



## Classification of the Histones

The classification of the histones that is generally used at present is shown in Table I (cf. Introduction). On the basis of their amino acid content, the histones are divided into three groups: "arginine-rich" histones, slightly lysine-rich histones, and very lysine-rich histones. The slightly lysine-rich histones are divided into two groups: one is largely composed of the *N*-proline histone, and the other is largely composed of the *N*-acetylalanine histone. None of the members of these groups of proteins has been isolated in pure form to this point. All the groups of histones isolated previously were mixtures of proteins equally or more complex than those obtained at present. As a result, a variety of systems of classification have been developed and the considerable confusion in the literature is not easily resolved. In essence, the methods employed for classification of the histones have been based on such chemical properties as amino acid analysis, precipitation from solution in various solvents, and the $NH_2$-terminal

TABLE 2-I
BASIS OF NOMENCLATURE OF HISTONE FRACTIONS

| | Chemical | | | Physical | |
|---|---|---|---|---|---|
| Amino acid composition | $NH_2$-terminal amino acid (21, 25–28, 37) | Precipitation (25) | (11) | Chromatography (6) | Electrophoresis (7, 10) |
| Very lysine-rich | (blocked) | F1 or | II | A | $\alpha$ |
| Slightly lysine-rich | 1. Proline | F2b | | | |
| | 2. Acetylalanine | F2a | | B | $\gamma$ |
| | 3. Others | | | | |
| "Arginine-rich" | Alanine | F3 or | I | — | $\beta$ |

amino acid or have been based on such physical properties as electrophoretic mobility, chromatography, and sedimentation behavior. The abbreviations based on these various systems of classification are shown in Table 2-I.

## Amino Acid Composition of Histones

*Lysine and Arginine Content.* A logical development from the isolation and characterization of the protamines was a search for "arginine-rich" proteins in nuclei of other types of cells. When the "arginine-rich" histones were found, Kossel (29) suggested that the protamines were degradation products of the histones and that the very "arginine-rich" segments of the histones were the origins of the protamines. He ascribed the lower arginine content of the histones to the building up of peptide chains around protamines with amino acids other than arginine. The finding of the lysine-rich histones by Daly and Mirsky (12) made it apparent that there were at least two classes of histones as determined by amino acid analysis. Later evidence by Cruft *et al.* (7–11) and Johns *et al.* (25–28) made it possible to separate the histones into the five categories shown in Fig. 2-1. These are (i) "arginine-rich" histones, (ii) the slightly lysine-rich 2b or *N*-proline histone fraction, (iii) the slightly lysine-rich 2a or *N*-acetylalanine histone fraction, (iv) the very lysine-rich histones, and (v) α-1, a fraction found by Cruft *et al.*

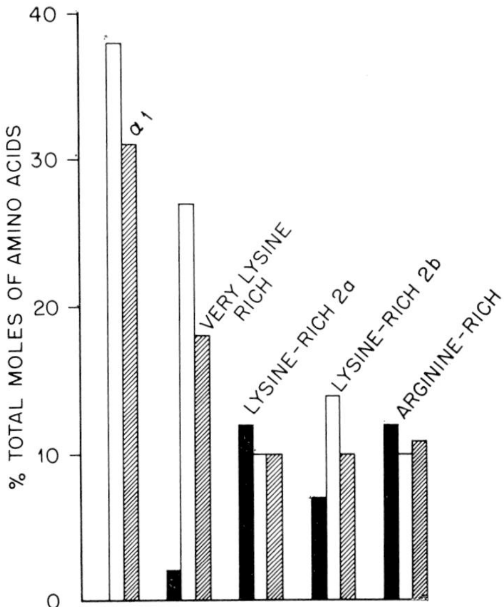


FIG. 2-1. Lysine, arginine, and alanine content of various histone fractions. [From Busch *et al.* (5).]

(7–11) to have an extraordinarily large content of lysine and alanine. The α-1 fraction has not been found by other workers and is excluded from the general classification in Table I.

*Alanine.* As a major component of the histones in terms of percentage of the total amino acid residues, alanine comprises a larger share of the amino acids than arginine in the slightly lysine-rich 2b or *N*-proline histone fraction or the very lysine-rich histones. In these fractions, alanine accounted for 10 and 18% of the total amino acids. In the α-1 fraction of Cruft *et al.* (7–11) lysine and alanine accounted for almost 70% of the amino acids. It is not completely clear whether this fraction is a distinct protein entity or whether it is a breakdown product of a fraction with a higher molecular weight, as Johns (24) has recently suggested.

One of the reasons for the early consideration of histones as "arginine-rich" proteins is the fact that amino acid content including arginine content was determined at one time solely by Kjehldahl analysis. Since the nitrogen content of arginine is four times that of most other amino acids, it is not surprising that the values for arginine appeared high in the histones when the amino acids were compared on the basis of percentage of the total nitrogen in the histones.

*Amino Acid Composition of "Whole Histone."* Table 2-II presents modern values for amino acid composition of crude calf thymus histones or "whole histone" prior to fractionation. At one time, marked differences

TABLE 2-II
AMINO ACID COMPOSITION OF CALF THYMUS HISTONES PRIOR TO FRACTIONATION

| Amino acid | Per cent[a] |
|---|---|
| Alanine | 13.2 |
| Arginine | 8.3 |
| Aspartic acid | 5.1 |
| Glutamic acid | 8.8 |
| Glycine | 8.4 |
| Histidine | 1.9 |
| Isoleucine | 4.3 |
| Leucine | 7.6 |
| Lysine | 14.6 |
| Methionine | 0.9 |
| Phenylalanine | 2.0 |
| Proline | 5.1 |
| Serine | 5.8 |
| Threonine | 6.0 |
| Tyrosine | 2.2 |
| Valine | 6.3 |

[a] The values are percentages of total moles of amino acids recovered in the particular amino acid. The data are averaged from representative studies (6, 21, 25–28, 32, 44).

were found in different laboratories in the values for lysine, leucine, and valine content of the histones. However, the values for arginine were quite similar in four of the five series shown in Table 2-III. Only Crampton *et al.* (6) had the advantage of the modern techniques of Spackman, Moore, and Stein (43) for the analysis of amino acids, and their analysis for whole calf thymus histone has now been repeatedly verified within the current limits of experimental error (21, 25–28, 32, 44). Johns and Butler (26) studied the amino acid composition of

TABLE 2-III

EARLY STUDIES ON THE AMINO ACID COMPOSITION[a] OF CALF THYMUS HISTONES PRIOR TO FRACTIONATION

| Starting material: | Nucleohistone | Isolated nuclei | Nucleoprotein | Chromosomal material | Nucleoprotein |
|---|---|---|---|---|---|
| References: | Kossel (29) | Daly *et al.* (13) | Hamer (18–20) | Morris and Harper (33) | Crampton *et al.* (6) |
| Histone extraction: | dil. $H_2SO_4$ | 0.2 *N* HCl | 0.1 *N* HCl | 0.2 *N* HCl | 2.6 *M* NaCl |
| Histone precipitation: | Ammonia | NaOH to pH 10.0 | Ammonia | NaOH to pH 10.4 | Ethanol |
| Amino acid | | | | | |
| Alanine | 5.4 | 11.2 | 9.8 | 14.2 | 13.5 |
| Arginine | 9.6 | 8.5 | 11.0 | 9.3 | 8.3 |
| Aspartic acid | — | 6.1 | 5.5 | 6.0 | 4.8 |
| Cystine | — | 0.4 | 0.03 | — | 0.0 |
| Glutamic acid | 0.8 | 9.2 | 9.8 | 9.4 | 8.2 |
| Glycine | 0.8 | 9.0 | 9.3 | 7.8 | 8.3 |
| Histidine | 0.9 | 1.7 | 2.0 | 2.5 | 2.0 |
| Isoleucine | — | 4.4 | — | 6.3 | 4.3 |
| Leucine | 18.0 | 8.5 | 14.8 | 7.3 | 7.7 |
| Lysine | 6.1 | 7.9 | 8.0 | 11.6 | 14.7 |
| Methionine | — | 0.8 | 0.9 | 0.6 | 0.9 |
| Phenylalanine | 3.4 | 2.4 | 3.0 | 1.9 | 2.2 |
| Proline | 2.3 | 4.5 | 3.8 | 4.4 | 4.9 |
| Serine | — | 5.1 | 4.3 | 4.8 | 5.9 |
| Threonine | — | 6.0 | 6.0 | 6.6 | 5.7 |
| Tryptophan | — | — | 0.21 | 0.0 | 0.0 |
| Tyrosine | 8.0 | 2.1 | 2.7 | 2.8 | 2.5 |
| Valine | — | 5.9 | 8.7 | 4.7 | 6.2 |

[a] The values are percentages of total moles of amino acids recovered in the particular amino acid. The data were recalculated from the original papers. The values reported by Crampton *et al.* (6) are now accepted as standard values since they have been confirmed by most later studies (21, 25–28, 32, 44).

whole histone of wheat germ. They found a higher alanine and lysine content and a lower arginine content than in calf thymus histones (Table 2-IV).

TABLE 2-IV
AMINO ACID COMPOSITION OF WHEAT GERM HISTONES PRIOR TO FRACTIONATION

| Amino acid | Per cent[a] |
|---|---|
| Alanine | 15.5 |
| Arginine | 7.3 |
| Aspartic acid | 4.4 |
| Cystine | — |
| Glutamic acid | 8.6 |
| Glycine | 8.1 |
| Histidine | 1.5 |
| Isoleucine } Leucine } | 12.3 |
| Lysine | 17.6 |
| Methionine | — |
| Phenylalanine | 2.2 |
| Proline | 5.1 |
| Serine | 4.9 |
| Threonine | 5.4 |
| Tryptophan | — |
| Tyrosine | 1.7 |
| Valine | 5.5 |

[a] The values are percentages of total moles of amino acids recovered in the particular amino acid. The histones were extracted from deoxyribonucleoproteins. Data of Johns and Butler (26).

## Amino Acid Composition of Products of Recent Fractionation Procedures

The advent of improved techniques for the isolation of histones (see Chapter III) has brought with it the realization that most of the previous data on the amino acid compositions of the histones were necessarily the composite values for mixtures of fractions. With the procedures of Johns *et al.* (25–28) it was possible to further fractionate the histones of the calf thymus, the Walker tumor, and other tissues (21). The amino acid compositions of representative fractions are shown in Table 2-V. Fraction 1 consists of the very lysine-rich histones, and the amino acid composition is like those previously reported; the content of lysine and alanine were both very high (Table 2-VI). When fraction 1 was obtained by precipitation with trichloroacetic acid (fraction 1T) the fraction had a higher lysine and lower alanine content than when it was obtained by chromatography (fraction 1C).

This difference in amino acid composition may reflect the change in the relative amounts of the subgroups of this fraction that were present (21) as shown in Figs. 2-2 and 2-3 (pp. 50, 51).

TABLE 2-V
AMINO ACID COMPOSITION OF REPRESENTATIVE HISTONE SUBFRACTIONS

| Composition: Chemical fractions (20–22): | Very lysine-rich F1 | Slightly lysine-rich *N*-acetylalanine F2a | Slightly lysine-rich *N*-proline F2b | "Arginine-rich" F3 |
|---|---|---|---|---|
| Amino acid | | | | |
| Alanine | 23.5 | 10.5 | 10.5 | 12.5 |
| Arginine | 2.5 | 11.5 | 7.5 | 13.0 |
| Aspartic acid | 2.8 | 6.0 | 5.5 | 5.0 |
| Glutamic acid | 6.0 | 8.5 | 9.0 | 11.0 |
| Glycine | 6.8 | 12.5 | 7.0 | 6.5 |
| Histidine | 0.5 | 2.0 | 2.5 | 2.1 |
| Isoleucine | 1.6 | 4.5 | 5.0 | 5.0 |
| Leucine | 4.4 | 10.5 | 6.0 | 8.5 |
| Lysine | 26.3 | 10.5 | 14.5 | 9.0 |
| Methionine | — | — | 0.7 | 0.7 |
| Phenylalanine | 0.8 | 1.6 | 2.0 | 2.5 |
| Proline | 7.9 | 3.0 | 4.5 | 4.5 |
| Serine | 6.2 | 3.1 | 9.0 | 4.5 |
| Threonine | 5.5 | 5.6 | 6.5 | 7.0 |
| Tyrosine | 0.5 | 3.0 | 3.1 | 2.0 |
| Valine | 5.0 | 7.0 | 6.8 | 6.0 |

[a] The values are percentages of total moles of amino acids recovered in the particular amino acid. The data are averages from representative studies (21, 22, 25–28).

The "arginine-rich" fraction 3 contained 10–14% of arginine and alanine. When isolated by chromatography (fraction 3C) it contained more glutamic acid than when precipitated by ammonia. This result suggests that a fraction rich in glutamic acid is present in this group of histones, and recently a fraction containing 20% glutamic acid and 10% aspartic acid was separated from this fraction. The ratio of lysine to arginine in the slightly lysine-rich fraction 2a, the fastest moving histone fraction on gel electrophoresis, was essentially the same as that of the "arginine-rich" histone fraction. The fraction differed from the "arginine-rich" fraction in the lower content of glutamic acid and higher content of glycine. Fraction 2a has been referred to as the "glycine-rich" histone (21) or as the *N*-acetylalanine histone.

The other slightly lysine-rich fraction is the 2b histone fraction of which the major component is the *N*-proline histone. The lysine content of this fraction was found to be 14% of the total amino acid residues and the alanine content was only about 10% of the total amino acid residues. The *N*-proline histone fraction has a composition quite similar to that of fraction B (Table 2-VI) of Crampton *et al.* (6).

***Amino Acids in Low Concentration in Histones.*** Some of the amino acids are present in low concentration in histones. In all instances, the concentration of methionine, cystine, cysteine, and tryptophan was very low. Small amounts of histidine, tyrosine, and phenylalanine were found in all the histone fractions but the concentrations of these amino acids were very low in the very lysine-rich histones.

***Earlier Studies.*** Table 2-VI presents amino acid compositions of fractions obtained in earlier studies. There are some similarities to values

TABLE 2-VI
EARLY STUDIES ON AMINO ACID COMPOSITION OF VARIOUS CALF THYMUS HISTONE FRACTIONS[a]

| Reference: Name of fraction: | Daly and Mirsky (12) | | Davison and Butler (14, 15) | | Gregoire *et al.* (16, 17) | |
|---|---|---|---|---|---|---|
| | I | II | Fast | Slow | P | S |
| Amino acid | | | | | | |
| Alanine | 12.1 | 19.1 | 11.6 | 27.4 | 9.5 | |
| Arginine | 11.3 | 3.0 | 11.6 | 2.7 | 10.4 | 5.5 |
| Aspartic acid | 6.1 | 2.4 | 4.9 | 2.7 | 6.5 | |
| Cystine | 0.4 | 0.0 | | | 0.4 | |
| Glutamic acid | 9.9 | 4.0 | 8.5 | 2.3 | 7.7 | |
| Glycine | 9.8 | 7.0 | 8.7 | 7.9 | 9.3 | |
| Histidine | 1.9 | 0.0 | 3.2 | 0.0 | 1.4 | 1.3 |
| Isoleucine | 3.4 | 1.5 | 6.5 | 1.3 | | |
| Leucine | 8.1 | 4.9 | 9.3 | 3.1 | 17.0 | |
| Lysine | 11.5 | 33.7 | 8.4 | 26.2 | 10.5 | 15.2 |
| Methionine | 1.1 | 0.2 | 1.7 | 0.0 | 0.7 | |
| Phenylalanine | 2.3 | 0.8 | 2.8 | 0.0 | 2.1 | |
| Proline | 4.0 | 7.7 | 2.3 | 8.9 | 3.4 | |
| Serine | 5.0 | 6.0 | 2.7 | 5.9 | 5.4 | |
| Threonine | 6.1 | 4.4 | 6.4 | 5.8 | 5.1 | |
| Tryptophan | | | | | 0.2 | |
| Tyrosine | 2.5 | 0.8 | 4.5 | 0.7 | 3.4 | 2.0 |
| Valine | 4.3 | 4.5 | 6.9 | 5.0 | 6.9 | |

[a] Starting materials and extraction procedures are the same as in Table 2-III. Values are percentages of total moles of amino acids recovered in the particular amino acid. The data were recalculated from the original papers.

in Table 2-V, but for the most part the values differ, presumably because of the relative amounts of different histones in the fractions.

***Relative Amounts of Histone Fractions.*** The relative amounts of the histones in the total crude histone fraction are not precisely known. The estimate made for the percentage of histone fractions in the total histones is shown in the accompanying tabulation (21, 24):

| Fraction | Walker tumor (% total histone) | Calf thymus (% total histone) |
|---|---|---|
| Fraction 1 | 10 | 20 |
| Fraction 2a | 30–40 | 35 |
| *N*-proline histone (fraction 2b) | 30 | 25 |
| Fraction 3 | 20–30 | 20 |

TABLE 2-VI (*Continued*)

| Reference: Name of fraction: | Crampton *et al.* (6) | | | Cruft *et al.* (7–11) | | | | | |
|---|---|---|---|---|---|---|---|---|---|
| | A | B | C | $\alpha_1$ | $\alpha_2$ | $\alpha_3$ | β | 0.8 S | 1.6 S |
| Amino acid | | | | | | | | | |
| Alanine | 24.5 | 11.3 | 19.6 | 30.4 | 22.8 | 19.5 | 11.4 | 17.7 | 11.3 |
| Arginine | 2.4 | 7.3 | 4.7 | 0.0 | 3.3 | 4.3 | 11.4 | 4.8 | 8.1 |
| Aspartic acid | 2.1 | 5.2 | 3.3 | 0.8 | 2.4 | 4.2 | 4.9 | 5.6 | 6.5 |
| Cystine | 0.0 | 0.0 | 0.0 | | | | | | |
| Glutamic acid | 3.6 | 8.2 | 5.8 | 1.1 | 4.1 | 5.1 | 9.8 | 6.5 | 8.9 |
| Glycine | 7.1 | 8.0 | 7.4 | 3.8 | 9.0 | 11.0 | 8.1 | 9.7 | 8.1 |
| Histidine | 0.0 | 2.4 | 1.1 | 0.0 | 0.8 | 1.7 | 3.3 | 1.6 | 3.2 |
| Isoleucine | 1.1 | 4.5 | 2.4 | 0.0 | 1.6 | 2.5 | 4.9 | 2.4 | 4.9 |
| Leucine | 4.7 | 8.0 | 5.9 | 0.8 | 4.1 | 6.8 | 9.8 | 7.3 | 8.9 |
| Lysine | 26.0 | 12.6 | 18.8 | 38.0 | 26.0 | 20.4 | 8.1 | 17.7 | 11.3 |
| Methionine | 0.0 | 0.9 | 0.5 | 0.0 | 0.0 | 0.0 | 1.6 | 0.8 | 1.6 |
| Phenylalanine | 0.7 | 1.3 | 1.4 | 0.0 | 0.8 | 8.5 | 2.4 | 1.6 | 1.3 |
| Proline | 9.2 | 4.4 | 7.6 | 13.7 | 9.8 | 6.8 | 4.9 | 4.8 | 4.0 |
| Serine | 7.1 | 7.0 | 6.8 | 3.0 | 4.9 | 6.8 | 4.1 | 7.3 | 6.5 |
| Threonine | 5.7 | 4.9 | 5.8 | 4.6 | 4.9 | 4.2 | 6.5 | 4.8 | 5.7 |
| Tryptophan | | | | | | | | | |
| Tyrosine | 0.7 | 3.0 | 2.0 | 0.0 | 0.8 | 2.2 | 3.2 | 1.6 | 3.2 |
| Valine | 5.3 | 6.4 | 4.7 | 3.8 | 4.9 | 5.1 | 5.7 | 5.6 | 6.5 |

*Methods for Amino Acid Analysis.* Even with the elegant methods available at present for amino acid analysis, small errors occur because of the different rates of destruction of the amino acids in the course of hydrolysis of the protein. These errors can be minimized by studies on the time of hydrolysis and extrapolation of the values to zero-time of hydrolysis. Another problem is the method for actual analysis of the amino acids. The procedure of Spackman *et al.* (43) for determination of amino acids on automatic amino acid analyzers eliminates many limitations in precise quantitation of amino acids which are inherent in paper electrophoresis, chromatography of dinitrophenyl derivatives, bacterial assays, and other less direct methods. However, the increasing evidence that some of the terminal residues in the histones may be acetylated (39) and that ε-*N*-methyllysine (34) is present in the histones makes it necessary to accept the values shown in Table 2-V as very good approximations that are subject to minor corrections. Thus far, there are no satisfactory values reported for the content of glutamine and asparagine in the various histone fractions.

*ε-N-Methyllysine.* Murray (34) has reported that ε-*N*-methyllysine is present in histones of calf thymus, liver, and spleen; rabbit liver, kidney, and spleen; and liver of rat and lamb. This amino acid accounted for only 0.02% of all the moles of the amino acids of the protein. The significance of its presence is not yet clear, particularly in view of the fact that it was not found in histones of chicken erythrocytes, wheat germ, or pea embryos (42). The source of the methyl group was found to be methionine, but it remains to be established whether the lysine is methylated when in peptide linkage in the protein or whether lysine is first methylated and then incorporated into the histones.

## $NH_2$-Terminal Amino Acid Analysis of Histones

Luck and his colleagues (30, 31) first noted that $NH_2$-terminal amino acids of histones included alanine, glycine, and leucine (Table 2-VII). When the histones were fractionated into light and heavy groups by ultracentrifugation, Luck and his colleagues (30, 31, 40) reported the presence of a terminal dipeptide, valyllysine, in the group of $NH_2$-terminals. All the $NH_2$-terminal amino acids in the "light" histones were also found in the "heavy" histones but the $NH_2$-terminal dipeptide valyllysine was not found in the latter group. In addition, Luck *et al.* (30, 31) made studies on the C-terminal amino acids and reported that the latter were alanine, valine, leucine, and tyrosine. The studies by Luck *et al.* (30, 31, 40) on the terminal amino acids of the histones supported the idea that there was a variety of proteins in the histones, but it was not clear whether they were only four or five histones or many more.

Shortly after Luck *et al.* (30, 31) reported their studies on the $NH_2$-terminal amino acids, Phillips (37) modified the Sanger procedure (41) and improved the paper chromatographic analysis of dinitrophenyl (DNP)-amino acids. He recognized that DNP-proline

TABLE 2-VII
$NH_2$-TERMINAL AMINO ACIDS OF HISTONES

| Reference | $NH_2$-terminal | Histone type |
|---|---|---|
| Luck *et al.* (30, 31, 40) | Alanine, glycine, leucine | Heavy |
| | Alanine, glycine, leucine, valyllysine | Light |
| Phillips (37) | Proline | Slightly lysine-rich |
| | Alanine | Arginine-rich |
| | Lysine, phenylalanine, serine, glycine | Others |
| Phillips (39) | Acetylalanine | Slightly lysine-rich |
| Biserte and Sautiere (1) | Proline, alanine, histidine, lysine | Whole histone |

had a much lower molar absorption coefficient than the dinitrophenyl derivatives of other amino acids. As a result, there was a misleading calculation of $NH_2$-terminal concentration unless this point was considered. Phillips (37) was the first to show that the slightly lysine-rich histones mainly had proline as the $NH_2$-terminal amino acid and that "arginine-rich" histones mainly had an alanine as the $NH_2$-terminal amino acid. Lysine, phenylalanine, serine, and glycine have also been found to be present as $NH_2$-terminal amino acids along with small amounts of threonine, valine, and aspartic and glutamic acids (21, 44). Proline, alanine, histidine, and lysine were also found by Biserte and Sautiere (1) to be $NH_2$-terminal amino acids of histones. In view of the presence of all these amino acids as the $NH_2$-terminal amino acids, it does not seem that a limitation on the number of histones could be set on the basis of the $NH_2$-terminal amino acids. However, some of these are present in such small amounts that it is not certain whether they are present in the histones or in minor contaminants of histone preparations.

*N-Proline Histone.* One of the fractions, coded as 2b, has been isolated in a highly purified state. Since proline is its major $NH_2$-terminal amino acid, tentatively the protein may be classified as the *N*-proline histone (Table 2-I). At the moment, however, one cannot exclude the possibility that several *N*-proline histones may exist, although on the basis of starch gel electrophoresis, $NH_2$-terminal analysis, ultracentrifugation, and peptide mapping, the *N*-proline histone of fraction 2b has been highly purified (5). Another fraction has as its $NH_2$-terminal an acetylated alanine residue; this protein may be referred to as the *N*-acetylalanine histone (25, 39). For the future, nomenclature on the basis of $NH_2$-terminals would appear to have the virtue of providing a specific structural basis for the identification of the histones.

## Physical Methods for Classification of the Histones

*Electrophoretic Mobility.* In addition to the classification of the histones on the basis of amino acid composition, particularly lysine and arginine, it has been possible to classify the histones on the basis of

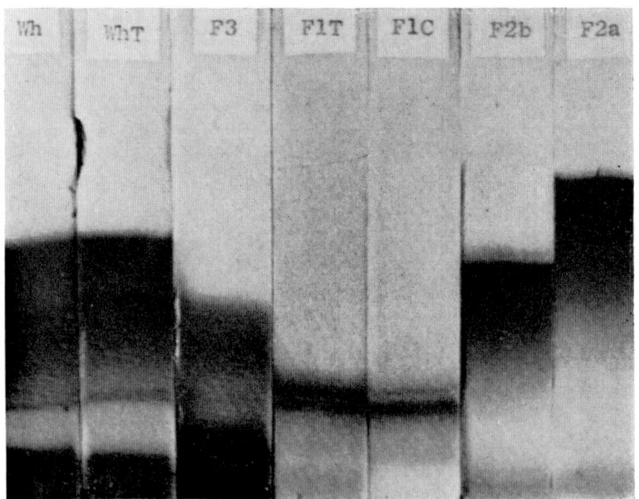


FIG. 2-2. Starch gel electrophoresis of histone fractions. F1C, F2a, and F2b are fractions obtained by chromatography. F1T was obtained by precipitation with 20% trichloroacetic acid. F3 was obtained by precipitation with 0.06 *N* $NH_4OH$ of proteins recovered from F3 fractions obtained by chromatography. Wh is unfractionated histone from Walker tumor; WhT is the same sample precipitated with 20% trichloroacetic acid. The proteins were stained with Amido Black 10B. [From Hnilica and Busch (21).]

electrophoretic mobility. Cruft *et al.* (7–11) reported that calf thymus histones could be separated into 4 or 6 groups by means of moving boundary electrophoresis (Table 2-VI). Whether they were able to derive pure proteins by this technique has not been established, but they did separate the very lysine-rich fractions referred to as α-frac-

FIG. 2-3. Starch gel electrophoresis of very lysine-rich histones. F1C was obtained by chromatography (see Chapter III). F1T was obtained by precipitation with trichloroacetic acid. The starch gels were prepared from 12% suspensions of starch in a solution that was 4 *M* with respect to urea and 0.01 *N* with respect to HCl. A gradient of 4 volts per centimeter was maintained for 6 hours. The proteins were stained with Amido Black 10B. [From Hnilica and Busch (21).]

tions from the β- or "arginine-rich" histone. In the same study they also found the γ- or slightly lysine-rich histones. The possibility has been suggested that the most lysine-rich of the various α-fractions may be the product of partial degradation of the very lysine-rich histones (24). Mauritzen and Stedman (32) reported that the amino acid composition of the β- or "arginine-rich" histones differed when the histones were extracted from the erythrocytes, spleen, or liver of the chickens. They concluded that the β-histones were cell specific.

*Starch Gel Electrophoresis.* On starch gel electrophoresis of the histones, the fastest moving histones (Fig. 2-2) are the slightly lysine-rich histones (21, 25–28). Of these, fraction 2a moves fastest and the 2b or the *N*-proline histone fraction moves more slowly. The very lysine-rich histones are next to the slowest moving fraction. When this fraction was treated with urea, several small components were noted in addition to the main component, suggesting that as many as five fractions were present (Fig. 2-3). The "arginine-rich" fraction is the fraction of lowest mobility in starch gel. At present, it does not seem desirable to develop a special classification of the histones based upon their electrophoretic mobility, but rather to use this characteristic as a means for identification of the histone fractions.

## Sedimentation Analysis of the Histones

The histones can be separated into "heavy" and "light" fractions by means of ultracentrifugation (see Chapter III). This method has not proved useful for fractionation or nomenclature of the histones because of their tendency to aggregate at pH above 4 and the lack of evidence for a clear-cut fractionation of discrete chemical entities. As mentioned previously, ultracentrifugation was utilized by Luck *et al.* (30, 31) in early studies on the $NH_2$-terminal amino acids of the histones. At present, no method of nomenclature of histones is completely satisfactory, including those based on electrophoretic mobility or amino acid composition, since no method provides a completely pure histone fraction.

## The Number of Histones

From the fact that there are three classes of histones on the basis of amino acid composition and that these classes of lysine-rich, slightly lysine-rich, and arginine-rich histones contain 2, 3, and 2 or 3 fractions, respectively, it would appear at the present time that the total number of histones would be eight or more in calf thymus preparations. It is difficult at present to set upper limits on the number of these proteins, since all the histone fractions are still heterogeneous. As shown in Fig. 2-3, it seems that the *very lysine-rich fraction* contains 5 components. On the other hand, these may result from breaking apart of strands of a single molecule by a degradative process or disruption of van der Waals forces through the interaction of urea on some of the bonding forces. Evidence for multiple components in the slightly lysine-rich fraction was also obtained by studies of the $NH_2$-terminal amino acids (see Chapter III). Recently, Johns (24) has reported separation of three very lysine-rich histone fractions (Table 2-VIII). One of these had an amino acid composition equivalent to that of the original very lysine-rich histone fraction, but the other two fractions were distinctly different inasmuch as they contained large amounts of glutamic acid and aspartic acid. The total number of acidic amino acid residues approximated 31% of the total amino acids in these fractions.

TABLE 2-VIII

Amino Acid Composition[a] of Fractions of Lysine-Rich Histones[b]

| Amino acid | Peak 1 | Peak 2 | Peak 3 |
|---|---|---|---|
| Alanine | 10.1 | 8.3 | 24.3 |
| Arginine | 4.2 | 4.2 | 1.8 |
| Aspartic acid | 11.4 | 30.9 | 6.2 |
| Glutamic acid | 20.1 | | |
| Glycine | 5.6 | 6.5 | 7.2 |
| Histidine | 1.3 | 0.9 | — |
| Leucine + isoleucine | 5.6 | 4.2 | 6.0 |
| Lysine | 19.4 | 19.0 | 26.8 |
| Phenylalanine | 3.2 | 3.5 | 0.9 |
| Proline | 5.8 | 7.2 | 9.2 |
| Serine | 5.6 | 7.6 | 5.6 |
| Threonine | 2.9 | 2.3 | 5.6 |
| Tyrosine | 2.4 | 3.0 | 0.9 |
| Valine | 2.4 | 2.5 | 5.4 |

[a] The values are percentages of total moles of amino acid recovered in the particular amino acid.

[b] From Johns (24).

Some inferences can be drawn from the study of the *N*-proline histone. As indicated earlier, the 2b fraction that contains this protein consists of 30% of all of the histones in calf thymus or the Walker tumor. The *N*-proline histone comprises approximately 80–95% of the total protein residues in the 2b fraction. Thus, a single protein possibly accounts for 25–30% of all the histones. In addition, studies on the histone of fraction 2a have shown that this fraction is also highly purified and consists of at most two proteins. Thus, the 50–60% of the total histones that are in the slightly lysine-rich fraction could be composed of three types of proteins. In addition, fraction 3 may contain four or five proteins and fraction 1 may contain five proteins. From these considerations, it would seem most reasonable that at present the number of histones be estimated to be approximately 10–15 rather than a very large number (35).

## Distribution of Histones in Nature

Histones have been found in a variety of plant and animal tissues (38). However, there is some question whether they are present in some single-cell species.

*Histones in Bacteria.* The question of whether histones are present in bacteria has been approached by a number of workers (8, 45). Zubay and Watson (45) have stated the *Escherichia coli* do not contain histones, but Cruft and Leaver (8) reported that a basic protein fraction can be isolated from *Staphylococcus aureus.* On starch gel electrophoresis, the basic proteins that were extracted with 0.1 $N$ $H_2SO_4$ separated into three components (8). Large amounts of lysine, arginine, alanine, leucine, and proline were found in these proteins. Similar results were obtained with *Micrococcus lysodeikticus.* A DNA-protein fraction referred to as a deoxyribonucleohistone was previously reported by Palmade *et al.* (36) to be present in *Escherichia coli.*

*Histones in Other Single-Cell Organisms.* A number of studies have suggested that histones are present in amebas and a variety of other single-

TABLE 2-IX
AMINO ACID COMPOSITIONS[a] OF HISTONE PREPARATIONS FROM CHLORELLA CELLS AND RICE EMBRYOS[b]

| Amino acid | *Chlorella* | Rice embryos Peak 1 | Peak 2 | Peak 3 |
|---|---|---|---|---|
| Alanine | 17.8 | 16.6 | 10.2 | 6.7 |
| Arginine | 4.0 | 8.2 | 10.9 | 13.2 |
| Aspartic acid | 3.9 | 5.1 | 6.1 | 6.8 |
| Cystine | 0.8 | 0 | 0.2 | 2.3 |
| Glutamic acid | 8.9 | 8.7 | 13.8 | 18.2 |
| Glycine | 6.1 | 9.2 | 10.1 | 11.3 |
| Histidine | 1.2 | 3.2 | 2.3 | 5.4 |
| Isoleucine | 1.7 | 3.8 | 4.6 | 2.8 |
| Leucine | 3.3 | 6.0 | 7.0 | 4.8 |
| Lysine | 26.7 | 14.0 | 7.3 | 5.4 |
| Phenylalanine | 0.9 | 1.3 | 3.2 | 2.6 |
| Proline | 8.7 | 7.1 | 4.7 | 4.1 |
| Serine | 4.6 | 5.6 | 5.8 | 6.1 |
| Threonine | 4.2 | 4.2 | 4.4 | 2.9 |
| Tyrosine | 1.2 | 1.3 | 2.2 | 1.9 |
| Valine | 5.1 | 4.9 | 6.4 | 4.6 |

[a] The values are percentages of total moles of amino acids recovered in the particular amino acid.
[b] From Iwai (23).

cell species. As in the case of other species including bacteria, there is relatively little biochemically satisfactory evidence to support this idea. Such reports have been based primarily upon staining with Fast Green or other stains for basic proteins. A similar kind of evidence is available that histones are present in chromosomes in a number of insects including *Drosophila* and *Chironomus*. Recently, Iwai (23) has reported the isolation of a histone fraction from *Chlorella ellipsoidea*. The amino acid composition of the fraction is shown in Table 2-IX.

**Histones in Plants.** Histones have been reported to be present in a variety of plants including wheat, broad beans, corn, onions, *Lilium henryi*, *Pinus sibirica*, and *Tradescantia paludosa*. More recently, histones of pea seedlings (42), wheat (p. 44), and rice (Table 2-IX) have been analyzed. Histones of birds have also been studied; as already indicated, histones were found initially in goose erythrocytes (29). Subsequently, histones were studied in a variety of birds, including ducks and chickens.

**Histones in Animal Tissues.** Histones have been found in various tissues of animals including tumors, thymus, testis, spleen, pancreas, liver, kidney, and placenta (38). In addition, histones of ova and lymphocytes have been studied. The changing patterns of histones to protamines and other basic proteins in spermatogenesis has been detailed by Bloch and Hew (2–4). In many instances, satisfactory analytical data are not available (see Chapter V, p. 134).

## References


1. Biserte, G., and Sautiere, P.: Groupes α-amines terminaux des histones du thymus de veau et de tumeurs expérimentales du rat. *Compt. Rend. Acad. Sci.* **246**: 1764-1766 (1958).
2. Bloch, D. P.: On the derivation of histone specificity. *Proc. Natl. Acad. Sci. U.S.* **48**: 324-326 (1962).
3. Bloch, D. P.: Synthetic processes in the cell nucleus. I. Histone synthesis in non-replicating chromosomes. *J. Histochem. Cytochem.* **10**: 137-143 (1962).
4. Bloch, D. P., and Hew, H. Y. C.: Changes in nuclear histones during fertilization, and early embryonic development in the pulmonate snail, *Helix aspersa*. *J. Biophys. Biochem. Cytol.* **8**: 69-81 (1960).
5. Busch, H., Steele, W. J., Hnilica, L. S., Taylor, C. W., and Mavioglu, H.: Biochemistry of histones and the cell cycle. *J. Cellular Comp. Physiol.* **62** (Suppl. 1): 95-110 (1963).
6. Crampton, C. F., Moore, S., and Stein, W. H.: Chromatographic fractionation of calf thymus histone. *J. Biol. Chem.* **215**: 787-801 (1955).

7. Cruft, H. J., Hindley, J., Mauritzen, C. M., and Stedman, E.: Amino acid composition of the six histones of calf thymocytes. *Nature* **180**: 1107-1109 (1957).
8. Cruft, H. J., and Leaver, J. L.: Isolation of histones from *Staphylococcus aureus*. *Nature* **192**: 556-557 (1961).
9. Cruft, H. J., Mauritzen, C. M., and Stedman, E.: Abnormal properties of histones from malignant cells. *Nature* **174**: 580-585 (1954).
10. Cruft, H. J., Mauritzen, C. M., and Stedman, E.: The nature and physico-chemical properties of histones. *Phil. Trans. Roy. Soc. London Ser.* **B241**: 93-145 (1957).
11. Cruft, H. J., Mauritzen, C. M., and Stedman, E.: The isolation of β-histone from calf thymocytes and the factors affecting its aggregation. *Proc. Roy. Soc.* **B249**: 21-41 (1958).
12. Daly, M. M., and Mirsky, A. E.: Histones with high lysine content. *J. Gen. Physiol.* **38**: 405-413 (1954-1955).
13. Daly, M. M., Mirsky, A. E., and Ris, H.: The amino acid composition and some properties of histones. *J. Gen. Physiol.* **34**: 439-462 (1950-1951).
14. Davison, P. F., and Butler, J. A. V.: The fractionation and composition of histones from thymus nucleoprotein. *Biochim. Biophys. Acta* **15**: 439-440 (1954).
15. Davison, P. F., and Butler, J. A. V.: The chemical composition of calf thymus nucleoprotein. *Biochim. Biophys. Acta* **21**: 568-573 (1956).
16. Gregoire, J., Gregoire, J., and Reynaud, J.: The heterogeneity of thymo-histone. *Compt. Rend. Acad. Sci.* **236**: 1922-1924 (1953).
17. Gregoire, J., and Limozin, M.: Heterogeneity and composition of preparations of thymus histone. *Bull. Soc. Chim. Biol.* **36**: 15-30 (1954).
18. Hamer, D.: Amino acid composition of thymus histone. *Nature* **167**: 40 (1951).
19. Hamer, D.: Aspects of the chemistry of the proteins in the nucleus. A short review and some experimental results. *Brit. J. Cancer* **5**: 130-139 (1951).
20. Hamer, D.: A comparison of different protein fractions obtained from thymus nuclei isolated in an aqueous medium. *Brit. J. Cancer* **7**: 151-156 (1953).
21. Hnilica, L. S., and Busch, H.: Fractionation of the histones of the Walker 256 carcinosarcoma by combined chemical and chromatographic techniques. *J. Biol. Chem.* **238**: 918-924 (1963).
22. Hnilica, L. S., Johns, E. W., and Butler, J. A. V.: Observations on the species and tissue specificity of histones. *Biochem. J.* **82**: 123-129 (1962).
23. Iwai, K.: Histones of rice embryos and of chlorella. *In* "The Nucleohistones" (J. Bonner and P. Ts'o, eds.), pp. 59-65. Holden-Day, San Francisco, California, 1964.
24. Johns, E. W.: Studies on lysine-rich histones. *In* "The Nucleohistones" (J. Bonner and P. Ts'o, eds.), pp. 52-57. Holden-Day, San Francisco, California, 1964.
25. Johns, E. W., and Butler, J. A. V.: Further fractionation of histones from calf thymus. *Biochem. J.* **82**: 15-18 (1962).
26. Johns, E. W., and Butler, J. A. V.: Studies on histones. 4. The histones of wheat germ. *Biochem. J.* **84**: 436-439 (1962).

27. Johns, E. W., Phillips, D. M. P., Simson, P., and Butler, J. A. V.: Improved fractionation of arginine-rich histones from calf thymus. *Biochem. J.* **77**: 631-636 (1960).

28. Johns, E. W., Phillips, D. M. P., Simson, P., and Butler, J. A. V.: The electrophoresis of histones and histone fractions on starch gel. *Biochem. J.* **80**: 189-193 (1961).

29. Kossel, A.: "The Protamines and Histones." Longmans, Green, London, 1921.

30. Luck, J. M., Cook, H. A., Eldredge, N. T., Haley, M. I., Kupke, D. W., and Rasmussen, P. S.: On the fractionation of thymus histone. *Arch. Biochem. Biophys.* **65**: 449-467 (1956).

31. Luck, J. M., Rasmussen, P. S., Satake, K., and Tsvetikov, A. N.: Further studies on the fractionation of calf thymus histone. *J. Biol. Chem.* **233**: 1407-1414 (1958).

32. Mauritzen, C. M., and Stedman, E.: Cell specificity of β-histones in the domestic fowl. *Proc. Roy. Soc.* **B150**: 299-311 (1959).

33. Morris, M. D., and Harper, H. A.: Amino acid composition of thymus nucleo-histone. *Proc. Soc. Exptl. Biol. Med.* **82**: 482-484 (1953).

34. Murray, K.: The occurrence of ε-*N*-methyl lysine in histones. *Biochemistry* **3**: 10-15 (1964).

35. Ohtaka, Y., and Spiegelman, S.: Translational control of protein synthesis in a cell-free system directed by a polycistronic viral RNA. *Science* **142**: 493-497 (1963).

36. Palmade, C., Chevallier, M.-R., Knobloch, A., and Vendrely, R.: Isolement d'une déoxyribonucleohistone à partir d'*Escherichia coli. Compt. Rend. Acad. Sci.* **246**: 2534-2537 (1958).

37. Phillips, D. M. P.: The *N*-terminal groups of calf thymus histones. *Biochem. J.* **68**: 35-40 (1958).

38. Phillips, D. M. P.: The Histones. *Progr. Biophys. Biophys. Chem.* **12**: 211-280 (1961).

39. Phillips, D. M. P.: The presence of acetyl groups in histones. *Biochem. J.* **87**: 258-263 (1963).

40. Rasmussen, P. S., Murray, K., and Luck, J. M.: On the complexity of calf thymus histone. *Biochemistry* **1**: 78-89 (1962).

41. Sanger, F.: The free amino groups of insulin. *Biochem. J.* **39**: 507-515 (1945).

42. Setterfield, G., Neelin, J. M., Neelin, E. M., and Bayley, S. T.: Studies on basic proteins from ribosomes of buds of pea seedlings. *J. Mol. Biol.* **2**: 416-424 (1960).

43. Spackman, D. H., Stein, W. H., and Moore, S.: Automatic recording apparatus for use in the chromatography of amino acids. *Anal. Chem.* **30**: 1190-1205 (1958).

44. Steele, W. J., and Busch, H.: Studies on the acidic nuclear proteins of the Walker tumor and the liver. *Cancer Res.* **23**: 1153-1163 (1963).

45. Zubay, G. L., and Watson, M. R.: The absence of histone in the bacterium *Escherichia coli*. I. Preparation and analysis of nucleoprotein extract. *J. Biophys. Biochem. Cytol.* **5**: 51-54 (1959).

# CHAPTER III

# Isolation of the Histones



## Introduction

The problems involved in the isolation of the histones are part of the overall problem of isolation of nuclear components from cells. The first of these problems is that of isolation of native nuclei from cells;

even now this problem is not completely solved. The second problem is the isolation of the gels, particles, and soluble fractions from the nuclei in a native state. Finally, there is the problem of extraction of histones in sufficient yield to permit their subfractionation into individual molecular species. Although several methods have been developed for the isolation of nuclei from various types of tissues, none of the methods is completely satisfactory and all require considerable effort. As a result, methods have been worked out for the isolation of a crude deoxyribonucleoprotein fraction from nuclei that are based on broader procedures for fractionation of nuclear proteins with saline solutions.

The methods for extraction of histones from the deoxyribonucleoproteins involve either direct extraction of the histones with acid or preliminary extraction with acid-ethanol solutions. Purification of the individual histone fractions may be achieved by selective precipitation with ethanol, acetone, or trichloroacetic acid and by chromatography, generally on carboxymethylcellulose. The criteria for purity of the histone fractions are the patterns obtained by starch gel electrophoresis, the amino acid analysis, the $NH_2$-terminal amino acid composition, and to a lesser extent the sedimentation characteristics. Thus far, a completely pure histone has not been obtained despite the intensive efforts of many workers. However, the progress that has been made now permits the isolation of one histone fraction, the *N*-proline histone, in purity ranging from 85 to 95%.

## Isolation of Nuclei

The initial problem in the isolation of the nuclear proteins is ascertaining that they come from the nucleus, and that cytoplasmic proteins are not present in the products isolated. Theoretically, more perfect isolation procedures than are available today would permit isolation of nuclei from cells in such a way that "1) the nuclei are anatomically identical to those of the whole cell, 2) the contents of the nuclei as they exist in the cell should all be present in the isolated product, and 3) the isolated nuclei should not contain cytoplasmic constituents" (9). The attainment of these important objectives is still a considerable distance away (33–38). The development of the now classical procedure of Chauveau *et al.* (17) for the isolation of nuclei of liver has permitted many important advances in studies on the nuclei of normal liver cells. Yet even in this case, the nuclei are not a perfect morphological replica of the nuclei of the normal liver cell unless the concentration of divalent ions is less than $5 \times 10^{-4}\,M$ in the media employed.

In the normal liver cell, as Schneider (81) pointed out, the nucleus is a pale object, with a very faint nucleolus or perhaps several faintly visible nucleoli, as seen by phase microscopy. The nuclear membrane is pale or scarcely visible, and the separation between the nucleus and the cytoplasm is more of a boundary than a doubled or birefringent membrane. Within the nucleus, there are faint shadows, but there are no visible particles.

*Procedures Employing Direct Homogenization of Tissues.* When the nucleus is isolated by the technique of Chauveau *et al.* (17) as well as by a variety of other methods in which $Ca^{++}$ is present in the medium, it has a doubly refractile nuclear membrane, the nucleoli are dense and condensed objects that differ sharply in refractive index from the nucleoplasm, and, in addition, there are other dense masses in the nucleus that are more or less irregularly shaped. The latter might be referred to as "micronucleoli" or condensed ribosomes but more likely are condensed nucleoprotein masses.

When other techniques are employed for isolation of the nuclei (12) in which divalent ions are omitted from the medium, the nucleus appears to be a homogeneous structure bounded by a membrane that is more refractile than the surrounding medium. Moreover, the nucleolus is not visible and neither are any of the condensed masses that are characteristic of the nuclei that are "hardened" with $Ca^{++}$.

*Perinuclear Ribonucleoprotein Layer.* If $Ca^{++}$ (0.003 $M$) is added to the media in which Walker tumor cells of the rat are homogenized, it is not possible to remove the cytoplasm or cytoplasmic tags from the nuclei, either by prolonged homogenization with loose homogenizers or with homogenizers with a very narrow pestle clearance (0.003 inch). Georgiev *et al.* (40) have indicated that a perinuclear ribonucleoprotein layer remains around nuclei of transplantable tumor cells when they are isolated by homogenization techniques. This layer is particularly difficult to separate from tumor nuclei when $Ca^{++}$ is added to the medium. With rat liver cells, however, it is very simple to remove the surface cytoplasm even when loose homogenizers are employed. The same is apparently true for the nuclei of acinar cells of the rat pancreas (16). Although the perinuclear ribonucleoproteins have been a laboratory nuisance in purification of the nuclei of the rat tumor cells, the possibility exists that in fact they are a site of active synthesis of proteins in dividing cells. In recent studies of human tumor cells in this laboratory, it was found that nuclei could be isolated in good yield, and with a morphology that was virtually the same as that of nuclei in the tumor cells, with minor modifications of the technique of Chauveau *et al.* (17).

*Procedures Employing Homogenization after Preliminary Treatment.* In some studies (33–38) hardening of nuclei has been attempted by means of citric acid. In others, cells have been pretreated with dilute saline solutions or distilled water so that the *osmotic shock* to the cell membrane renders it more susceptible to damage. A number of workers, including Lettré (61), Sauer *et al.* (80), Samarina (79), and Hudack *et al.* (53, 54), have found that ascites tumor cells were very resistant to destruction by direct homogenization, but after osmotic shock the cells were readily broken up by homogenization. The two serious disadvantages of this procedure are that the nuclear components may be leached out of the cells by the dilute solutions employed and that hydrolytic enzymes may be released from lysosomes and may then produce partial autolysis of the isolated cells and nuclei (13).

*Detergents.* Acceleration of disruption of cells by means of Triton-X (55) and other wetting agents (39, 61) has been reported to be a useful means for the isolation of nuclei. Although the cytoplasm is removed almost completely, the appearance of the nuclei suggests that some of the nuclear lipoprotein (Chapter VIII) has been removed. Since the nuclear membrane is virtually denuded, the method achieves the purpose of isolation of the nuclei with their membranes virtually free of contamination.

*Techniques Employing Organic Solvents.* At first it would seem that treatment of the cells with organic solvents would remove so much of the lipoprotein and lipid that the product would differ markedly in content and structure from the original cell mass. Apparently this has not turned out to be the case. The development of the technique for isolation of nuclei in organic solvents by Behrens (5) was predicated on the idea that aqueous media would tend to remove from cells the soluble components of small and large molecular weight that were important to cell function. With the aid of organic solvents, such substances would not be affected; indeed, it seemed possible that if they were properly employed there would be no appreciable change in the morphology of the cell or the cell nucleus. The original procedure of

Behrens (5) has been modified by Allfrey *et al.* (2) and more recently by Siebert *et al.* (83–85) so as to include rapid removal of the tissue from the animal, rapid freezing at temperatures approximating those of liquid nitrogen, and quick drying in a lyophilizer. Fragmentation of the tissue is carried out in a ball mill containing a medium of carbon tetrachloride and cyclohexane which serves to remove lipid, but protects against loss of proteins and enzymes.

The microscopic appearance of such nuclei obtained in this laboratory has not been satisfactory because the nuclei were crenated and contained cytoplasmic contaminants. The appearance of the nuclei was very inferior to the product obtained by other procedures for isolation of the nuclei (17, 36). The primary problem with regard to the procedure of Behrens (5) and its subsequent modification is the satisfactory removal of cytoplasm without adherence of cytoplasmic components to the nuclei. Some of the nuclei are dry, misshapen, and filled with crevasses. It would seem almost impossible to exclude significant cytoplasmic contamination from these indentations. Moreover, the dehydration of the cells may produce a layer of dehydrated cytoplasm adjacent to the nuclear membrane. Nonetheless, the method has been continuously improved and found to have advantages; it would seem to be a procedure of choice under some circumstances (see Chapter IX).

Another procedure that utilizes organic solvents is that of Georgiev *et al.* (41–43). In this technique, tissue samples are treated with phenol in an effort to block most degradative reactions in the nucleus (59). For the purpose of isolation of proteins, the phenol procedure would seem to be of very limited value in view of the marked denaturation of proteins produced by phenol. Other methods for isolation of nuclei in organic media include those described by Schneider (81) for the isolation of nuclei in glycerin-containing systems and modifications of this technique described by Dallam (25).

*Limitations of Procedures for Isolation of Nuclei.* Any of the procedures for isolation of nuclei is subject to a variety of experimental hazards (33–38) including:

1. adherence of cytoplasm to the nucleus;
2. destruction of nuclear components by released lysosomal hydrolases;
3. loss of nuclear soluble components;
4. loss of cofactors from the nucleus.

At the moment, none of the procedures available surmounts all these difficult problems; it would seem necessary to utilize several of the available procedures for handling nuclear components before final conclusions would be completely acceptable regarding the presence or absence of one molecular species from the nucleus.

*Isolation of Nuclear Subfractions.* The procedures for isolation of nuclear components are summarized in Table 3-I. Methods are being improved for isolation of nucleoli, chromosomes, nuclear ribosomes,

TABLE 3-I

A SUMMARY OF PROCEDURES FOR ISOLATION OF NUCLEAR COMPONENTS[a]

A. Following initial isolation of nuclei
   1. *Isolation of nucleoli:* Either by sonication of nuclei prepared in 0.0033–0.005 *M* $CaCl_2$ and 0.25 *M* sucrose or by compression and rapid decompression of nuclear preparations in the French pressure cell; purification by differential centrifugation
   2. *Isolation of chromosomes:* By gentle procedures employing cells in metaphase; aspiration and ejection from syringes followed by centrifugation in sucrose solutions 0.0005 *M* with respect to $Mg^{++}$ and $Ca^{++}$
   3. *Isolation of nuclear ribonucleoproteins:* Extraction from nuclei of calf thymus by 0.15 *M* NaCl or 0.01 *M* Tris buffers containing 0.001 *M* $MgCl_2$ followed by differential centrifugation
   4. *Isolation of deoxyribonucleoproteins:* Either by extraction of nuclei with 2 *M* NaCl or with water followed by precipitation of the deoxyribonucleoproteins from solutions 0.10–0.20 *M* with respect to NaCl
   5. *Nucleolochromosomal apparatus:* A residual fraction obtained after successive extraction of nuclei with 0.15 *M* NaCl and 2 *M* NaCl; bears many similarities to the nuclear ribonucleoprotein network, but probably contains other components including the nuclear membrane

B. Without initial isolation of nuclei
   1. *Nucleoli:* Obtained from tumors without extensive nuclear preparation inasmuch as it is not possible to remove cytoplasmic components in the presence of calcium ions at concentrations required to maintain the integrity of the nucleoli. Techniques are the same as in A,1, above
   2. *Deoxyribonucleoproteins:* Obtained as a residue following prolonged treatment of nuclear preparations with isotonic saline solutions

[a] From Busch and Steele (13).

and deoxyribonucleoproteins. For the isolation of histones, the methods for isolation of deoxyribonucleoproteins are of greatest importance. The extraction with either dilute salt solutions or with tris(hydroxymethyl)aminomethane (Tris) buffer is the procedure of choice (1, 98–100) for the isolation of nuclear ribonucleoproteins. The residual fraction that remains after extraction of the ribonucleoprotein and deoxyribonucleoprotein fractions (2 *M* NaCl) is referred to as the "nucleolochromosomal apparatus" by Zbarsky and his colleagues (42, 43, 101–103). This designation is one that primarily is operational rather than specific morphologically, since the whole nucleus is "nucleolochromosomal apparatus."

## Direct Isolation of Nucleoproteins

In view of the difficulties attending the direct isolation of nuclei and their components, efforts have been made to develop chemical procedures that would provide for direct isolation of nuclear proteins. In essence, this technique employing saline solutions is based upon the finding of Bensley (6) and Pollister and Mirsky (75) that nucleoproteins were soluble in concentrated salt solutions, i.e., about 5–10% NaCl or approximately 1–2 *M* NaCl. Although this technique has been subjected to a large number of variations, one of the presently employed procedures (91) for fractionation of nuclei is shown in Table 3-II, which demonstrates the key steps:

1. extraction with isotonic saline solution to remove the nuclear ribonucleoproteins and/or
2. extraction with Tris buffer at pH 7.6 to further remove ribonucleoproteins;
3. extraction with 2.0 *M* NaCl, by which deoxyribonucleoproteins are extracted;
4. extraction with 0.05 *N* NaOH to remove the acidic proteins.

Although the proteins extracted with dilute saline solution are referred to as the proteins of the "nuclear sap," it is equally likely that these include proteins of the nucleolus and of the chromatin since there is no satisfactory way at present to exclude this possibility.[1] Similarly, it is not possible to be precisely certain that all the proteins present in the deoxyribonucleoprotein extract (with 2 *M* NaCl) originate in the chromatin. Some may originate in the nucleolus and the nuclear RNP network (87). Others may represent portions of the soluble entities of the nucleus that are left behind when the initial saline extraction has been completed (42, 43). The deoxyribonucleoprotein extracted in 2 *M* NaCl contains histones, acidic proteins, RNA,

[1] Studies in this laboratory by Drs. Sankaranarayanan and Steele (unpublished results) have shown that a halo of perinucleolar ribonucleoprotein is extracted in steps 1 and 2, i.e., the Tris-saline extract.

and DNA; the histones and DNA are dissociated in this medium. Thus, the problem of isolation of a native deoxyribonucleoprotein from mammalian cells has not yet been resolved satisfactorily.

In one of the methods for isolation of the nucleoproteins, nuclei are not isolated (14, 15). Instead, the cells are directly extracted with buffered dilute saline solutions by stirring in a mixer. The mixers used have been magnetic stirrers, homogenizers, and blendors; the latter

TABLE 3-II

CHEMICAL PROCEDURE FOR ISOLATION OF NUCLEAR PROTEIN FRACTIONS[a]

- Isolated nuclei
  - 0.14 $M$ NaCl, 2 times → precipitate; "nuclear sap" proteins
- precipitate
  - 0.1 $M$ Tris pH 7.6 → precipitate; "nuclear sap" proteins
- precipitate
  - 2.0 $M$ NaCl → precipitate; deoxyribonucleoproteins-1
- precipitate
  - 2.0 $M$ NaCl → precipitate; deoxyribonucleoproteins-2
- precipitate
  - 0.05 $N$ NaOH, 3 times → "residual proteins"; acidic ribonucleoproteins
- deoxyribonucleoproteins-1
  - 0.5 $N$ $H_2SO_4$; extract twice with 0.2 $N$ $H_2SO_4$ → precipitate; histones
- precipitate
  - 6% PAS-phenol; 3 times → aqueous phase; phenol phases
- aqueous phase
  - 5% TCA, 90°C, 2 times → phenol-insoluble proteins; DNA RNA products
- phenol phases
  - methanol (2 volumes) → Acid-insoluble proteins

[a] From Steele and Busch (91).

have been shown to degrade high molecular weight RNA and may damage the nucleoproteins. The residue is treated with acid to extract the histones. The whitish residue that remains after many washings with 0.15 $M$ NaCl is referred to as "crude deoxyribonucleoprotein" (52). This preparation could suffer from the same deficiencies as the deoxyribonucleoprotein preparation referred to previously with the exception that it may also contain cytoplasmic contaminants. Operationally, the hazards of each of the procedures mentioned must be weighed against their rapidity and the further procedures to be employed in the course of the extraction and purification of individual types of protein.

*Extraction of Deoxyribonucleoprotein with Water.* Lilienfeld (62) and later Hammarsten (50) reported a procedure for extraction of nuclei with water to obtain nucleoprotein preparations. The product has recently been studied by Commerford *et al.* (18), who showed that the nucleoprotein contained about 5% RNA. The nucleoprotein was readily soluble in water containing ethylenediaminetetraacetic acid (EDTA). More than 90% of the nucleoprotein was extracted in 20 minutes. The molecular weight of the DNP was approximately two to three million. This product was probably markedly degraded from its native state, since this value is very low by comparison to others (14, 15, 59, 67, 82). Commerford *et al.* (18) attempted to determine the molarity of salt at which histone dissociated from DNA. At 1 *M* NaCl the histone and DNA remained associated, but with 6 *M* CsCl they were completely dissociated as determined by ultracentrifugation.

*Composition of the Products Obtained by Nuclear Extractions.* Table 3-III shows the composition of the products obtained in the various steps of the extraction procedure of Table 3-II (91). Approximately 15% of the nucleoprotein was extracted with dilute saline solution, and approximately another 5–15% was extracted with the Tris solution. More was extracted from the Walker tumor nuclei than was extracted from the nuclei of liver cells. The largest percentage, almost 60%, of the nucleoprotein was extracted with 2 *M* NaCl. In the liver, less of the total nucleoprotein was extracted with 0.05 *N* NaOH than was extracted in the tumor. Part of this greater extraction of components with Tris and NaOH in the tumor may have been related to the partial adherence of cytoplasmic contaminants to the tumor nuclear preparation (40).

Table 3-III also shows the composition of the various fractions. In the liver, the nucleic acids comprised only 5% of the total mass of the fraction extracted with dilute salt solution and 18% of the fraction extracted with Tris. In the tumor extracts, a larger percentage of the Tris fraction was composed of RNA. A much larger percentage of the fraction extracted with 2 *M* NaCl was composed of nucleic acids, i.e., about one-third; in this fraction, the amount of DNA was about 6 times that of RNA. In the other fractions, the amount of RNA was

TABLE 3-III

Fractionation of Isolated Nuclei of Liver and Walker 256 Carcinosarcoma and Nucleic Acid Content of Individual Fractions

| Fraction | Liver | | | | Walker tumor | | | |
|---|---|---|---|---|---|---|---|---|
| | Recovery | DNA | RNA | Protein | Recovery | DNA | RNA | Protein |
| 0.14 *M* NaCl extract | 17 | 1.5 | 3.4 | 95 | 12 | 0.1 | 5 | 95 |
| 0.10 *M* Tris extract | 5 | 6.8 | 11 | 82 | 14 | 1.5 | 26 | 72 |
| 2.0 *M* NaCl, 1st extract | 54 | 31 | 5 | 64 | 54 | 27 | 4.8 | 68 |
| 2.0 *M* NaCl, 2nd extract | 10 | 12 | 5 | 83 | 3 | 8 | 5.8 | 86 |
| 0.05 *N* NaOH extract | 6 | 0.3 | 8.9 | 91 | 12 | 0.3 | 12.6 | 87 |
| Residual | 2 | 0.0 | 0.6 | — | 2 | 0.0 | 0.3 | — |

[a] Data from Steele and Busch (91).

[b] The values for recovery are percentages of the lipid-free dry weight of the isolated nucleus in the fraction. The values for nucleic acids and protein are percentages of the dry weight of the individual fractions. The total recovery of dry weight in the nuclear fractions averaged 94% for liver and 97% for Walker tumor.

considerably higher than the amount of DNA. In both the liver and tumor fractions, there was some DNA in the Tris extract.

*Nucleoproteins Obtained with the Phenol Procedure.* The deoxyribonucleoprotein product obtained by the procedure of Kirby (39a) contains 53–81% DNA and 3–27% protein. The method for determination of the amino acids employed by Frearson and Kirby (39a) showed that the proteins in these products contained large amounts of acidic amino acids, i.e., 18–34% of the total residues. The deoxyribonucleoproteins obtained by this procedure were separated into a sedimentable and supernatant fraction by centrifugation for 5 hours at 20,000 rpm. The proteins in the supernatant fraction contained large amounts of lysine, i.e., 13–28% of the total amino acid residues. The content of acidic amino acids ranged from 16 to 48% of the total amino acid residues. However, the differences were not great in the amino acid composition of the supernatant and sedimentable fractions obtained from a transplantable tumor. In the sediment from other tissues, the concentration of acidic amino acids was greater than in the supernatant fraction. Although the authors suggested that they had separated a DNA fraction containing a lysine-rich histone fraction from another DNA fraction, further studies are required to establish the nature of the histones in both of these fractions.

*Extraction of Histones.* As noted previously (p. 10), the standard method for separation of histones from deoxyribonucleoproteins is extraction with HCl, stemming from the early experiments of Kossel (60). There have been attempts to substitute the alcohol extraction procedure for the acid extraction and also to substitute the use of $H_2SO_4$ for HCl, but thus far, these other agents have not been widely used. As shown in Table 3-IV, the methods for extraction of histones have been limited to extraction with acid or selective precipitation of DNA with ethanol to leave histones dissolved in concentrated salt solutions (19). The procedure employing acid extraction has received important support from the X-ray diffraction studies of Zubay and Wilkins (104). In studying the histones isolated by the acid extraction procedure and the histones isolated by the procedure employing ethanol precipitation of deoxyribonucleic acid, it became apparent that the former had the natural or α-configuration of the proteins linked to DNA and the latter were largely in the β-form; the β-configuration suggests that they were partially or completely denatured in the course of the extraction procedure.

## Fractionation of the Histones

The procedures for the isolation of histone fractions include chemical fractionation, chromatography, and, to a lesser extent, electrophoresis (see Table 3-IV). All these separated the histones into two groups, i.e., arginine and lysine-rich, heavy and light, and fast and slow-moving electrophoretically. Until recently, it was apparent that none of these fractions approached the requirements of chemical purity, i.e., they had several end groups and multiple bands on electrophoresis. In fact, even getting the histones into solution for solubility tests was difficult on occasion since, on lyophilization, some histones tend to become denatured in part.

*Chemical Fractionation of the Histones.* Improvements introduced by Johns *et al.* (56–58) have been embodied in the procedure shown in Table 3-V, which presents the steps involved in the isolation of histones of the Walker tumor. In this scheme, the critical step is the initial separation of histones into two groups by extraction with a solution which is 0.25 *N* HCl in 80% ethanol. This extract contains a mixture of fractions designated as 1, 2a, and 3 (see Table 3-V). The residue contains a mixture of fractions 1, 2b, and 3 (see Table 3-V). Further fractionation of the histones obtained by the initial acid–alcohol extract is achieved by means of chromatography on carboxymethylcellulose as shown in Figs. 3-1 and 3-2.

The residual fraction is extracted with 0.25 *N* HCl, and its components can be fractionated either by initial chromatography on carboxymethylcellulose (Fig. 3-2) or by treatment with 5% trichloroacetic acid (Table 3-V). After treatment with 5% trichloroacetic acid, the precipitate contains fraction 3 and fraction 2b; the supernatant fraction contains the more soluble lysine-rich fraction (F1) that is precipitable with 20% trichloroacetic acid.

Johns (55a) has recently modified the extraction procedures to provide relatively simple chemical methods that separate the histones into the four fractions. To extract the more soluble fraction 1, crude DNP was treated with 5% perchloric acid and the protein extracted was precipitated with 18% trichloroacetic acid. The residue remaining after the extraction with perchloric acid was then treated successively with 0.25 *N* HCl in 80% ethanol to extract fractions 2a and 3 and with 0.25 *N* HCl to extract fraction 2b. The last part of the procedure is similar to that shown in Table 3-V. The yields obtained in this modi-

TABLE 3-IV
FRACTIONATION OF CALF THYMUS HISTONES

| Methods of fractionation | Number of fractions | Characteristics of fractions | Starting material | Histone extraction | References |
|---|---|---|---|---|---|
| I. Differential precipitation with | | | | | |
| Ethanol | 2 | Arginine-rich and lysine-rich | Isolated nuclei | 0.1 *N* $H_2SO_4$ | (90) |
| Ethanol | 2 | Arginine-rich and lysine-rich | Nucleohistone | 0.2 *N* HCl | (7) |
| Ethanol | 2 | Arginine-rich and lysine-rich | Isolated nuclei | 0.5 *N* $H_2SO_4$ | (93, 97) |
| Ethanol | 2 | Arginine-rich and lysine-rich | Nucleoprotein | 10% NaCl | (45, 46) |
| Alkali and ethanol | 2 | Arginine-rich and lysine-rich | Isolated nuclei | 0.5 *N* $H_2SO_4$ | (26) |
| Ammonia and acetone | 2 | Arginine-rich and lysine-rich | Nucleoprotein | 0.2 *N* HCl | (32) |
| NaCl (saturation) | 2 | Arginine-rich and lysine-rich | Nucleoprotein | 0.3 *N* HCl | (88) |
| NaCl (successive extraction) | 6 | Inverse proportionality between arginine and lysine | Nucleoprotein | | (65) |
| II. Electrophoresis | 2 | Arginine-rich and lysine-rich | Nucleoprotein | 0.2 *N* HCl | (15, 31) |
| III. Ultracentrifugation | 2 | Heavy and light | Nucleoprotein | 0.2 *N* HCl | (15) |
| | 2 | Heavy and light | Isolated nuclei | 0.25 *N* HCl | (63) |
| | 2 | Heavy and light | Nucleoprotein | HCl pH 2.5 | (4) |
| | 2 | Heavy and light | Nucleoprotein | 0.1 *N* HCl | (47, 49) |

| IV. Electrophoresis and ultracentrifugation | 6 | 2 fractions rich in arginine and four fractions rich in lysine | Isolated nuclei | 0.1 *N* $H_2SO_4$ | (21) |
|---|---|---|---|---|---|
| V. Column chromatography: | | | | | |
| Ba IRC-50 column eluted with $Ba(AC)_2$ | 3 | 1 fraction rich in arginine and 2 fractions rich in lysine | Nucleoprotein | 2.6 *M* NaCl-ethanol | (19) |
| Ba IRC-50 column eluted with $Ba(AC)_2$ and guanidinium chloride | 6 | | Nucleoprotein | 2.6 *M* NaCl-ethanol | (63) |
| Amberlite IRC-50 column eluted with guanidinium chloride | 2 | Arginine-rich and lysine-rich | Nucleoprotein | dil. $H_2SO_4$ | (64) |
| Carboxymethylcellulose column eluted with NaCl | 3 | 1 fraction rich in dicarboxylic amino acids and 2 fractions rich in lysine | Nucleoprotein | 0.2 *N* HCl | (29) |
| Diethylaminoethylcellulose column eluted with NaCl | 2 | Arginine rich and lysine-rich | Nucleoprotein | | (3) |
| VI. Combined Ethanol-HCl and HCl extraction; chromatography on carboxymethylcellulose | 4 | Lysine-rich, slightly lysine-rich, arginine-rich | Nucleoprotein | 0.25 *N* HCl (20%) in ethanol (80%); 0.25 *N* HCl | (52, 56–58) |

fied procedure were very similar to those obtained in the other procedure developed by Johns *et al.* (56–58).

TABLE 3-V (52)
SCHEME FOR FRACTIONATION OF HISTONES OF THE WALKER TUMOR

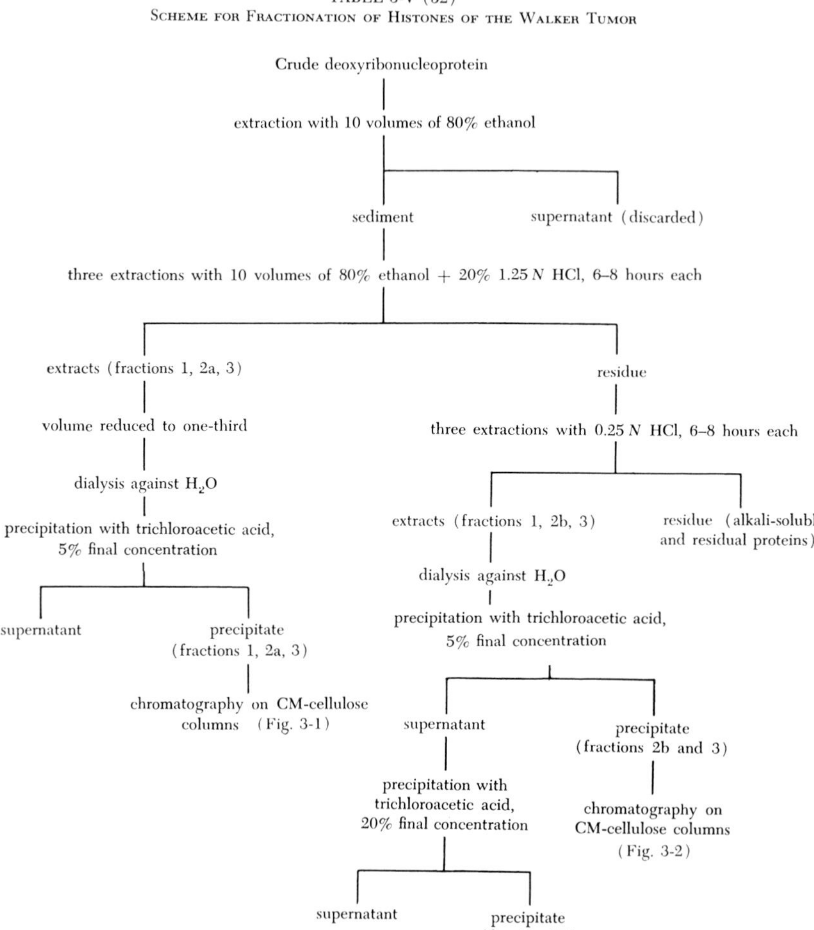


*Separation of Fractions of the Very Lysine-Rich Histones.* Johns (55a) chromatographed fraction 1 on carboxymethylcellulose and obtained three fractions. The samples were added to the columns in a borate buffer at pH 9, and the proteins were eluted with a linear gradient of NaCl in the same buffer. About 85% of the protein was in the third fraction eluted, which had an amino acid composition very similar to that of the crude fraction 1. The amino acid compositions of the proteins in the other two peaks were very similar but were remarkable for the very large amounts of acidic amino acids present (see p. 53, Table 2-VIII).

*Electrophoresis of the Histone Fractions.* The fractionation scheme employed in this laboratory provides a group of fractions with the electrophoretic pattern shown in Fig. 2-2. There are four groups of bands on

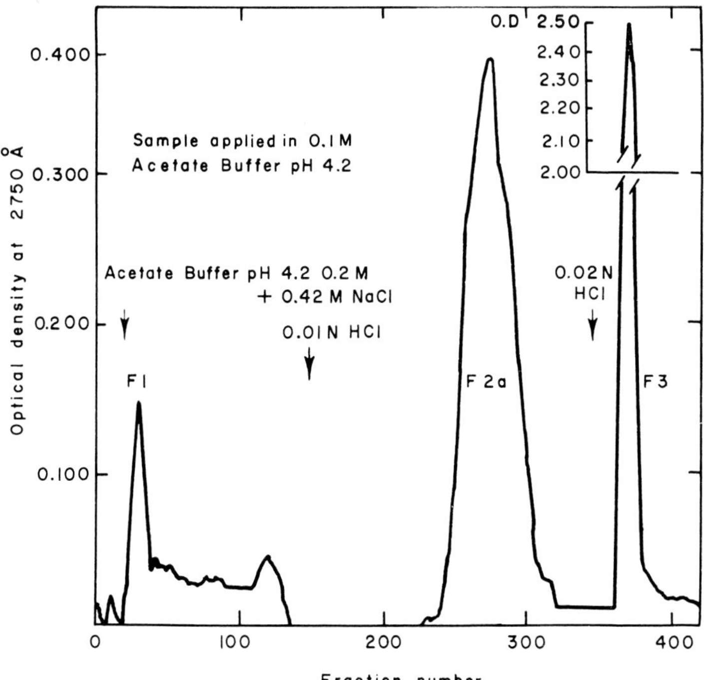


FIG. 3-1. Representative elution pattern for the histones of the Walker tumor extracted with ethanol-HCl (see Table 3-V). [From Hnilica and Busch (52).]

electrophoresis of histones on starch gels according to the procedure described by Johns *et al.* (56–58). The technique employed for fractionation of the histones does not provide single zones on starch gel electrophoresis. For example, there are several bands in fraction 3. There is one dense and one light band in fraction 1 and small amounts of more diffuse contaminants. At least two zones were found in fraction 2b; the major one was slower moving and the other moved more rapidly. A similar number of zones was found in fraction 2a. On staining, the 2b and 2a zones were dense and the contaminants were very pale by comparison. When urea was added to the gels, there was a separation of some of the components of the F1 band (Fig. 2-3). However, it is not certain whether these components are subunits of the main band, individual protein fractions, or products of denaturation of the protein of this band (52); their relationship to the fractions described by Johns (55a) is not yet clarified (see p. 53).

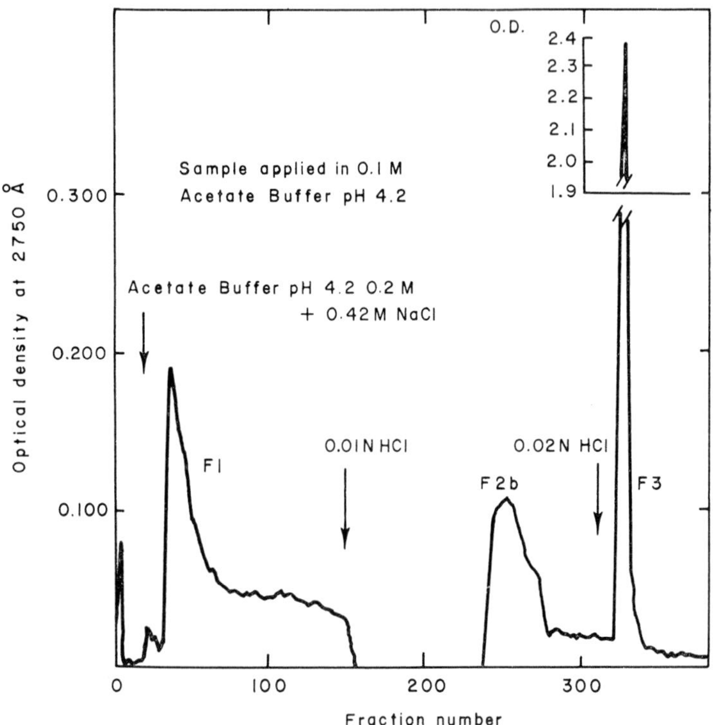


Fig. 3-2. Representative elution pattern of the histones of the Walker tumor extracted with 0.25 *N* HCl and precipitated with 5% trichloroacetic acid as shown in Table 3-V. [From Hnilica and Busch (52).]

***$NH_2$-Terminal Acids of the Histone Fractions.*** One of the criteria of purity of these proteins is their content of various $NH_2$-terminal amino acids (Table 3-VI). In the fractions from the Walker tumor (52) there were several $NH_2$-terminal amino acids in each of the fractions, but the amounts varied from fraction to fraction. The purest fraction would appear to be the 2b fraction, in which proline accounted for 80.8% or more of the $NH_2$-terminals. In fraction 2a, two-thirds of the $NH_2$-

TABLE 3-VI

$NH_2$-TERMINAL AMINO ACIDS OF HISTONES FROM WALKER TUMOR[a, b]

| Amino acid | Fraction 1 (trichloro-acetic acid) | Fraction 1 (chroma-tography) | Fraction 2a | Fraction 2b | Fraction 3 (chroma-tography) | Fraction 3 ($NH_4OH$) |
|---|---|---|---|---|---|---|
| Alanine | 10.6 | 21.1 | 66.5 | 6.2 | 51.2 | 75.0 |
| Aspartic + glutamic acids | 3.9 | 5.6 | 1.2 | 2.7 | 6.5 | 1.5 |
| Glycine | 23.5 | 18.4 | 19.5 | 4.8 | 3.9 | 7.3 |
| Leucine + isoleucine | 2.2 | 2.0 | — | 0.6 | 1.6 | — |
| Lysine | 17.5 | 18.4 | 4.9 | 3.3 | 5.8 | 4.2 |
| Proline | 14.6 | — | 6.7 | 80.8 | 21.6 | 9.3 |
| Serine | 18.2 | 17.5 | 0.9 | 0.3 | 4.4 | — |
| Threonine | 6.5 | 14.9 | — | 1.5 | 3.9 | 2.2 |
| Valine | 3.0 | 2.1 | — | 1.0 | 1.2 | — |

[a] From Hnilica and Busch (52).

[b] The values for $NH_2$-terminal amino acids are molar percentages of the total found. The standard error for the value for $NH_2$-terminal proline in fraction 2b was 3.9. The standard errors for the values for $NH_2$-terminal alanine and glycine in fraction 2a were 4.4 and 1.0, respectively. Five determinations were carried out for each fraction.

terminals were alanine residues and approximately 20% were glycine residues. In fraction 1 and fraction 3, alanine was also present as an $NH_2$-terminal amino acid. Similar results were obtained for fractions of calf thymus histone (56–58).

These results are subject to some corrections in view of the finding of Phillips (73, 74) that some of the $NH_2$-terminal amino acids of the histones may be acetylated and the methods for determination of the $NH_2$-terminal amino acid would not detect such substituted amino acids. He noted that $NH_2$-terminal amino acids of the very lysine-rich histones include proline, alanine, lysine, serine, and glycine. The $NH_2$-terminal amino acids of fraction 2a were alanine, glycine, proline, and lysine. In view of the fact that the major $NH_2$-terminal of fraction 3, the "arginine-rich" histone, was alanine and the major terminal of the *N*-proline histone (fraction 2b) was proline, the possibility exists that both the very lysine-rich histones and fraction 2a were contaminated in part with these fractions. On the basis of the total $NH_2$-terminals, including the acetylated $NH_2$-terminals, the minimal molecular weights of the proteins in fractions 1 and 2a ranged from 9000 to 12,000 and 12,000 to 14,000, respectively. On the same basis, the minimal molecular weights of the proteins of fraction 2b and fraction 3 were approximately 10,000. These findings are in accord with some earlier sedimentation studies (92). However, these molecular weights are significantly smaller than the values derived from studies on $NH_2$-terminals in which the degree of acetylation was not taken into account (52, 56–58).

## Older Methods for Fractionation of the Histones

*Chemical Fractionation.* The histones were considered to be one type of substance for many years after their discovery by Kossel (60) and the development of procedures for their isolation in mass amounts (62). Even in Greenstein's review (44) the opinion was held that there were two classes of histones, those in salt-like linkages with nucleic acids and the other, presumably globins, in conjugated states with hemoglobin. Isolation of the former group with 1 *M* NaCl was first achieved by Bensley (6) and by Mirsky (67). It was not until Daly and Mirsky (26) reported that there was a high content of lysine in the histones that were not precipitated at pH 10.6 as compared to those precipitated at that pH that a method was evolved for the separation of these two entities as well as the demonstration that these proteins were not homogeneous. The procedure of Daly and Mirsky consisted of extraction of nucleoproteins with $H_2SO_4$, elevation of the pH to 10.6, and separation of the supernatant solution from the precipitate. Daly and Mirsky (26) obtained similar protein fractions from nuclei of calf thymus, turtle red cells and liver nuclei. They suggested that there might be other histones of intermediate types, a prediction that was later amply borne out.

One of the reasons for the progressive loss of interest in the methods employed by Daly and Mirsky (26) as a means for fractionation of histones was the finding of Cruft *et al.* (23, 24) that remarkable aggregation of histones occurred at pH above 4. Although at pH 2 relatively small amounts of the "arginine-rich" histone were in the aggregated state, all the histone was aggregated at pH 5.5 and above. The molecular weight of the aggregate was 10 times or more the molecular weight of the original unaggregated histone. Hirschbein *et al.* (51) have suggested that some of the aggregation was reversible on the basis of starch gel electrophoresis of the aggregates that had been dialyzed against buffers at low pH.

Many subsequent fractionations have been made in which methods for selective precipitation of the individual histones were employed, including the procedure for fractionation of histones with cold ethanol (7, 93–97), a procedure that has now become part of the method employed by Johns *et al.* (56–58), as mentioned earlier in this chapter. Davison *et al.* (32) reported another procedure for differential precipitation of histones with ammonia and acetone; although it was utilized in part in studies in this laboratory (10, 27) it has not been sufficiently specific to be incorporated into any other more advanced procedure up to the present time. Procedures employing differential amounts of NaCl for extraction of histones have been reported (65, 88) to provide some fractionation of the histones, but analytical data are not available that are comparable to those for other fractionation techniques.

## Chromatography of the Histones

The first endeavors to isolate histones by chromatography were made by Crampton *et al.* (19), who in 1955 employed a column of IRC-50 in the barium form to adsorb the histones. They eluted the histones with increasing concentrations of barium acetate and obtained fractions that in the aggregate accounted for 35% of the total histones added to the column. Later, Neelin and Butler (69) reported that the yields of the histones could be improved by modifications of the technique. The three fractions obtained (19, 69) included two lysine-rich fractions, A and C, and an "arginine-rich" fraction, B, that was rather low in arginine. Fractions B and C (19) appear to be a mixture of the lysine and "arginine-rich" histones in view of the fact that the content of almost all amino acids was intermediate between the lysine and "arginine-rich" fractions. Luck and his colleagues (63, 64, 78) also utilized IRC-50 columns in attempts to further fractionate the histones of calf thymus. With an interrupted gradient of guanidinium chloride, the histones were eluted in five peaks, of which the second and third were the largest. The peaks containing the histones were not homogeneous inasmuch as rechromatography of the peaks showed the presence of two or more components. Rasmussen *et al.* (78) showed that chromatography on IRC-50 columns was improved with an initial elution by barium acetate and later elution by guanidinium chloride. However, the fractions obtained by any of the procedures employed in Luck's laboratory provided mixtures of proteins, as shown by the complex patterns on starch gel electrophoresis. Reasonably satisfactory separations were obtained for some of the slower moving fractions from some of the faster moving fractions.

*Chromatography on Carboxymethylcellulose.* The first use of carboxymethylcellulose for fractionation of the histones was that reported by Davison (28, 29), who eluted the histones from the cation exchanger with increasing concentrations of NaCl. In the initial experiments, he found three fractions that comprised 3, 12, and 80% of the total histones, respectively. The first of these was rich in dicarboxylic acids; the second consisted of lysine-rich histones; and the third was a mixture of proteins as indicated by changing molar ratios of arginine:lysine from the leading to the trailing edges of the peak. The components of the histone fractions obtained in the three peaks were partly analyzed by chromatography on the system employed by Crampton *et al.* (19). The lysine-rich fraction of Crampton *et al.* (19) or peak A corresponded to the second fraction of Davison (28, 29). The third fraction of Davison corresponded to fraction B of Crampton *et al.* (19), and probably both represented rather substantial mixtures of proteins. One of the results obtained by Davison (28, 29) was interesting because of its relationship to the "aggregation" of histones; when the pH for elution was increased to 6.5, more peaks appeared, and their presence was probably related to the tendency of the histones to aggregate at higher pH (23, 24, 32). Although efforts have been reported to chromatograph histones on DEAE-cellulose, an anion exchanger (3), these have not been successful in this laboratory since the histones passed through the columns without adhering.

The technique reported by Davison (28, 29) was of apparent value because it permitted the recovery of virtually all the histones added to the column. However, efforts to repeat these experiments in this laboratory failed, presumably because of the high pH of the salt solutions employed by Davison for elution of the histones from the columns (27). In an effort to keep the pH low and yet permit the elution of histones in a dilute gradient from the carboxymethylcellulose, formic acid was utilized in much the way found to be effective for elution of acids of the citric acid cycle from Dowex-1 (11, 27). In early experiments, it was found that the methods for isolation of histones from tissues of the rat provided material for further analysis. To circumvent this difficulty, whole-acid extracts of nuclear preparations were chromatographed on carboxymethylcellulose as shown in Fig. 3-3. The protein peaks are indicated in block letters. When radioactive lysine was injected into the rats one hour prior to the termination of the experiment, the radioactivity was found in the peaks indicated by arabic numerals. The elution patterns of radioactivity and protein provided a relatively specific pattern for each of the tissues studied. Although not all the proteins were histones in these elution patterns, presumably all would be sufficiently basic to adhere to carboxymethylcellulose.

Chromatography on carboxymethylcellulose has been employed by Klyszejko *et al.* (59a) to fractionate the histones of calf pancreas, calf thymus, and human placenta. Four fractions were obtained, but they differed in amino acid composition from the fractions reported by other workers, and starch gel electrophoretic patterns were not shown. Some differences were obtained in the products derived from different tissues.

*Chromatography of Histones on Other Types of Columns.* Although chromatography of histones on substituted celluloses has advanced to a more satisfactory level, improvements in the techniques for fractionation of the histones are required. As shown in Fig. 3-4, lengthening the carboxymethylcellulose columns permits a further fractionation of nuclear proteins (86). Cruft (20) has noted that carboxymethyl-Sephadex columns also provide an enhancement of the fractionation of the histones. However, detailed data have not been published to the present time which would show that a significant improvement has been achieved by the use of Sephadex columns or carboxymethyl–Sephadex columns. Among other chromatographic adsorbents being tested are carboxyethyl and sulfoxyethyl celluloses.

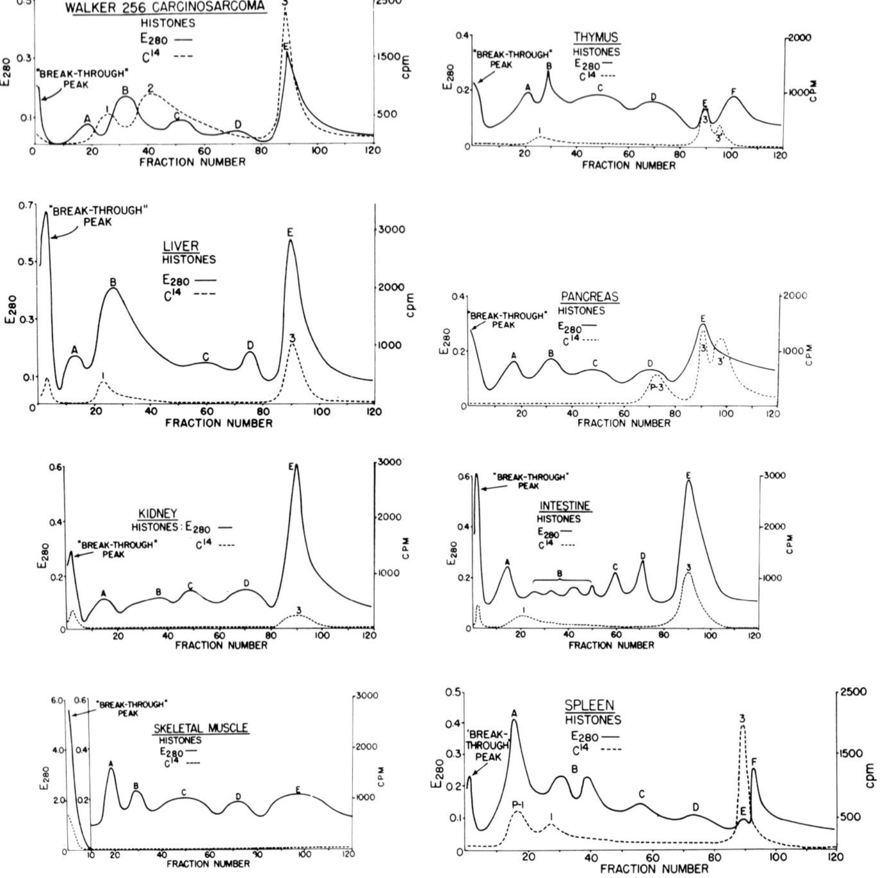


FIG. 3-3. Composite figure showing the comparative chromatograms of cationic nuclear proteins of Walker tumor and other tissues. The ordinates are specific activity and optical density at 280 mμ. The solid lines are protein concentration, and the dashed lines represent the radioactivity in the fractions. Peak 2, coded as RP2-L, was found only in neoplastic tissues. [From Davis and Busch (27).]

## Electrophoresis of Histones

*Moving Boundary Electrophoresis.* Cruft *et al.* (21–23) were the first to utilize moving boundary electrophoresis for fractionation of the histones. They determined the amino acid composition of the fractions obtained in moving boundaries and showed that the histones were divisible into several fractions on the basis of electrophoretic mobility. The α-fractions were lysine-rich fractions, and one of these contained very large amounts of both lysine and alanine (see page 47). The β-fraction closely resembled the "arginine-rich" fraction described by Davison and Butler (30) in that alanine and arginine each comprised 11% of the total amino acid residues. Of the other fractions obtained by Cruft *et al.* (21), the slower sedimenting fraction contained about 18% each of lysine and alanine and the faster sedimenting fraction contained 11% each of lysine and alanine. These findings represented the first actual demonstration of the slightly lysine-rich histones, although the amino acid analyses do not exactly match those of fractions obtained later.

Recently, columns of the type developed by Porath (76) have been

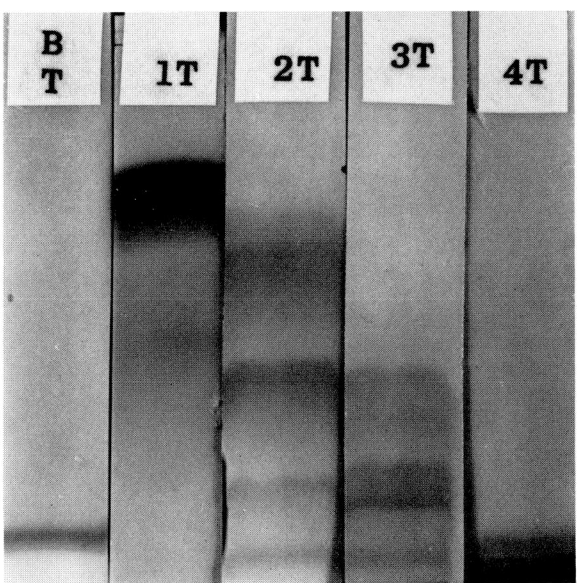


FIG. 3-4. Starch gel electrophoresis of fractions of acid-soluble nuclear proteins of the Walker tumor obtained from 180-cm carboxymethylcellulose columns by elution by increasing concentrations of formic acid. The fraction shown as 4T was eluted with 4 *N* formic acid and contains very acidic proteins[2] (see Chapter VIII).

[2] Studies in which nuclei were carefully isolated have suggested that some of these very acidic proteins are cytoplasmic proteins.

further utilized by Sorof and his colleagues (89) to study the behavior of nuclear proteins of livers and tumors. In their studies, one positive and eight negatively charged classes of proteins were found in the nuclear preparations. Of these, there was less of the slower positive component in tumors and more of the faster negative components. At the moment, analytical information on these proteins is not available, because the authors are of the opinion that the proteins are not yet at the stage of purification where such data would be meaningful. deNooij and Niemeijer (72) have indicated that one of the problems in electrophoresis of histones is the discongruence of ascending and descending boundaries. This problem was resolved in their studies when electrophoresis was carried out at pH 8.2 and a Tris buffer was employed.

*Starch Gel Electrophoresis.* Although electrophoresis has not yet been satisfactorily adapted to the isolation of histones in quantities sufficient for further purification, the development of starch gel electrophoresis by Poulik and Smithies (77) has provided an important technique for the determination of the number and types of proteins in a preparation. Neelin and his colleagues (69–71) first used starch gel electrophoresis (Fig. 3-5) for separation of histones, and later this technique was modified by Johns *et al.* (56–58) and others (8, 66). In essence, the histones can be separated into four groups of bands by the rates of movement through the starch (Fig. 2-2). The fastest moving band (Fig. 2-2) contains one or two proteins that are components of fraction 2a. The second fastest moving band contains the *N*-proline histone. The slowest moving fractions comprise the F3 fraction, which is obviously a mixture of several proteins. Those that remain closest to the origin are probably neutral or partially denatured components. The very lysine-rich histones are the ones that move electrophoretically at intermediate rates between the F3 and the *N*-proline histone fractions.

The number of bands that are found on starch gel electrophoresis of the various histone fractions is dependent in part upon the conditions employed for the electrophoresis. As shown in Fig. 3-5, the bands appear to move more rapidly at the lower pH ranges than at higher values. In theory, this is quite logical since at lower pH the ionization of the carboxyl groups is suppressed and all the amines are protonated. However, at higher pH the histones tend to aggregate (24); although the carboxyl groups become ionized, the lower mobility of the fractions is the resultant of these two effects. It seems logical to extend this exquisite method to large scale isolation of histones, and an effort has been made by Murray (68) to adapt the electrophoresis of histones to a continuous process. Thus far, the method has not yielded

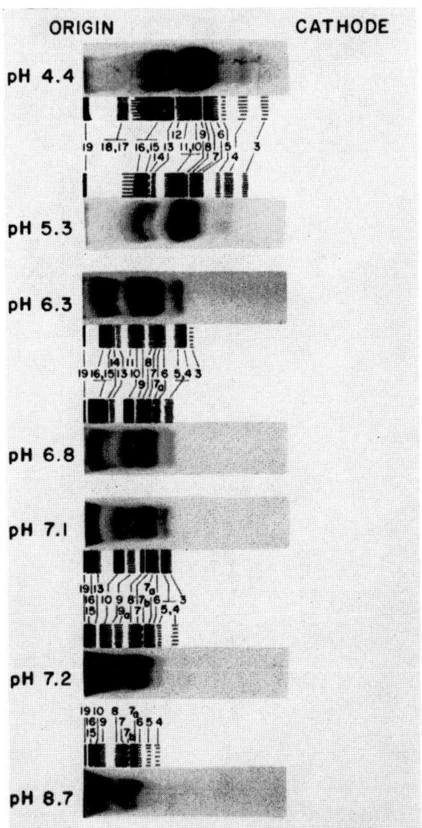


Fig. 3-5. Starch gel electrophoresis of chicken erythrocyte histone. [From Neelin and Connell (70).]

the same degree of separation as was found in the analytical starch gel electrophoresis.

## Sedimentation of the Histones

Studies on the sedimentation constants of histones have shown that the molecular weight of these proteins are in the range of 8000-130,000 (Table 3-VII). The general range of $S_{20}$ values is 0.6–28 S. Two fractions were present in almost all the studies, the "light" and the "heavy" fractions. The sedimentation constants for the light fractions ranged from 0.8 to 1.8 S, and molecular weights ranging from 8000 to 20,000 were assigned to these proteins. The sedimentation constants for the heavy fractions ranged from 1.5 to 2.6 S, and molecular weights ranging from 37,000 to 51,000 were reported for this fraction. These two were the only groups reported to be present in the histones. In the pH range of 6.5–8.1, the sedimentation constants increased to a range of

TABLE 3-VII
SEDIMENTATION CONSTANTS ($S_{20}$)[a] AND MOLECULAR WEIGHT OF HISTONE FRACTIONS OF VARIOUS AUTHORS[b]

| $S_{20}$ | | | Molecular weight | | | |
|---|---|---|---|---|---|---|
| Light fraction | Heavy fraction | Aggregation product | Light fraction | Heavy fraction | Aggregation product | References |
| 0.9 | 2.6 | — | 17,000 | 51,000 | — | (15) |
| 0.6 | 2.0 | — | 8,400 | 37,000 | — | (93–97) |
| 0.8 | 1.5 | — | — | — | — | (7) |
| 0.9 | 2.3 | — | — | — | — | (88) |
| 1.0 | 2.0 | 10–23 | 18,000 | — | — | (32) |
| 1.7 | — | 8.0 | — | — | — | (7) |
| 1.6 | — | 8.4 | 11,000 | — | 132,000 | (4) |
| 1.8 | — | 28.0 | 8,100 | — | 9,200 | (63) |

[a] Given as Svedberg units (S).
[b] Starting materials and extraction procedures are the same as in Table 3-IV.

8.0–28.0 S (22–24, 82, 93–97), and the higher sedimentation constants were ascribed to the formation of aggregation products of high molecular weight. It is not yet clear whether these aggregation products represent agglomerations of all the histones or whether they simply represent the aggregation of a few types of the histones. These results may be related to the finding that histones extracted from tissues at neutral pH are electrophoretically more complex than those extracted with dilute acids (15).

Trautman and Crampton (92) were concerned about the possibility that histones normally exist as dimers or polymers. They determined the minimum molecular weights of the histones by amino acid analysis and by ultracentrifugation employing the Archibald principle. Fraction A, the very lysine-rich fraction, had a molecular weight of 10,000 ± 2000 and did not dissociate in urea. Fraction B, which was a slightly lysine-rich fraction, had a molecular weight of 32,000 but dissociated into monomers of molecular weight of 16,000 ± 1600. They also determined that the molecular weight of ribonuclease was 14,000; this protein has been found as a contaminant of histones (see Chapter V).

Although ultracentrifugation has been a useful method for determination of the molecular weights of the histones and for separation of the "heavy" and "light" fractions, this technique has not been used for fractionation of the histones. This may be related to the fact that the amounts used are too small for the procedure to be useful in fractionation of proteins.

## References


1. Allfrey, V. G.: Nuclear ribosomes, messenger-RNA, protein synthesis. *Exptl. Cell Res. Suppl.* **9**: 183-212 (1963).
2. Allfrey, V. G., Stern, H., Mirsky, A. E., and Saetren, H.: The isolation of cell nuclei in nonaqueous media. *J. Gen. Physiol.* **35**: 529-555 (1952).
3. Bakay, B., and Kirschner, L. B.: Heterogeneity of calf thymus nucleoprotein. *Federation Proc.* **17**: 184 (1958).
4. Bakay, B., Kolb, J. J., and Toennies, G.: On the component proteins of calf thymus nucleoprotein. *Arch. Biochem. Biophys.* **58**: 144-168 (1955).
5. Behrens, M.: Untersuchungen an isolierten Zell- und Gewebstandtheilen. I. Mitteilung: Isolierung von Zellkernen des Kalbsherzmuskels. *Z. Physiol. Chem.* **209**: 59-74 (1932).
6. Bensley, R. R.: Chemical structure of cytoplasm. *Science* **96**: 389-393 (1942).
7. Bijvoet, P.: Ethanol precipitation analysis of thymus histone. *Biochim. Biophys. Acta* **25**: 502-512 (1957).
8. Biserte, G., Sautiere, P., Houard, C., and Devys, M.: Etude comparative du comportement en électrophorèse en gel d'amidon des histones du thymus de veau. *Compt. Rend. Soc. Biol.* **156**: 1823-1827 (1962).
9. Busch, H., and Davis, J. R.: Nuclear proteins of tumors and other tissues. *Cancer Res.* **19**: 1241-1256 (1958).
10. Busch, H., Davis, J. R., Honig, G. R., Anderson, D. C., Nair, P. V., and Nyhan, W. L.: The uptake of a variety of amino acids into nuclear proteins of tumors and other tissues. *Cancer Res.* **19**: 1030-1039 (1959).
11. Busch, H., Hurlbert, R. B., and Potter, V. R.: Anion exchange chromatography of acids of the citric acid cycle. *J. Biol. Chem.* **196**: 717-727 (1952).
12. Busch, H., Starbuck, W. C., and Davis, J. R.: A method for isolation of nuclei from cells of the Walker 256 carcinosarcoma. *Cancer Res.* **19**: 684-687 (1959).
13. Busch, H., and Steele, W. J.: Nuclear proteins of neoplastic cells. *Advan. Cancer Res.* **8**: 41-120 (1964).
14. Butler, J. A. V., and Davison, P. F.: Deoxyribonucleoprotein, a genetic material. *Advan. Enzymol.* **18**: 161-190 (1957).
15. Butler, J. A. V., Davison, P. F., James, D. W. F., and Shooter, K. V.: The histones of calf thymus deoxyribonucleoprotein. I. Preparation and homogeneity. *Biochim. Biophys. Acta* **13**: 224-232 (1954).

16. Chauveau, J.: Technique d'isolement des noyaux cellulaires. *Rev. Franç. Etudes Clin. Biol.* **3**: 503-506 (1958).
17. Chauveau, J., Moulé, Y., and Rouiller, C.: Isolation of pure and unaltered liver nuclei, morphology and biochemical composition. *Exptl. Cell Res.* **11**: 317-321 (1956).
18. Commerford, S. L., Hunter, M. J., and Oncley, J. L.: The preparation and properties of calf liver deoxyribonucleoprotein. *J. Biol. Chem.* **238**: 2123-2134 (1963).
19. Crampton, C. F., Moore, S., and Stein, W. H.: Chromatographic fractionation of calf thymus histone. *J. Biol. Chem.* **215**: 787-801 (1955).
20. Cruft, H. J.: The fractionation of histones on Sephadex G-75. *Biochim. Biophys. Acta* **54**: 611-613 (1961).
21. Cruft, H. J., Hindley, J., Mauritzen, C. M., and Stedman, E.: Amino acid composition of the six histones of calf thymocytes. *Nature* **180**: 1107-1109 (1957).
22. Cruft, H. J., Mauritzen, C. M., and Stedman, E.: Abnormal properties of histones from malignant cells. *Nature* **174**: 580-585 (1954).
23. Cruft, H. J., Mauritzen, C. M., and Stedman, E.: The nature and physicochemical properties of histones. *Proc. Roy. Soc.* **B241**: 93-145 (1957).
24. Cruft, H. J., Mauritzen, C. M., and Stedman, E.: The isolation of β-histone from calf thymocytes and the factors affecting its aggregation. *Proc. Roy. Soc.* **B249**: 21-41 (1958).
25. Dallam, R. D.: The chemical composition of nucleic and cytoplasmic granules. *Arch. Biochem. Biophys.* **54**: 24-37 (1955).
26. Daly, M. M., and Mirsky, A. E.: Histones with high lysine content. *J. Gen. Physiol.* **38**: 405-413 (1954).
27. Davis, J. R., and Busch, H.: Chromatographic analysis of radioactive cationic nuclear proteins of tissues of tumorbearing rats. *Cancer Res.* **19**: 1157-1166 (1959).
28. Davison, P. F.: Histones from normal and malignant cells. *Biochem. J.* **66**: 703-707 (1957).
29. Davison, P. F.: Chromatography of histones. *Biochem. J.* **66**: 708-712 (1957).
30. Davison, P. F., and Butler, J. A. V.: The fractionation and composition of histones from thymus nucleoprotein. *Biochim. Biophys. Acta* **15**: 439-440 (1954).
31. Davison, P. F., and Butler, J. A. V.: The chemical composition of calf thymus nucleoprotein. *Biochim. Biophys. Acta* **21**: 568-573 (1956).
32. Davison, P. F., James, D. W. F., Shooter, K. V., and Butler, J. A. V.: The histones of calf thymus deoxyribonucleoprotein. II. Electrophoretic and sedimentation behavior and a partial fractionation. *Biochim. Biophys. Acta* **15**: 415-424 (1954).
33. Dounce, A. L.: Enzyme systems of isolated cell nuclei. *Ann. N.Y. Acad. Sci.* **50**: 982-989 (1950).
34. Dounce, A. L.: The significance of enzyme studies on isolated cell nuclei. *Intern. Rev. Cytol.* **3**: 199-223 (1954).
35. Dounce, A. L.: The isolation and composition of cell nuclei and nucleoli.

*In* "The Nucleic Acids" (E. Chargaff and J. N. Davidson, eds.) Vol. II, pp. 93-153. Academic Press, New York, 1955.

36. Dounce, A. L.: The isolation of nuclei from tumor cells. *Exptl. Cell Res. Suppl.* **9**: 126-143 (1963).
37. Dounce, A. L., Tishkoff, G. H., Barnett, S. R., and Freer, R. M.: Free amino acids and nucleic acid content of cell nuclei isolated by a modification of Behren's technique. *J. Gen. Physiol.* **33**: 629-642 (1950).
38. Dounce, A. L., Witler, R. F., Monty, K. J., Pate, S., and Cottine, M. A.: A method for isolating intact mitochondria and nuclei from the same homogenate and the influence of mitochondrial destruction on the properties of cell nuclei. *J. Biophys. Biochem. Cytol.* **1**: 139-154 (1955).
39. Fisher, H. W., and Harris, H.: The isolation of nuclei from animal cells in culture. *Proc. Roy. Soc.* **B156**: 521-523 (1962).

39a. Frearson, P. M., and Kirby, K. S.: Nucleoproteins. II. Fractionation of deoxyribonucleoproteins into acidic proteins and lysine-rich histones associated with deoxyribonucleic acid. *Biochem. J.* **90**: 578-583 (1964).

40. Georgiev, G. P., Yermolayeva, L. P., and Zbarsky, I. B.: The ratio of protein and nucleoprotein fractions in the cell nuclei of various tissues. *Biokhimya* **25**: 318-322 (1960).
41. Georgiev, G. P., and Mantieva, V. L.: The isolation of cell nuclei by a phenol method and a study of nuclei characteristics. *Biokhimiya* **25**: 143-150 (1960).
42. Georgiev, G. P., and Mantieva, V. L.: The isolation of DNA-like RNA and ribosomal RNA from the nucleolo-chromosomal apparatus of mammalian cells. *Biochim. Biophys. Acta* **61**: 153-154 (1962).
43. Georgiev, G. P., and Mantieva, V. L.: Methods of isolation and nucleotide composition of informational and ribosomal ribonucleic acids of nucleolo-chromosomal apparatus. *Biokhimiya* **27**: 949-957 (1962).
44. Greenstein, J. P.: Nucleoproteins. *Advan. Protein Chem.* **1**: 209-287 (1944).
45. Gregoire, J., Gregoire, J., and Reynaud, J.: The heterogeneity of thymohistone. *Compt. Rend. Acad. Sci.* **236**: 1922-1924 (1953).
46. Gregoire, J., and Limozin, M.: Heterogeneity and composition of preparations of thymus histone. *Bull. Soc. Chim. Biol.* **36**: 15-30 (1954).
47. Hamer, D.: Amino acid composition of thymus histone. *Nature* **167**: 40 (1951).
48. Hamer, D.: Aspects of the chemistry of the proteins in the nucleus. A short review and some experimental results. *Brit. J. Cancer* **5**: 130-139 (1951).
49. Hamer, D.: A comparison of different protein fractions obtained from thymus nuclei isolated in an aqueous medium. *Brit. J. Cancer* **7**: 151-156 (1953).
50. Hammarsten, E.: Zur Kenntnis der biologischen Bedeutung des Nucleinsäureverbindungen. *Biochem. Z.* **144**: 383-466 (1924).
51. Hirschbein, L., de Mende, M. S., and Khouvine, Y.: Action de pH sur l'association des histones du placenta humain. *Compt. Rend. Acad. Sci.* **248**: 870-872 (1959).
52. Hnilica, L. S., and Busch, H.: Fractionation of the histones of the Walker 256 carcinosarcoma by combined chemical and chromatographic techniques. *J. Biol. Chem.* **238**: 918-924 (1963).

53. Hudack, E. D., and Baker, N.: Studies on Ehrlich ascites cell nuclei. I. Methods of isolation of nuclei. *Exptl. Cell Res.* **22**: 327-337 (1961).

54. Hudack, E. D., and Brummond, D. O.: Studies on Ehrlich ascites cell nuclei. IV. Determination of nicotinamide adenosine dinucleotide pyrophosphorylase activity in nuclei isolated by an improved technique. *Exptl. Cell Res.* **29**: 343-348 (1963).

55. Hymer, W. C.: The isolation of nuclei from mammalian tissues with the use of Triton X-100. *Federation Proc.* **22**: 473 (1963).

55a. Johns, E. W.: Preparative methods for histone fractions from calf thymus. *Biochem. J.* **92**: 55-59 (1964).

56. Johns, E. W., and Butler, J. A. V.: Further fractionation of histones from calf thymus. *Biochem. J.* **82**: 15-18 (1962).

57. Johns, E. W., Phillips, D. M. P., Simson, P., and Butler, J. A. V.: Improved fractionation of arginine-rich histones from calf thymus. *Biochem. J.* **77**: 631-636 (1960).

58. Johns, E. W., Phillips, D. M. P., Simson, P., and Butler, J. A. V.: The electrophoresis of histones and histone fractions on starch gel. *Biochem. J.* **80**: 189-193 (1961).

59. Kirby, K. S.: A new method for the isolation of deoxyribonucleic acids: evidence on the nature of bonds between deoxyribonucleic acid and protein. *Biochem. J.* **66**: 495-504 (1957).

59a. Klyszejko, L., de Mende, M. S., and Khouvine, Y.: Désoxyribonucleoprotéines du pancreas de boeuf. III. Fractionnement des histones. *Bull. Soc. Chim. Biol.* **46**: 111-128 (1964).

60. Kossel, A.: Ueber einen peptonartigen Bestandtheil des Zellkerns. *Z. Physiol. Chem.* **8**: 511-515 (1884).

61. Lettré, H.: Ueber das Verhalten von Bestandtheilen von Tumorzellen bei der Transplantation. III. Mitteilung. Zellkerne, Plasmagranulen und gequollene Zellen. *Z. Krebsforsch.* **57**: 345-352 (1951).

62. Lilienfeld, L.: Zur Chemie der Leukocyten. *Z. Physiol. Chem.* **18**: 472-486 (1893).

63. Luck, J. M., Cook, H. A., Eldredge, N. T., Haley, M. I., Kupke, D. W., and Rasmussen, P. S.: On the fractionation of thymus histone. *Arch. Biochem. Biophys.* **65**: 449-467 (1956).

64. Luck, J. M., Rasmussen, P. S., Satake, K., and Tsvetikov, A. N.: Further studies on the fractionation of calf thymus histone. *J. Biol. Chem.* **233**: 1407-1414 (1958).

65. Lucy, J. A., and Butler, J. A. V.: Fractionation of deoxyribonucleoprotein. *Biochim. Biophys. Acta* **16**: 431-432 (1955).

66. McAllister, H. C., Jr., Wan, Y. C., and Irvin, J. L.: Electrophoresis of histones and histone fractions on polyacrylamide gels. *Anal. Biochem.* **5**: 321-329 (1963).

67. Mirsky, A. E.: Chromosomes and nuclear proteins. *Advan. Enzymol.* **3**: 1-34 (1943).

68. Murray, K.: A continuous elution method of preparative starch gel electrophoresis. *Anal. Biochem.* **3**: 415-428 (1962).

69. Neelin, J. M., and Butler, G. C.: A comparison of histones from chicken

tissues by zone electrophoresis in starch gel. *Can. J. Biochem. Physiol.* **39**: 485-491 (1961).

70. Neelin, J. M., and Connell, G. E.: Zone electrophoresis of chicken erythrocyte histone in starch gel. *Biochim. Biophys. Acta* **31**: 539-541 (1959).
71. Neelin, J. M., and Neelin, E. M.: Zone electrophoresis of calf thymus histone in starch gel. *Can. J. Biochem. Physiol.* **38**: 355-363 (1960).
72. de Nooij, E. H., and Niemeijer, J. A.: Free-boundary electrophoresis of histones. *Biochim. Biophys. Acta* **65**: 148-149 (1962).
73. Phillips, D. M. P.: The presence of acetyl groups in histones. *Biochem. J.* **87**: 258-263 (1963).
74. Phillips, D. M. P.: A micrcmethod for the determination of *N*- and *O*-acetyl groups. *Biochem. J.* **86**: 397-401 (1963).
75. Pollister, A. W., and Mirsky, A. E.: The nucleoprotamine of trout sperm. *J. Gen. Physiol.* **30**: 101-115 (1946-1947).
76. Porath, J.: Methodological studies of zone electrophoresis in vertical columns. *Biochim. Biophys. Acta* **22**: 151-175 (1956).
77. Poulik, M. D., and Smithies, W.: Comparison and combination of the starch gel and filter paper electrophoretic methods applied to human sera: Two-dimensional electrophoresis. *Biochem. J.* **68**: 636-643 (1958).
78. Rasmussen, P. S., Murray, K., and Luck, J. M.: On the complexity of calf thymus histone. *Biochemistry* **1**: 79-89 (1962).
79. Samarina, O. P.: Incorporation of labeled amino acids into protein fractions of the cell nuclei of liver and Ehrlich ascitic carcinoma. *Biokhimiya* **26**: 61-69 (1961).
80. Sauer, L. A., Martin, A. P., and Stotz, E.: Cytochemical fractionation of the Lettré-Ehrlich ascites tumor. *Cancer Res.* **20**: 251-256 (1960).
81. Schneider, R. M.: The effect of anions on the optical properties of rat liver nuclei isolated in glycerol solutions. *Exptl. Cell Res.* **8**: 24-34 (1955).
82. Shooter, K. V., Davison, P. F., and Butler, J. A. V.: Physical properties of thymus nucleoprotein. *Biochim. Biophys. Acta* **13**: 192-198 (1954).
83. Siebert, G.: Enzyme und Substrate der Glykolyse in isolierten Zellkernen. *Biochem. Z.* **334**: 369-387 (1961).
84. Siebert, G.: Enzymes of cancer nuclei. *Exptl. Cell Res. Suppl.* **9**: 389-417 (1963).
85. Siebert, G., Bassler, K. H., Hannover, R., Adloff, E., and Beyer, R.: Enzymaktivitäten in isolierten Zellkernen in Abhängigkeit von der mitotischen Aktivität. *Biochem. Z.* **334**: 388-400 (1961).
86. Singh, E. J., and Busch, H.: Unpublished results.
87. Smetana, K., Steele, W. J., and Busch, H.: A nuclear ribonucleoprotein network. *Exptl. Cell Res.* **31**: 198-202 (1963).
88. Smillie, L. B., Butler, G. C., and Smith, D. B.: Properties of calf thymus histone isolated by three different methods. *Can. J. Biochem. Physiol.* **36**: 1-13 (1958).
89. Sorof, S., Young, E. M., McCue, M. M., and Fetterman, P. L.: Zonal electrophoresis of the soluble proteins of liver and tumor in azo dye carcinogenesis. *Cancer Res.* **23**: 864-882 (1963).
90. Stedman, E., and Stedman, E.: Probable function of histone as a regulator of mitosis. *Nature* **152**: 556 (1943).

91. Steele, W. J., and Busch, H.: Studies on acidic nuclear proteins of the Walker tumor and liver. *Cancer Res.* **23**: 1153-1163 (1963).
92. Trautman, R., and Crampton, C. F.: Application of the Archibald principle for the ultracentrifugal determination of the molecular weight in urea solutions of histone fractions from calf thymus. *J. Am. Chem. Soc.* **81**: 4036-4040 (1959).
93. Ui, N.: Preparation, fractionation and properties of calf thymus histone. *Biochim. Biophys. Acta* **25**: 493-502 (1957).
94. Ui, N.: Sedimentation and diffusion studies of calf thymus histone. *Bull. Chem. Soc. Japan* **30**: 801-806 (1957).
95. Ui, N.: Sedimentation and diffusion studies of calf thymus histone aggregation. *Bull. Chem. Soc. Japan* **30**: 806-815 (1957).
96. Ui, N.: Sedimentation and diffusion studies of calf thymus histone. Electrophoretic studies. *Bull. Chem. Soc. Japan* **30**: 815-822 (1957).
97. Ui, N.: Sedimentation and diffusion studies of calf thymus histone. Studies on the preparation. *Bull. Chem. Soc. Japan* **30**: 822-826 (1957).
98. Wang, T.-Y.: Globulin of calf thymus nuclei and the *in vitro* incorporation of $C^{14}$ adenosine triphosphate into globulin-RNA. *Biochim. Biophys. Acta* **45**: 8-14 (1960).
99. Wang, T.-Y.: Metabolic activities of nuclear proteins and nucleic acids. *Biochim. Biophys. Acta* **68**: 52-61 (1963).
100. Wang, T.-Y.: Physico-chemical and metabolic properties of nuclear ribosomes. *Exptl. Cell Res. Suppl.* **9**: 213-219 (1963).
101. Zbarsky, I. B., and Dmitrieva, N. P.: Some features of cytochemistry of tumor cell nuclei. *Acta Unio Intern. Contra Cancrum* **18**: 123-126 (1962).
102. Zbarsky, I. B., Dmitrieva, N. P., and Yermolayeva, L. P.: On the structure of tumor cell nuclei. *Exptl. Cell Res.* **27**: 573-576 (1962).
103. Zbarsky, I. B., and Georgiev, G. P.: Cytological characteristics of protein and nucleoprotein fractions of cell nuclei. *Biochim. Biophys. Acta* **32**: 301-302 (1959).
104. Zubay, G., and Wilkins, M. H. F.: An X-ray diffraction study of histone and protamine in isolation and in combination with DNA. *J. Mol. Biol.* **4**: 444-450 (1962).

# CHAPTER IV

# Spatial Relationships between DNA and Histones



## Introduction

***Proteins and Chromosome Structure.*** Three types of chromosomal products have been available for histochemical and biochemical analysis, i.e., chromatin from interphase nuclei, chromosomes of various insect, plant, and animal cells *in situ*, and isolated chromosomes obtained from cells in metaphase. Although there has been a tendency to draw conclusions that seem to be relevant to all three types of chromosomal products, it is likely that these products vary in their content of RNA, acidic proteins, and histones. The chromosomes of the cells in metaphase are the structures that are generally thought of as chromosomes, and thus far, relatively little analytical information is available on these structures (15, 62) because they have not been isolated in amounts sufficient for biochemical analysis (10). Studies on the composition of the deoxyribonucleoproteins of the interphase chromatin have been discussed in Chapters II and III. In many studies on the chromosomes of the *Drosophila* (31, 32, 68–70), staining techniques have been employed. Information has been obtained about the DNA and histone content of these chromosomes, but relatively little information has been obtained about the acidic proteins.

*Continuity of DNA in Chromosomes.* Substantial evidence has been obtained that DNA is the thread that is continuous in some chromosomes, particularly in lampbrush chromosomes (70) of the oocyte of the newt. Evidence has been obtained that the treatment of these chromosomes with DNase destroys the chromosome but treatment with RNase and proteinases has the effect of removing much of the surface material without destroying the linear axial fiber of the chromosome. Support for this experiment has been reported by Chorhazy *et al.* (15), who found that DNase destroyed the metaphase chromosomes isolated from mouse leukemia cells. Swift (68, 69) made microphotometric analyses of the DNA content of interchromomeric regions in *Drosophila* chromosomes and found that although the amount was small there was some DNA present, so he has suggested that DNA is continuous throughout these chromosomes as well.

*Proteins and Chromosome Continuity.* However, it should be noted that DNA is not the only substance essential to the integrity of the mammalian chromosomes isolated by Chorhazy *et al.* (15) since trypsin also completely destroyed the chromosomes. RNase had no effect on the morphology of the chromosomes. This evidence, and earlier evidence (9, 45, 46), suggests that both protein and DNA are "linkers" essential to the continuity of the mammalian chromosome, but the question that is raised is what proteins are involved. Evidence that histones are not essential to the continuity of the chromosomes has been obtained by extraction of the chromosomes with acid (62), which does not seem to alter the morphology of the chromosomes and actually provides a medium in which they can be preserved for months. A number of reports have emphasized the strong binding between some proteins and DNA. Frearson and Kirby (28) endeavored to remove as much protein as possible from interphase chromatin by the phenol procedure and found that it was not possible to remove all the protein (Chapter III). The amount of protein remaining linked to DNA was variable for different cells and species. The largest percentage of protein in the deoxyribonucleoprotein complex was 26.7% in the product from the rat liver and the smallest was 3.4% in the product from the rat spleen. Large amounts of aspartic and glutamic acids were found in these products, i.e., about 30% of the total moles of amino acids recovered. The strength of binding of some proteins to DNA is also apparent from the fact that small amounts of protein remain linked to DNA even after extraction of DNP with acid and alkali. Jones and Marsh (34) recommended the use of sodium dodecylsulfate followed by treatment with chloroform and octanol to remove the remainder of the protein from DNA. Saline solutions were ineffective for removing proteins from bacterial nucleoproteins.

*"Linkers."* The possibility that the acidic proteins or peptides could serve as "linkers" for DNA chains in chromosomes was suggested by Bendich *et al.* (5), who found that a variety of amino acids were present in DNA preparations from bull sperm. These amino acids included aspartic and glutamic acids, valine and serine, and lesser amounts of other amino acids. The presence of serine in substantial amounts in their proteins as well as products obtained by other workers (28) prompted them to suggest that the phosphoester bonds of phosphoserine might serve as a linkage point of peptide and nucleotide.

The role of "linkers" in maintenance of the structure of chromatin and repair of chromosomes damaged by radiation has been emphasized by Taylor (70), who has suggested that in fact there are four types of such linkers, which have been named H, 5′, 3′, and 3′R. The 5′-linkers would serve to join two 5′-phosphate ends of DNA and provide for a reversal in polarity. The 3′-linker would presumably join two 3′-phosphate groups and serve to maintain the complementarity of the sequences of deoxyribonucleotides. H-linkers would provide a kind of backbone for the whole system to stabilize a ladderlike arrangement of the chains. The 3′R linker would function during replication to close the chains which have been opened at the 3′ ends for initiation of replication. Taylor (70) does not assume that all the "linkers" are proteins but he has not specified the nature of the linkers.

## Relationship of Histones to Chromosome Structure

*Intranuclear Localization of Histones.* As shown in Fig. 4-1A and Fig. 4-1B, there are a number of types of structures in the interphase

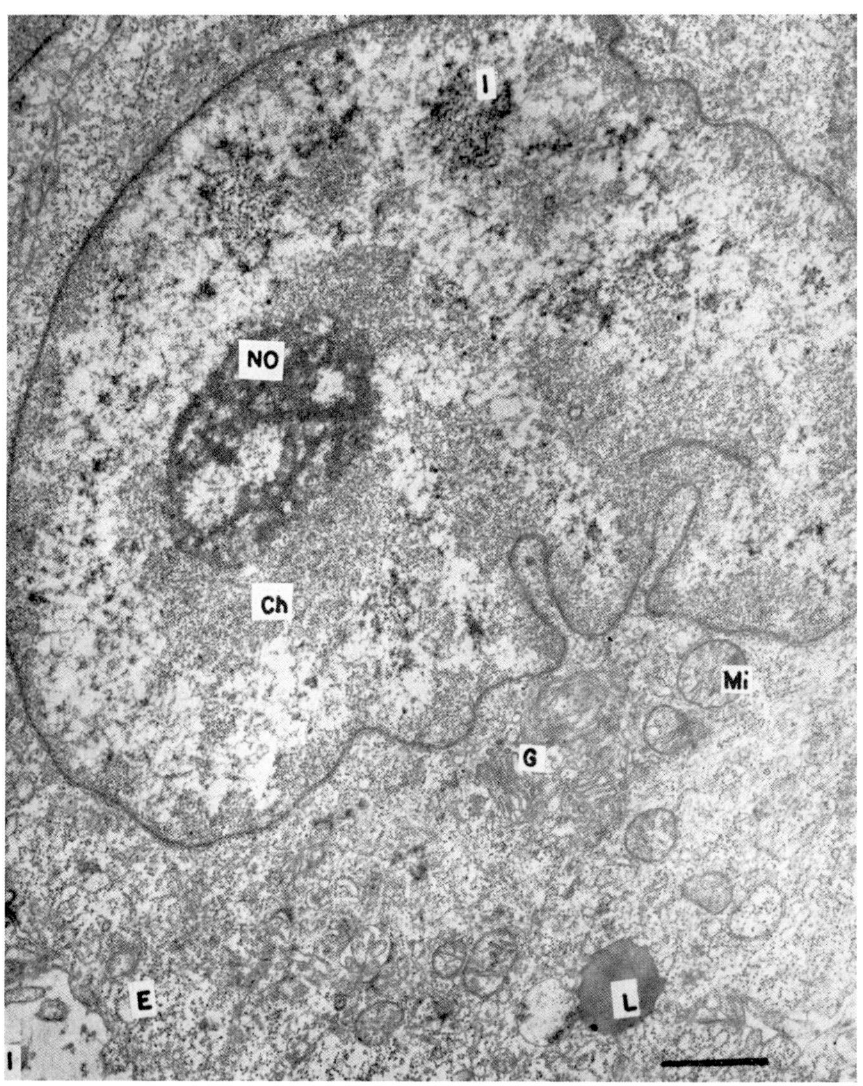


Fig. 4-1A. Nuclear structures. Nucleus of a cell of the Walker tumor. NO = nucleolus; Ch = chromatin; G = Golgi body; Mi = mitochondria; L = lipid; E = endoplasmic reticulum. The measured line indicates 1 μ (× 23,500). [From K. Smetana and H. Busch, *Cancer Res.* 23: 1600-1603 (1933).]

nucleus. Although this nucleus may vary in appearance depending upon the concentration of divalent ions in the medium (Chapter III) one or several nucleoli usually can be seen. In addition, there is generally a sharply defined nuclear membrane. Although there is not much question that the chromatin contains most of the histones, there is uncertainty about the histone content of other structures. For example, the nucleolus contains relatively little histone as determined by direct measurements of either the isolated nucleoli or nucleoli stained with

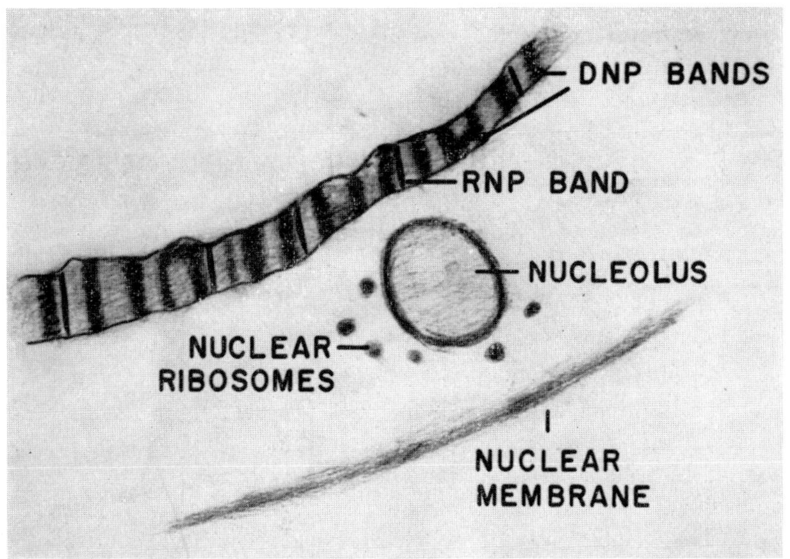


Fig. 4-1B. Diagram of intranuclear structures. Each of these structures may contain histones. [From Busch (9).]

Fast Green Fast (1–4, 31). The nuclear ribosomes contain mainly acidic proteins (64). It is not yet known whether "free" histones are present in the nuclear sap.

*Basic Proteins of the Cytoplasm.* It is generally accepted that most histones are in the nucleus, but recently some studies have been made on proteins in other cellular components that appear to be similar to the histones. The cytoplasmic ribosomes have been reported to contain some histone-like proteins (11, 12, 16, 20). The basic proteins extracted from the microsomes are similar in amino acid composition to the slightly lysine-rich histones; i.e., the basic amino acid residues and acidic amino acid residues composed approximately 24 and 18% of the total amino acid residues (16). Glycine, serine, and proline were found to be the major $NH_2$-terminal amino acids. The calculated molecular weight was 36,000. Horn (30) found that there are basic proteins in yolk platelets of oocytes of frogs. He suggested that these proteins were histones on the basis of electrophoretic mobility, sedimentation characteristics, and amino acid composition. The amounts of lysine and arginine were not very great in these proteins, but they have not yet been well characterized. Spicer (63) has reported that acid mucopolysaccharides may be associated with basic proteins in the cytoplasm of mucous cells, goblet cells, and mast cells, but these proteins have not been characterized. It has been pointed out previously that there are a number of proteins that are quite basic in cells that are not histones, including cytochromes, globins, portions of the globulins, lysozymes, interferons, and ribonucleases. Basicity alone is not a sufficient criterion to establish that a protein is a histone (see page 13).

*Localization of Histones in Chromatin.* A very close spatial relationship has been established between DNA and histones in the chromatin of salivary cells of *Drosophila* (31, 68, 69). At every point on the chromosomes of the *Drosophila* where there is a high concentration of DNA, there is a high concentration of histones (Fig. 4-2). In those studies, DNA was determined by the Feulgen stain and the histones were detected by staining with alkaline Fast Green, a stain that is regarded as specific for substances containing large numbers of basic amino acids (1–4). Each of the chromomeres had a high concentration of DNA, as indicated by the dense staining with the Feulgen reaction. The interchromomeric regions were stained to a much lesser extent, if at all, with the Feulgen technique. Swift (68, 69) and others have found that in the interband or interchromomeric regions DNA and histones were present in very low concentrations but, as noted previously, were not completely absent. These studies have supported the concept that there is a continuous DNA thread through the chromosome, at least in *Drosophila*, and further suggest that the chromomeres

---

FIG. 4-2. Intranuclear localization of the histones. The figures A and B are from identical sections through chromosomes of the *Drosophila melanogaster* stained with Feulgen stain (A) for DNA and with Fast Green (B) for histones. Comparison of the segments reveals the precise localization of the histones at the sites of localization of the DNA. [From Horn and Ward (31).]

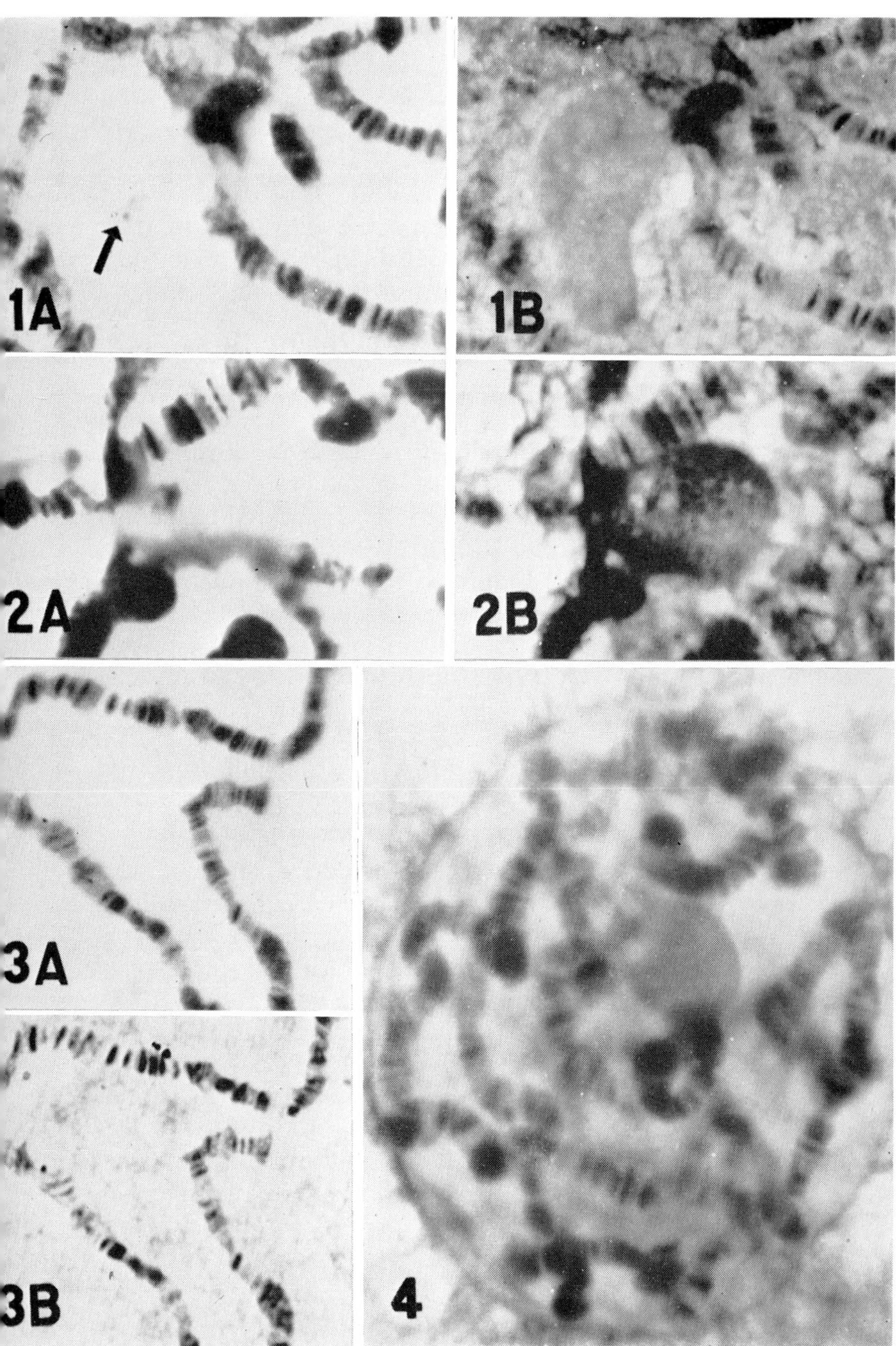
1A
1B
2A
2B
3A
3B
4

represent condensations or tight coiling of the DNA at particular loci (60).

It was particularly interesting that there was a precise equivalence of the localization of the histones and DNA as well as an optically equivalent concentration. Some evidence for the biological specificity of the localizations of DNA and histone comes from the study of Littau (39), who found that, after all the nucleic acids had been initially extracted from fixed tissues with hot trichloroacetic acid, added DNA combined with proteins in nucleolar and cytoplasmic sites as well as with the proteins of the chromatin.

Horn (30) found that the nuclei of amphibian ova do not contain substances that take the stain with alkaline Fast Green (1–4). In unfertilized eggs, fertilized eggs, and their divisions up to the morula, cytoplasmic substances were found that stained positively with Fast Green. At the first level of differentiation, the positively staining substances disappeared from the cytoplasm and appeared in the nucleus. It is known that some of the DNA is in the cytoplasm of these eggs and other structures (58). The same is apparently true for histones. With the inception of differentiation, the histones entered the nucleus and conceivably functioned to block out certain aspects of genetic totipotency.

Evidence has been provided by Prescott and Bender (59) that the proteins of the chromosomes are not permanently linked to DNA and do not persist in the chromosomes through successive mitoses. Although the label of tritiated thymidine persisted in DNA through at least four successive mitoses, neither the label in RNA nor label in protein was similarly retained on the chromosome. One interesting point was that much of the nuclear protein left the nucleus during mitosis of amebas (59). When mitosis was completed, a large amount of labeled protein returned to the nucleus. Like the RNA which is extruded from the nuclear area of cells undergoing division some nuclear proteins may also temporarily be located outside the nucleus and then return to the nucleus in telophase (see also cytonucleoproteins, page 215).

Thus, the localization of histones in chromosomes, their turnover, and their ready extraction from the chromosomes suggest that histones are not essential to the elementary structure of the chromosomes. Instead, they seem to be surface structures of chromatin. Some of the acidic nuclear proteins (see Chapter VIII) would appear to be more related to the structure of metaphase chromosomes and may serve as "linkers" for DNA molecules.

## Models of the Structure of the Chromosome

*Metaphase Chromosomes.* An important accomplishment of modern cytogenetics has been the development of techniques for the identification of the chromosomes (29, 32). As shown in Fig. 4-3, the metaphase chromosomes of man consist of a variety of structures of dif-

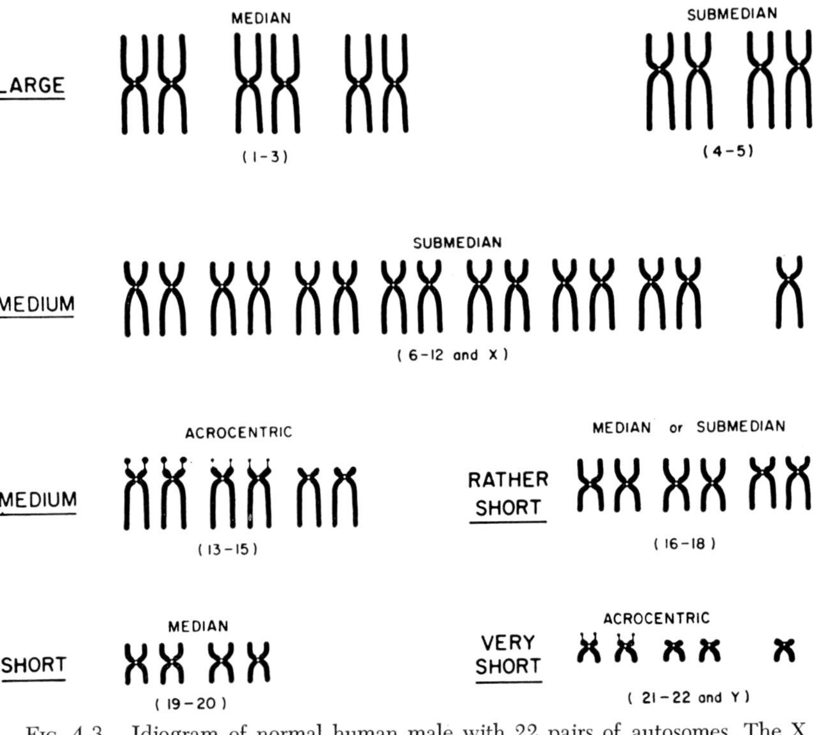


FIG. 4-3. Idiogram of normal human male with 22 pairs of autosomes. The X and Y sex chromosomes are separated from the autosomal pairs. The chromosomes are arranged according to their height primarily and also according to the position of the centromere. [From A. R. Sohval, *Am. J. Med.* **31**: 397-441 (1961).]

ferent sizes and shapes that are grouped as large, medium, rather short, short and very short, depending upon their size, and as median, submedian or acrocentric, depending upon whether their centromere is at the center or toward the end of the chromosome.

*Electron Microscopy of Chromosomes.* Recent electron microscopic studies of metaphase chromosomes (17) have made it apparent that the structure of the mammalian chromosome is complex (Fig. 4-4). Each

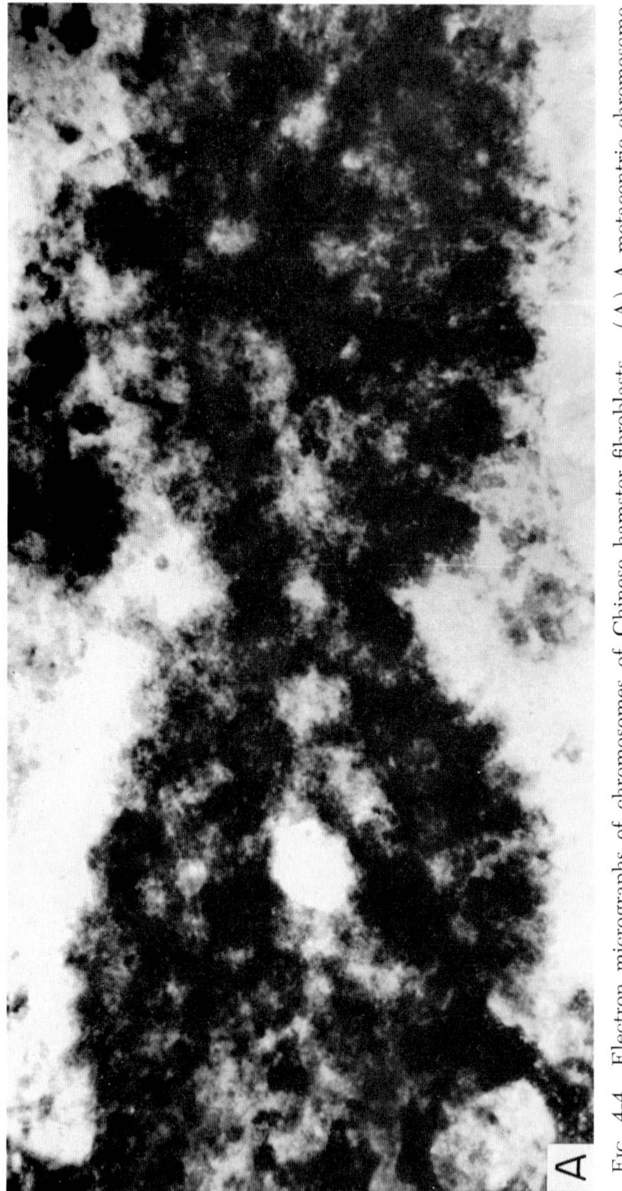


Fig. 4-4. Electron micrographs of chromosomes of Chinese hamster fibroblasts. (A) A metacentric chromosome. (B) The telomere of another chromosome. (These photographs were generously provided by Dr. Arthur Cole, of the M. D. Anderson Hospital.)

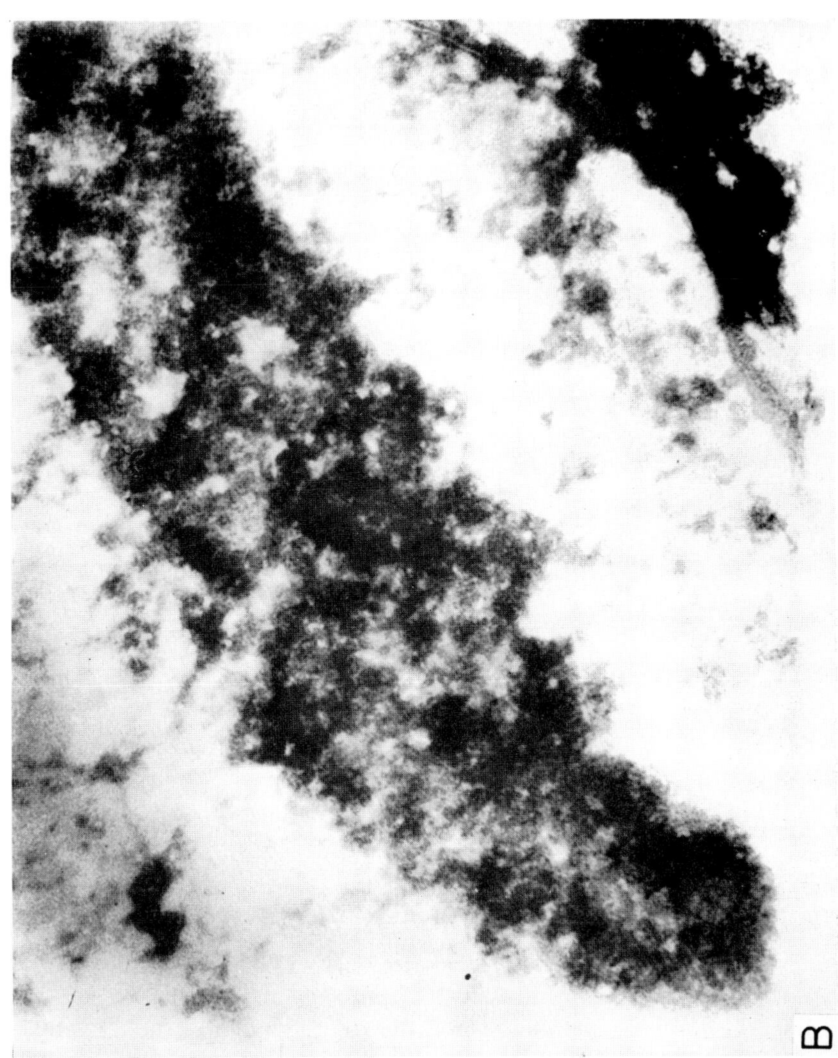
B

chromatid apparently consists of 64 or 128 of the elementary chromosomal fibrils of Ris (60). These are apparently intertwined and joined with one another in a network. Both the interrelations of the chromatids at the telomeres and the twisting strands at the centromere also appear to be quite complex. One element of uncertainty about the electron microscopic studies is the extent of the possible aggregation or extraction of components of the chromatin. Thus, one cannot be certain yet that the varying densities of chromatin reflect twisting or condensation of chromatin. Since the chromosomes are very large and are readily visible with the ordinary light microscope, it is somewhat disappointing that more structural detail is not apparent. One model that seems to reflect the coiling and twisting is the complex rope structure of Steffensen (65) is shown in Fig. 4-5.

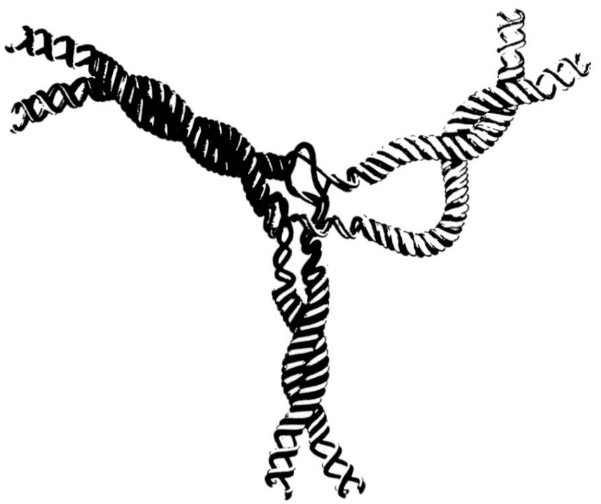

FIG. 4-5. The coiled rope concept of chromosomal structure. [From Steffensen (65).]

*Proteins in Chromosome Models.* Before chromosomal models are considered, it is essential that a number of points be stated. The first of these relates to the organization of the centromere. This junctional point in metaphase chromosomes is the meeting point of the maternal chromatid with the newly synthesized chromatid, as Taylor (70) has demonstrated. It seems unlikely that this junctional area contains only DNA in view of the fact that the double helices of one chromatid could not readily bond to double helices in the other chromatid. It is much more likely that either protein or lipid present in the centromere is related to the organization of this region of the chromosome. Similarly, at the telomere, the type of coiling and angulation that exist suggest that protein or lipid governs the shape of the region or the doubling back of the DNA.

Another point to consider is the effect of low concentrations of trypsin on the structure of the chromosomes. High concentrations of trypsin cause disintegration of the chromosomes (15), but in this laboratory it was observed that the chromosomes merely swelled into large blobs when treated with small amounts of trypsin. This finding suggests that proteins are partly responsible for the overall structure of the chromosomes.

Mirsky and Ris (45, 46) first suggested that proteins aid in defining the structure of chromatin and the interphase chromosomes. Their concept is embodied in the structure shown in Fig. 4-6, which shows that a protein filament runs through the chromosome. This idea was based upon the finding of an acidic protein fraction, Tr.Pr., that re-

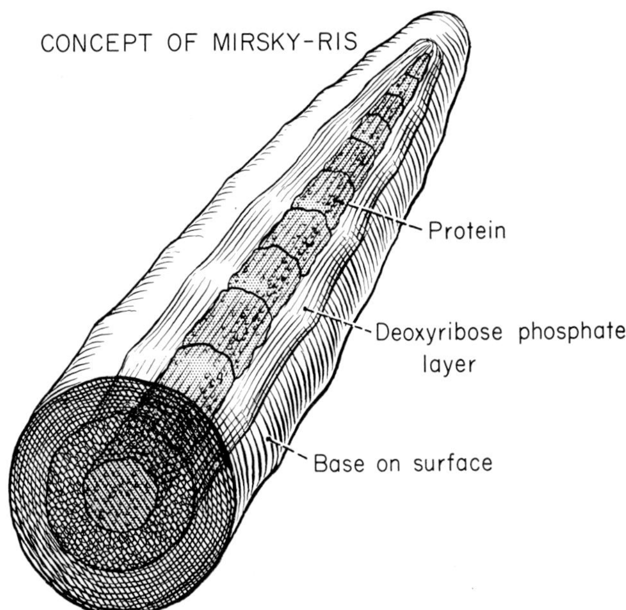


FIG. 4-6. Schematic representation of a segment of a chromosome. Relationships of DNA and protein are indicated in terms of a scheme which suggests that the protein is the inner "core" of the chromosome, and the DNA is the surface structure. [From Busch (9).]

mained after histones and DNA were both extracted from the chromatin (Chapter VIII). The Tr.Pr. fraction was insoluble in acid but was slowly soluble in dilute alkali (see Chapter VIII).

Mirsky and Ris (45, 46) regarded the Tr.Pr. protein as a linear filament of the chromosome around which the nucleic acids were laid down. The length of the linear filament was not clear, and the possibility exists that the protein could be the continuous mass shown in Fig. 4-6 or a discontinuous mass, as shown in Fig. 4-7. Either of these

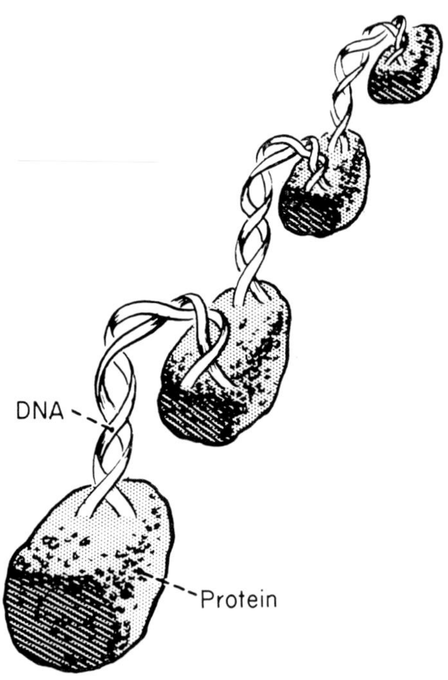


FIG. 4-7. Schematic representation of a segment of the chromosome in which protein serves to bind ends of DNA helices together. In this representation the proteins are discontinuous masses, but the possibility has been suggested that this protein could be a continuous mass. [From Busch (9).]

structures could account in part for intertwining of the DNA strands if disulfide or other bridges occurred between the protein strands at various points along the DNP fibers in the centromeres or at the telomeres.

Another structure is that in which a long strand of protein would have binding sites for the ends of a number of DNA helices in a modification of the one shown in Fig. 4-7. These DNA helices could begin and terminate as a series of loops (70), but the protein in Fig. 4-7 would be a continuous filament rather than a discontinuous series of molecules.

*Linkers in Chromosome Models.* As noted earlier in this chapter, models have been suggested in which proteins serve to link DNA chains in a variety of types of linkages. These more complex models are shown in Fig. 4-8 (70). Although four types of "linkers" are suggested, it is not clear whether one or more may be proteins (see page 93).

*Lipids in the Chromosomes.* In the studies of Wilkins and his associates (81–83, 87), it was suggested that sphingomyelin or other lipids were present in deoxyribonucleoprotein preparations. This suggestion has been criticized by Luzatti and Nicolaieff (42, 44), who had another interpretation for the X-ray diffraction studies. Since no evidence has been presented that there are indeed lipids in deoxyribonucleoproteins or chromosomes, it seems premature to invoke a role for them as binding substances. However, it is still not possible to exclude such a role.

*Tertiary and Quaternary Structures of the Histones.* Because the histones have not yet been completely purified either in crystalline form or amorphous states, completely satisfactory analysis of their structure has not been possible using either X-ray diffraction techniques or infrared analysis. Their very low concentrations of cysteine or cystine (Chapter II) have suggested that the histones are linear polymers without significant branching or crosslinking. The proline content of proteins has been related to their angulation (33). Most histones have relatively low concentrations of proline, including the "arginine-rich" group and the slightly lysine-rich histones (2a). The *N*-proline histone has slightly more proline than these fractions (Chapter II). The only fraction that has substantial amounts of proline is the very lysine-rich fraction in which proline comprises 8–10% of the total amino acid residues. The possibilities for angulation would appear to be greater in the very lysine-rich histones than in the other histone fractions.

*Spatial Relations of Some Histones to DNA.* Since there is a variety of histones it seems quite possible that the relationships of different histones to DNA are defined in part by their structures. The suggestion was made by Wilkins *et al.* (81–83) that the histones fit into the deep groove of the DNA molecule, but this has not been followed up with specific evidence. Others have suggested that there might be a folding

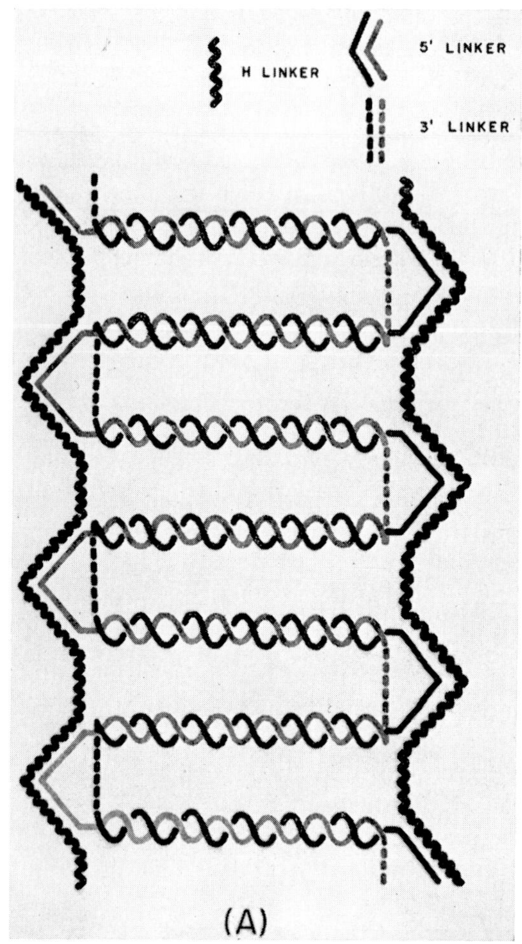


FIG. 4-8. (A) Chromosome models based upon various types of "linkers." 3′ and 5′ "linkers" join together the 3′ and 5′ ends of chains of DNA. The H linkers join together the linear strands of DNA to form a ladderlike arrangement in this model.

of the histones as they are linked to DNA such that the guanidinium or $NH_2$-residues would be in a position to neutralize the phosphate groups of DNA. Crampton *et al.* (21) reported that the ratio of basic amino acids per phosphate group was about 0.9, and Vendrely *et al.* (78) have concluded that the value ranges from 0.95 to 1.07. This parallelism has led to the opinion that one of the major functions of

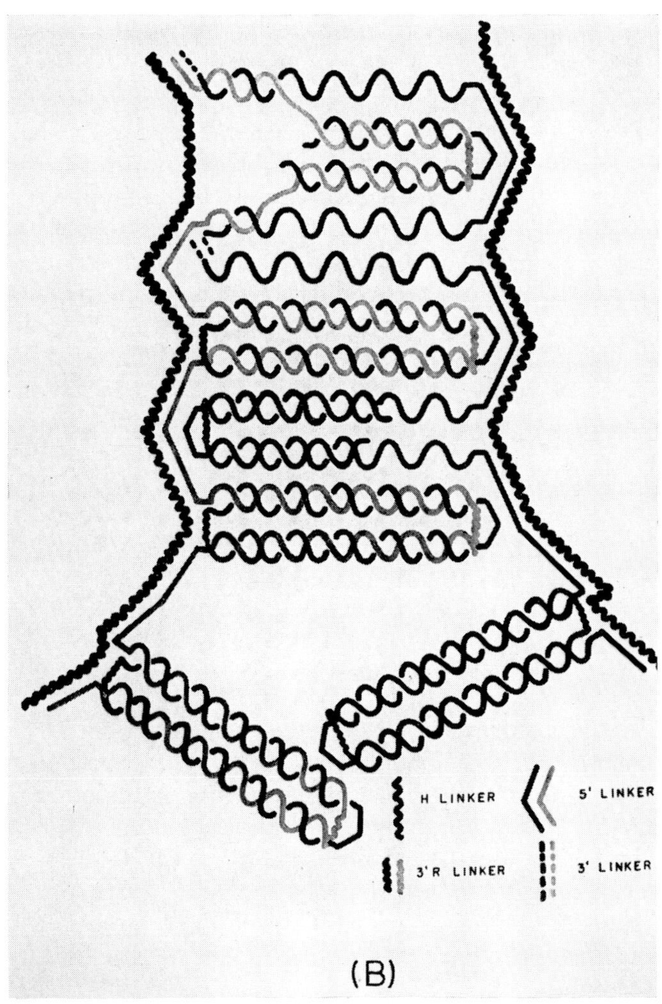


(B) On replication, a new "linker," the 3′ R linker, is assumed to be inserted and the growing 3′ ends are assumed to be closed by addition of 3′ R linkers. The two chromatids would consist of pairs of DNA attached to a single axial element. [Diagrams from Taylor (70).]

the histones is the *neutralization of the phosphate groups of DNA*. It should be noted that the precise ratio of amino nitrogen to phosphate groups is not yet completely clarified since values of 0.8 to 0.9 have been reported by many workers (37, 47, 48–55, 64). In addition, Dounce (27) has reported that the ratio of histone to DNA in the normal liver approaches 2. In regenerating liver and in tumors, the ratio was closer to 1.

Phillips (56) has studied the structural significance of the approximate equivalence of basic groups of the histones and the acidic groups of DNA. He estimated that 25–40% of all the basic amino acids were found in pairs in the "arginine-rich" histones. In some peptides, a number of nonbasic amino acids were found between the basic amino acids. Phillips and Simson (57) showed that after tryptic digestion of the histones, a fraction precipitated out of solution. In this fraction an *average* of 7 nonbasic amino acids were interposed between the basic residues. Thus, it would appear that histone structure is far more complex than would be required for the simple neutralization of the phosphate residues (see Chapter V). Since the binding of histone to DNA is largely electrostatic, it is likely that the basic residues play a critical role.

*Special Features of the Linkage of DNA and the Very Lysine-Rich Histones.* As mentioned previously, the very lysine-rich histones are richer in proline residues than the other histones. This interesting difference may account for a number of features of their solubility. For example, these proteins were more readily removed from DNA than the other histones. Using 0.07 *M* citric acid, Davison and Butler (23) found that the very lysine-rich histones were partly removed from DNP when other histones were not. In addition, these proteins have been readily extracted from DNP with acid at pH 1.5, whereas the other proteins were removed from DNP at pH 0.7, i.e., in the presence of more concentrated acid (6, 61). Low concentrations of salt, 0.6 *M* have been shown to selectively extract the very lysine-rich fraction (40, 41, 72–77). The relatively greater solubility of these proteins at pH 11 was demonstrated by the finding of Daly and Mirsky (22) that the very lysine-rich histones remained in solution when the other histones were precipitated by ammonia. In the interesting experiment of Ui (72–77) DNP was centrifuged through layers of 1 *M* and 2 *M* NaCl solutions. The upper layer contained only very lysine-rich histones and the layer with 2 *M* NaCl contained a mixture of different types of histones.

Evidence that the weaker binding of very lysine-rich histones and DNA may be related to a weaker affinity of these proteins to cation exchangers in general was suggested by Phillips (56), who noted an early elution of the very lysine-rich histones from carboxymethylcellulose columns. In the usual chromatographic procedure referred to in Chapter III, the buffer employed (pH 4.2) elutes the very lysine-rich histones and permits the other histones to remain attached to the carboxymethylcellulose.

There is little evidence at the moment to support the concept that histones are linked to DNA other than through ionic bonds. The fact that the strongly basic very lysine-rich histones are more weakly linked to DNA than the other histones suggests that although differences in electrostatic attraction may have a place in the differential functions of histones, differences in structure of the histones may be of greater significance. As noted previously, Frearson and Kirby (28) found that some very lysine-rich histones were apparently tightly bound to DNA, possibly by hydrogen bonding.

*X-Ray Analysis of the Physical Interrelationships of DNA and Histones.* Although there are models for chromosomes, none of these can be taken very seriously until the relationships between DNA and the histones become more adequately defined. One of the critical problems in defining these relationships is the fact that the deoxyribonucleoprotein complex is not crystalline and does not have a highly ordered structure on X-ray diffraction analysis. In addition, completely satisfactory pictures have not been taken with reconstituted products that are complexes of DNA with purified histones, such as the slightly lysine-rich, very lysine-rich, and other histone fractions. The lack of such information has limited workers in this field in their effort to provide a structure for the DNA–histone complex. In addition, there has been little study of the histone linked to the available purified DNA structures such as the AT-rich DNA obtained by enzymatic polymerization or by extraction from the crab (66, 67). Such information might also be valuable in defining the interrelationships between the histones and nucleic acids.

The two principal methods that have been employed for structural studies on the histones are X-ray analysis (42–44, 81–83, 85–87) and infrared analysis (7, 8, 24–26, 36, 38). The X-ray pattern for DNA has been compared with that of the deoxyribonucleohistone by Zubay and Wilkins (87). Undenatured isolated histone provides diffuse diffraction rings in the region of 4.5 and 10 Å. In general, the patterns of undenatured histones suggested that α-helices are a major component in the structure. Occasionally a sharp reflection was seen at 4.7 Å. This reflection was interpreted by Zubay and Wilkins (87) as suggesting that the β-type structure was present and had arisen from denaturation of the molecule. In freshly prepared nucleohistone, 50–70% of the protein was in α-helical form (7, 8).

When the structure of DNA was studied by X-ray diffraction, it was found that a structure with a regular order existed and it was possible to work out a structure with a high degree of regularity (79, 80). When histones were added to DNA, there was a diminution of the order of the structure. In nucleohistone preparations reflections were found at 20, 25, 34, 37, 55, and 60 Å. One possible arrangement of such a structure is shown in Fig. 4-9. In this model, the histones would

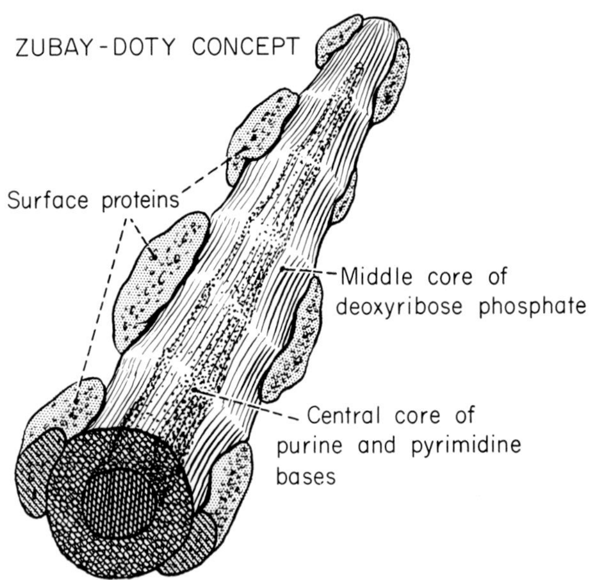


Fig. 4-9. Schematic representation of a chromosome in which the core is the nucleotide helix, with the deoxyribose phosphate groups on the surface of the inner nucleotide core. The proteins are on the surface of the chromosome in discrete bands or in discrete loci. [From Busch (9).]

not necessarily play a part in chromosomal structure, but rather would be surface proteins. Although this model does not completely define the chromosomal structure, particularly the points of branching and the centromere, it does predict that removal of proteins such as the histones would not alter the structure of the chromosomes. In studies on the histone content of chromosomes (62) it was found that 50% acetic acid, which is used to harden and preserve the chromosomes, effectively removes the histones from the chromosomal mass. In studies in which $C^{14}$-lysine was employed to label the chromosomal proteins, about 98% of the labeled proteins were removed from the chromosomes without altering their structure.

***Histones as Bridges between DNA Strands.*** A number of models of deoxyribonucleic acid and deoxyribonucleoproteins have been suggested as alternatives to the twin-stranded structure proposed by Watson and Crick (79, 80). Cavalieri and Rosenberg (14) have proposed a 4-stranded structure and Luzzati and Nicolaieff (42–44) have suggested a multistranded structure. Zubay and Doty (86) and others (42–44) have suggested that histones form bridges between DNA strands. The

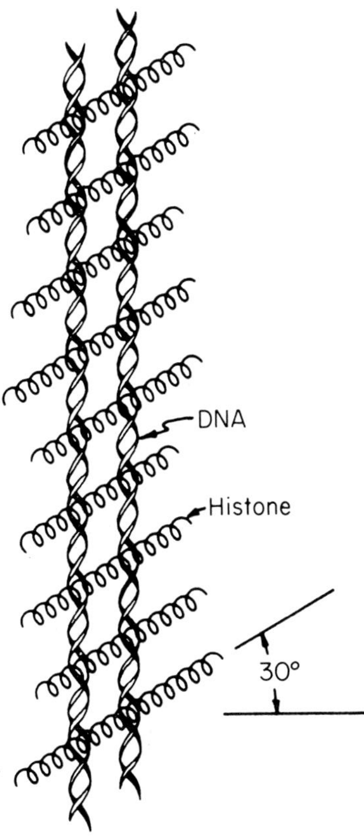


FIG. 4-10. A model of nucleohistone in which histones form bridges between DNA molecules. The long axis of these bridges would be at an angle of 60 degrees to the long axis of the DNA. [From Zubay (85).]

possibility exists that some histones are specifically linked to DNA in such a way that they promote coiling of DNA strands (33, 85). In this way, histones could maintain the spacing of genetic codes and thereby enhance or limit the read-out. For example, the very lysine-rich histones and protamines might limit the read-out by tightening the DNA coils, and other histones might serve to expand the coils and permit more frequent or more ready read-out of the codes (see page 129).

On the basis of the reflection at 37 Å and the evidence obtained from the infrared studies, Zubay (85) has proposed the latticelike arrangement in Fig. 4-10 as a model in which histones would intersect the DNA strands at an angle of approximately 55–60 degrees to the long axis of the DNA. One suggestion for the usefulness of an arrangement such as the lattice, or interlocking threads, is its ability to promote supercoiling of DNA as shown in Fig. 4-11. Some studies in progress support the idea that histones promote supercoiling of DNA.

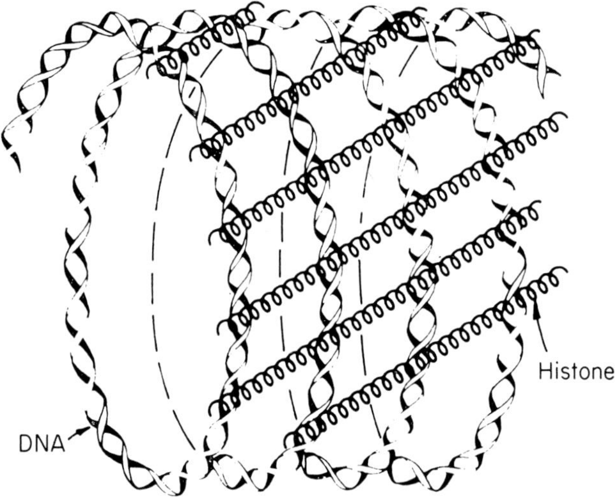


Fig. 4-11. A model suggesting that histones serve to enhance supercoiling of DNA in mitotic chromosomes. In this model a number of features of previous models are included. The possibility exists that molecules other than histones may be involved in supercoiling of DNA. [From Zubay (85).]

Studies of Bradbury *et al.* (7, 8) on the infrared analysis of nucleohistone structure provide support for the idea that either the lattice shown in Fig. 4-10 is correct, or that there is essentially no specific ordered interrelationship between the DNA and histone. In studies on freshly prepared nucleohistone, approximately 58% of the protein was slow in deuterating, and the interpretation was that it was probably in the $\alpha$-helical form. This value was very similar to the value of 66% of histone in the $\alpha$-helical form obtained in studies on optical rotation of histone preparations (86). Woodard and Swift (84) have pointed out that localized uncoiling of chromosomes may be induced by cold. The possibility exists that X-ray-induced "breaks" in chromosomes (70) may be due to local uncoiling. The relationship of histones to these effects are not defined.

*Stabilization of DNA against Thermal Denaturation by Histones.* Evidence that the $T_m$ of nucleohistone preparations is greater than that of DNA has recently been expanded by Huang *et al.* (33). The $T_m$ is the temperature at which the increase in optical density of DNA is halfway between the initial and final optical density as the sample is subjected to increasing temperature. In their preparations, the $T_m$ for DNA was 70°C and that for nucleohistone was 84°. When the nucleohistones were reconstituted with very lysine-rich histones, slightly lysine-rich, and "arginine-rich" histones, the respective values for the $T_m$ were 81°, 75°, and 71°. They had noted that there was an inflection point in their curve for nucleohistone at 69.5° and suggested that 80% of the DNA was complexed with histone and 20% was not. The values for the percentage of DNA complexed with histones were supported by the data on priming activity of the DNA for RNA synthesis and the amount of histone isolated in the chromatin (see Chapter V).

## Special Linkages of Histones and DNA

With respect to coding, DNA is an extremely complex structure, and, if there are only 10 to 20 kinds of histones, it is not clear how the histones are capable of specifying which components of DNA will be read out. If individual histones could have several types of linkages to DNA, it would seem that many different varieties of DNA–histone bonds could exist. This would be particularly true if histones were linked to DNA at two or three binding sites and the remainder of the molecule was not linked to DNA. In the very lysine-rich histones, where there are only two amino acids that are nonbasic for each lysine residue, there are many basic groups that could potentially neutralize the phosphate groups of DNA or bond with the hydroxyls of cytosine, guanine, and thymine. On the other hand, in the "arginine-rich" fraction 3, there are 4 nonbasic amino acids for each lysine and arginine residue. Some of the peptides isolated from the slightly lysine-rich histones have 11 or 12 nonbasic amino acids between the basic amino acids (Chapter VI). Such findings suggest that there are loops of peptides containing amino acids that are not linked to the DNA. These loops vary in number and size for the various histones and are not uniformly distributed through the histone molecules.

Phillips (56) has calculated that for one complete turn of the DNA double helix which contains 20 nucleotides (10 pairs), an approximate weight of histone of 8000–12,000 or protamine of 4000 would serve to neutralize the phosphate groups. These weights are about one-half to three-quarters of the molecular weights of these molecules (13, 61) and suggest that it would be possible for a single histone or protamine molecule to neutralize the phosphate groups of one to two turns of the helix; this idea would require coiling of the histone around the DNA helix. Phillips (56) suggested that the very lysine-rich histones resemble protamines much more in structure than the other histones, having a β-form and about 10% of the total residues as proline. In view of this similarity, the possibility was suggested that the very lysine-rich histones could also occupy the narrow groove of DNA (82, 83).

*The Relationship of Very Lysine-Rich Histones to GC-Rich DNA.* It is still not clear whether all histones are aligned to neutralize phosphate groups of DNA or some are more specifically linked to specific base sequences. A number of inferences have been made that suggest a close relationship between GC-rich components of DNA and the very lysine-rich histones (18, 19, 40, 41, 61a). As mentioned previously, the very lysine-rich histones appear to be more readily separated from DNA than the other histones by a variety of extraction procedures using acid or salt. When attempts were made to separate the deoxyribonucleoproteins by salt extractions, it was found that the histones with higher lysine content were extracted with DNA that was relatively richer in guanine and cytosine residues. Kent *et al.* (35) reported that stepwise addition of either dextran sulfate or heparin to solutions of deoxyribonucleoproteins resulted in the selective precipitation of histone fractions. The first fraction that was precipitated from solutions of deoxyribonucleoproteins of ox spleen was probably a very lysine-rich histone fraction. The DNA that was associated with this fraction was a GC-rich DNA.

Although it would be of great interest if a specific linkage of histone and DNA could be demonstrated, the evidence for the linkage of very lysine-rich histones and GC-rich DNA is the only evidence for such specificity. Even this has not been satisfactorily proved, and the concept remains to be further elaborated and extended to other molecular species of histones and to specific DNAs (61a).

## References


1. Alfert, M.: Chemical differentiation of nuclear proteins during spermatogenesis in the salmon. *J. Biophys. Biochem. Cytol.* **2**: 109-114 (1956).
2. Alfert, M.: Some cytochemical contributions to genetic chemistry. *In* "The Chemical Basis of Heredity" (W. D. McElroy and B. Glass, eds.), pp. 186-194. Johns Hopkins Press, Baltimore, Maryland, 1957.
3. Alfert, M.: Variations in cytochemical properties of cell nuclei. *Exptl. Cell Res. Suppl.* **6**: 227-235 (1958).
4. Alfert, M., and Geschwind, I. I.: A selective staining method for the basic proteins of cell nuclei. *Proc. Natl. Acad. Sci. U.S.* **39**: 991-999 (1953).
5. Bendich, A., Borenfreund, E., Korngold, G. C., Krim, M., and Balis, M. E.: Amino acids or small peptides as punctuation in the genetic code of RNA. *In* "Nucleic Acids and Their Role in Biology." Milan, 1963.
6. Bijvoet, P.: Ethanol precipitation analysis of thymus histone. *Biochim. Biophys. Acta* **25**: 502-512 (1957).
7. Bradbury, E. M., Price, W. C., and Wilkinson, G. R.: Polarized infrared studies on nucleoproteins. I. Nucleoprotamine. *J. Mol. Biol.* **4**: 39-49 (1962).
8. Bradbury, E. M., Price, W. C., Wilkinson, G. R., and Zubay, G.: Polarized infrared studies on nucleoproteins. II. Nucleohistone. *J. Mol. Biol.* **4**: 50-60 (1962).
9. Busch, H.: "An Introduction to the Biochemistry of the Cancer Cell." Academic Press, New York, 1962.
10. Busch, H., Starbuck, W. C., Singh, E. J., and Ro, T. S.: Chromosomal proteins. *In* "Chromosomes," Symposium of the Society for Growth, Amherst, Massachusetts, 1964.
11. Butler, J. A. V., and Cohn, P.: Studies on histones. 6. Observations on the biosynthesis of histones and other proteins in regenerating rat liver. *Biochem. J.* **87**: 330-334 (1963).
12. Butler, J. A. V., Cohn, P., and Simson, P.: The presence of basic proteins in microsomes. *Biochim. Biophys. Acta* **38**: 386-388 (1960).
13. Callanan, M. S., Carroll, W. R., and Mitchell, E. R.: Physical and chemical properties of protamine from the sperm of salmon (*Oncorhynchus tschanytscha*). I. Preparation and characterization. *J. Biol. Chem.* **229**: 279-287 (1957).
14. Cavalieri, L. F., and Rosenberg, B. H.: The replication of DNA. II. The number of polynucleotide strands in the conserved unit of DNA. *Biophys. J.* **1**: 323-336 (1961).
15. Chorhazy, M., Bendich, A., Borenfreund, E., and Hutchison, D. J.: Studies on the isolation of metaphase chromosomes. *J. Cell Biol.* **19**: 59-69 (1963).

16. Cohn, P., and Simson, P.: Basic and other proteins in microsomes of rat liver. *Biochem. J.* **88**: 206-212 (1963).
17. Cole, A.: Unpublished data.
18. Crampton, C. F., Lipshitz, R., and Chargaff, E.: Studies on nucleoproteins. I. Dissociation and reassociation of deoxyribonucleohistone of calf thymus. *J. Biol. Chem.* **206**: 499-510 (1954).
19. Crampton, C. F., Lipshitz, R., and Chargaff, E.: Studies on nucleoproteins. II. Fractionation of deoxyribonucleic acids through fractional dissociation of their complexes with basic proteins. *J. Biol. Chem.* **211**: 125-142 (1954).
20. Crampton, C. F., and Peterman, M. L.: The amino acid composition of proteins isolated from the ribonucleoprotein particles of rat liver. *J. Biol. Chem.* **234**: 2642-2644 (1959).
21. Crampton, C. F., Stein, W. H., and Moore, S.: Comparative studies on chromatographically purified histones. *J. Biol. Chem.* **225**: 363-386 (1957).
22. Daly, M. M., and Mirsky, A. E.: Histones with high lysine content. *J. Gen. Physiol.* **38**: 405-413 (1954-1955).
23. Davison, P. F., and Butler, J. A. V.: The fractionation and composition of histones from thymus nucleoprotein. *Biochim. Biophys. Acta* **15**: 439-440 (1954).
24. DeLozé, C.: Infrared spectra and structure of deoxyribonucleoproteins and their components. *Ann. Chim.* (*Paris*) [13] **3**: 145-203 (1958).
25. DeLozé, C.: Spectre infrarouge et structure de l'histone. *Compt. Rend. Acad. Sci.* **246**: 417-418, 599 (1958).
26. DeLozé, C., and Lenormant, H.: Effet des fixateurs sur la nucléohistone de thymus. *Bull. Soc. Chim. Biol.* **41**: 337-343 (1959).
27. Dounce, A. L.: The isolation of nuclei from tumor cells. *Exptl. Cell Res. Suppl.* **9**: 126-143 (1963).
28. Frearson, P. M., and Kirby, K. S.: Nucleoproteins. II. Fractionation of deoxyribonucleoproteins into acidic proteins and lysine-rich histones associated with deoxyribonucleic acid. *Biochem. J.* **90**: 578-583 (1964).
29. Hirschhorn, K., and Cooper, H. L.: Chromosomal aberrations in human disease. *Am. J. Med.* **31**: 442-470 (1961).
30. Horn, E. C.: Extranuclear histone in the amphibian oocyte. *Proc. Natl. Acad. Sci. U.S.* **48**: 257-265 (1962).
31. Horn, E. C., and Ward, C. L.: The localization of basic proteins in the nuclei of larval *Drosophila* salivary glands. *Proc. Natl. Acad. Sci. U.S.* **43**: 776-779 (1957).
32. Hsu, T. C.: Chromosomal evolution in cell populations. *Intern. Rev. Cytol.* **12**: 69-161 (1961).
33. Huang, R. C., Bonner, J., and Murray, K.: Physical and biological properties of soluble nucleohistones. *J. Mol. Biol.* **8**: 54-64 (1964).
34. Jones, A. S., and Marsh, G. E.: The deproteinization of nucleoproteins. *Biochim. Biophys. Acta* **14**: 559-566 (1954).
35. Kent, P. W., Hichens, M., and Ward, P. F. V.: Displacement fractionation of deoxyribonucleoproteins by heparin and dextran sulphate. *Biochem. J.* **68**: 568-572 (1958).
36. Klamerth, O.: Optical relations between deoxyribonucleic acid and histone. *Z. Naturforsch.* **12b**: 186-189 (1957).

37. Laurence, D. J. R., Simson, P., and Bulter, J. A. V.: Studies on histones. 5. The histones of the Crocker sarcoma and spontaneous mammary tumors of mice. *Biochem. J.* **87**: 200-205 (1963).
38. Lenormant, H., and DeLozé, C.: Effet du dioxone sur la nucléohistone de thymus. *Bul. Soc. Chim. Biol.* **41**: 331-337 (1959).
39. Littau, V. C.: Cytological evidence that both RNA and DNA may form a complex with the same protein. *J. Biophys. Biochem. Cytol.* **5**: 231-234 (1959).
40. Lucy, J. A., and Butler, J. A. V.: Fractionation of deoxyribonucleoprotein. *Biochim. Biophys. Acta* **16**: 431-432 (1955).
41. Lucy, J. A., and Butler, J. A. V.: Fractionation of deoxyribonucleoprotein. *Bull. Soc. Chim. Belges* **65**: 133-139 (1956).
42. Luzzati, V.: The structure of nucleohistones and nucleoprotamines. *J. Mol. Biol.* **7**: 758-759 (1963).
43. Luzzati, V., Luzzati, D., and Masson, F.: La structure des acides désoxyribonucléiques bactériens en solution. *J. Mol. Biol.* **5**: 375-383 (1962).
44. Luzzati, V., and Nicolaïeff, A.: The structure of nucleohistones and nucleoprotamines. *J. Mol. Biol.* **7**: 142-163 (1963).
45. Mirsky, A. E., and Ris, H.: The chemical composition of isolated chromosomes. *J. Gen. Physiol.* **31**: 7-18 (1947).
46. Mirsky, A. E., and Ris, H.: The composition and structure of isolated chromosomes. *J. Gen. Physiol.* **34**: 475-494 (1950).
47. Peacocke, A. R.: The structure and physical chemistry of nucleic acids and nucleoproteins. *Progr. Biophys. Biophys. Chem.* **10**: 55-113 (1960).
48. Perugini, S., Soldati, M., and Torelli, U.: Research on the protein component of blood cells. I. The protein content of nucleus in relation to its deoxyribonucleic acid content: Theoretical premises. *Riv. Istiochim. Norm. Patol.* **2**: 441-448 (1956).
49. Perugini, S., Soldati, M., and Torelli, U.: Research on the protein component of blood cells. II. The nuclear content of histone protein and of deoxyribonucleic acid in rat lymphocytes and hepatocytes. *Riv. Istiochim. Norm. Patol.* **2**: 449-460 (1956).
50. Perugini, S., Soldati, M., and Torelli, U.: Research on the protein component of blood cells. III. The nuclear content of total protein in lymphocytes and hepatocytes of normal rats. *Riv. Istiochim. Norm. Patol.* **2**: 461-468 (1956).
51. Perugini, S., Soldati, M., and Torelli, U.: Research on the protein component of blood cells. IV. The nuclear content of histone protein and deoxyribonucleic acid in lymphocytes and myelocytes of normal adult humans. *Riv. Istiochim. Norm. Patol.* **3**: 5-14 (1957).
52. Perugini, S., Soldati, M., and Torelli, U.: Research on the protein component of blood cells. V. The nuclear content of total protein in lymphocytes and myelocytes of normal adult humans. *Riv. Istiochim. Norm. Patol.* **3**: 15-22 (1957).
53. Perugini, S., Soldati, M., and Torelli, U.: Research on the protein component of blood cells. VI. The nuclear content of histone protein and of deoxyribonucleic acid in cells of lymphatic leukemia. *Riv. Istiochim. Norm. Patol.* **3**: 95-104 (1957).

54. Perugini, S., Soldati, M., and Torelli, U.: Research on the protein component of blood cells. VII. The nuclear content of total protein in cells of lymphatic leukemia. *Riv. Istiochim. Norm. Patol.* 3: 105-112 (1957).
55. Perugini, S., Torelli, U., and Soldati, M.: Differences in the deoxyribonucleoprotein complex of normal and leukemic human lymphocytes. *Experientia* **13**: 441-442 (1957).
56. Phillips, D. M. P.: The Histones. *Progr. Biophys. Biophys. Chem.* **12**: 211-280 (1961).
57. Phillips, D. M. P., and Simson, P.: Identification of some peptides from an arginine-rich histone and their bearing on the structure of deoxyribonucleohistone. *Biochem. J.* **82**: 236-241 (1962).
58. Pollard, C. J.: The deoxyribonucleic acid content of purified spinach chloroplasts. *Arch. Biochem. Biophys.* **105**: 114-119 (1963).
59. Prescott, D. M., and Bender, M. A.: Synthesis and behavior of nuclear proteins during the cell life cycle. *J. Cellular Comp. Physiol.* **62**: 175-194 (1963).
60. Ris, H.: Chromosome structure. *In* "The Chemical Basis of Heredity" (W. D. McElroy and B. Glass, eds.), pp. 23-62. Johns Hopkins Press, Baltimore, Maryland, 1957.
61. Satake, K., Rasmussen, P. S., and Luck, J. M.: Arginine peptides obtained from thymus histone fractions after partial hydrolysis with Streptomyces. *J. Biol. Chem.* **235**: 2801-2809 (1960).
61a. Skalka, A.: The effect of histones on the enzymatic synthesis of nucleic acids from a DNA template. *Federation Proc.* **23**: 526 (1964).
62. Somers, C. E., Cole, A., and Hsu, T. C.: Isolation of chromosomes. *Exptl. Cell Res. Suppl.* **9**: 220-234 (1963).
63. Spicer, S. S.: Basic protein visualized histochemically in mucinous secretions. *Exptl. Cell Res.* **28**: 480-488 (1962).
64. Steele, W. J., and Busch, H.: Studies on acidic nuclear proteins of the Walker tumor and liver. *Cancer Res.* **23**: 1153-1163 (1963).
65. Steffensen, D. A.: Comparative view of the chromosome. *Brookhaven Symp. Biol.* **12**: 103-118 (1959).
66. Sueoka, N., and Cheng, T.-Y.: Natural occurrence of a deoxyribonucleic acid resembling the deoxyadenylate-deoxythymidylate polymer. *Proc. Natl. Acad. Sci.* **48**: 1851-1856 (1962).
67. Sueoka, N., and Cheng, T.-Y.: Fractionation of nucleic acids with methylated albumin column. *J. Mol. Biol.* **4**: 161-172 (1962).
68. Swift, H.: Cytochemical studies on nuclear fine structure. *Exptl. Cell Res. Suppl.* **9**: 54-67 (1963).
69. Swift, H.: The histones of polytene chromosomes. *In* "The Nucleohistones" (J. Bonner and P. Ts'o, eds.), pp. 169-183. Holden-Day, San Francisco, California, 1964.
70. Taylor, J. H.: The replication and organization of DNA in chromosomes. *In* "Molecular Genetics" (J. H. Taylor, ed.), Part 1, pp. 65-111. Academic Press, New York, 1963.
71. Trautman, R., and Crampton, C. F.: Application of the Archibald principle for the ultracentrifugal determination of the molecular weight in urea

solutions of histone fractions from calf thymus. *J. Am. Chem. Soc.* **81**: 4036-4040 (1959).

72. Ui, N.: On the molecular weight of calf thymus histone. *Biochim. Biophys. Acta* **22**: 205-206 (1956).
73. Ui, N.: Preparation, fractionation and properties of calf thymus histone. *Biochim. Biophys. Acta* **25**: 493-502 (1957).
74. Ui, N.: Sedimentation and diffusion studies of calf thymus histone. *Bull. Chem. Soc. Japan* **30**: 801-806 (1957).
75. Ui, N.: Sedimentation and diffusion studies of calf thymus histone aggregation. *Bull. Chem. Soc. Japan* **30**: 806-815 (1957).
76. Ui, N.: Sedimentation and diffusion studies of calf thymus histone. Electrophoretic studies. *Bull. Chem. Soc. Japan* **30**: 815-822 (1957).
77. Ui, N.: Sedimentation and diffusion studies of calf thymus histone. Studies on the preparation. *Bull. Chem. Soc. Japan* **30**: 822-826 (1957).
78. Vendrely, R., Knobloch-Mazen, A., and Vendrely, O.: Recent studies on the relation between deoxyribonucleic acids and basic proteins of the nucleus. *Biochem. Pharmacol.* **4**: 19-27 (1960).
79. Watson, J. D., and Crick, F. H. C.: A structure for deoxyribose nucleic acid. *Nature* **171**: 737-738 (1953).
80. Watson, J. D., and Crick, F. H. C.: Genetic implications of the structure of deoxyribonucleic acid. *Nature* **171**: 964-967 (1953).
81. Wilkins, M. H. F., and Zubay, G.: X-ray diffraction study of the structure of nucleohistone and nucleoprotamines. *J. Mol. Biol.* **7**: 756-757 (1963).
82. Wilkins, M. H. F., Zubay, G., and Wilson, H. R.: X-ray diffraction studies of the structure of deoxyribonucleoprotein. *Trans. Faraday Soc.* **55**: 497 (1959).
83. Wilkins, M. H. F., Zubay, G., and Wilson, H. R.: X-ray diffraction studies of the molecular structure of nucleohistone and chromosomes. *J. Mol. Biol.* **1**: 179-185 (1959).
84. Woodard, J., and Swift, H.: The DNA content of cold-treated chromosomes. *Exptl. Cell. Res.* **34**: 131-137 (1964).
85. Zubay, G.: Nucleohistone structure and function. *In* "The Nucleohistones" (J. Bonner and P. Ts'o, eds.), pp. 95-107. Holden-Day, San Francisco, California, 1964.
86. Zubay, G., and Doty, P.: Isolation and properties of deoxyribonucleoprotein particles containing single nucleic acid molecules. *J. Mol. Biol.* **1**: 1-20 (1959).
87. Zubay, G., and Wilkins, M. H. F.: An X-ray diffraction study of histone and protamine in isolation and in combination with DNA. *J. Mol. Biol.* **4**: 444-450 (1962).

# CHAPTER V

# Functions of the Histones

## Introduction

In recent years, a variety of types of evidence has been provided that histones have functions that are related to the structure of DNA and the ability of DNA to serve as a primer for nucleic acid biosynthesis and possibly other types of roles (Table 5-I). The studies on the

TABLE 5-I

FUNCTIONS SUGGESTED FOR THE HISTONES

- I. Structural
  - A. "Cement" together DNA molecules
  - B. Enhance coiling of DNA; supercoil DNA
  - C. Unfold DNA
  - D. Stabilize DNA
  - E. Serve as backbones of chromosomes
  - F. Serve as ends of telomeres
  - G. Stabilize RNA
  - H. Neutralize negative charges of DNA phosphate or other acidic macromolecules
- II. Genetic
  - A. Suppress or enhance gene function, i.e., RNA synthesis
  - B. Block or accelerate DNA synthesis
  - C. Serve as ribonucleases
  - D. Release RNA from DNA
- III. Miscellaneous
  - A. Inhibitory effects on cells
  - B. Serve as interferons
  - C. Block or accelerate mitochondrial activity (cytochrome oxidase; ATPase)
  - D. Regulation of membrane ATPases and ion transport

structural relationships between DNA and histones (Table 5-I) and the effects of histones on chromosomal structure are dealt with in Chapter IV. In recent years, there has been a substantial expansion of evidence that histones may serve as gene modulators as was originally proposed by the Stedmans (88). In addition, a number of other cellular functions may be accelerated or inhibited by the histones or other polybasic substances.

## The Concept That Histones Are Gene Modifiers

Perhaps the earliest expression of the idea that histones might exert a function in control of the genome was that of Stedman and Stedman (88). Although in 1943, there was little doubt of the important genetic function of nucleic acids (4, 36, 52) little had been said about the role of the histones. Stedman and Stedman (88–90) had the impression that "chromosomin," an acidic protein complex (Chapter VIII), was related to the chemical basis of heredity. They relegated to the nucleic acids a role for formation of spindles and their component fibers, but they did not view the nucleic acids as being the major component of the chromosomes. Nonetheless, they suggested that the nucleic acids were important in the synthesis of proteins during the resting stages between the various stages of mitosis. The basis of the hypothesis of Stedman and Stedman (86–93) was the observation that the histones and "chromosomin" composed differing percentages of the total dry weight of the nuclei in various types of cells. In tumors and in chick embryo cells, the histones were found to compose 1.6–3% of the total dry weight of the nuclei while in other cells the histones composed up to 24% of the total dry weight of the nuclei. On the other hand, "chromosomin" composed 33–72.4% of the dry weights of the nuclei. In a variety of types of cells, such as those of the Walker tumor, mouse carcinoma 2146, embryonic tissue, spleen, erythrocytes, thymus, and sperm of a variety of species, they noted that nucleic acids composed about one-third of the dry weight of the nuclei and did not vary in amount as did the proteins.

In a study of the arginine content of histones of salmon tissues, Stedman and Stedman (87–93) found that the sperm proteins, largely protamines, had an arginine content of 87.7% (Chapter I) while the nuclear proteins of liver had an arginine content of 20.3%. Each of these values differed from the arginine content of nuclei of red cells, which was 19.0%. These findings and the findings obtained with dry weight of proteins of the various nuclei led Stedman and Stedman (87–93) to conclude that the high histone content of some cells produced blocks of the intermediate stages that lead to mitosis and cell division. They suggested that the low levels of histones in embryonic cells and in tumors were not sufficient to block formation of chromosomes and mitotic structures and therefore these cells proceed to division. Mauritzen and Stedman (69) also found some differences in the amino acid compositions of β-histones of the domestic fowl. They reported that the differences were sufficiently specific to justify the idea that the histones vary from tissue to tissue.

Some of their experimental points have not been borne out by later studies from this and other laboratories (20, 21, 49) since it has been found that there is essentially no difference in overall histone content in several tissues of a given species. However, the concentrations of individual types of histones have not been adequately studied in a variety of tissues (47, 49). Although their reasons do not seem to be as well based now as they did two decades ago, the concept developed by Stedman and Stedman (88) that histones suppress nuclear function has received considerable support (3, 5, 15, 16, 20a, 45, 53).

## Suppression of Biosynthesis of RNA

The development of systems for the study of the *in vitro* labeling of RNA by Weiss (95) followed the earlier experiments of Kornberg and his associates (8, 62) on the enzymatic synthesis of DNA. Although some aspects of the system differ, the basic requirements for biosynthesis of DNA *in vitro* were found to include deoxyribonucleoside triphosphates, $Mg^{++}$, the enzyme DNA polymerase, and a "primer" DNA. Similarly, Weiss (95) found that for incorporation of labeled ribonucleoside triphosphates into RNA, $Mg^{++}$, all four nucleoside triphosphates, and "primer" DNA were required for the reaction to proceed at maximal velocities. The use of a similar system enabled Bonner and his associates (15, 16, 53) to make one of the more interesting recent advances in the area of the function of histones.

In studies on biosynthesis of RNA in systems containing DNA of pea seedlings and the appropriate cofactors, Huang and Bonner (53) found a stoichiometric relationship between the blocking of RNA labeling and the histone concentration (Fig. 5-1). They also provided evi-

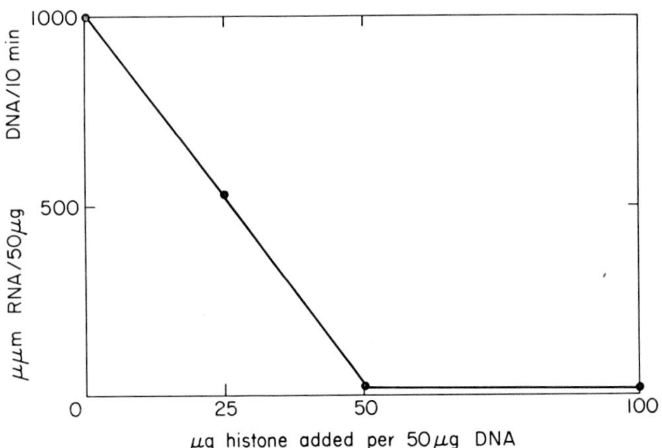


FIG. 5-1. Inhibitory effects of histones on priming activity of DNA. Nucleohistones were reconstituted by addition of histones to isolated DNA; the system employed was essentially the RNA polymerase system. A stoichiometric inhibitory effect of histones on RNA synthesis is apparent. [From (53).]

dence that the block was reversible inasmuch as DNA reisolated from complexes with histones was apparently "native," since it could again serve as a primer for these biosynthetic reactions. The findings were of considerable interest in view of their potentiality for explanation of mechanisms of gene control. One of the methods for preparation of the histones is questionable since Huang and Bonner employed conditions (25, 26) involving high concentrations of ethanol which have been shown (98) to denature histones. However, they also separated histones from DNA in 4 *M* CsCl; this procedure is more likely to provide a "native" histone product. The studies of Huang and Bonner (53) involved the use of pea seedlings, and studies on nativeness of the histones obtained from pea seedlings have not been made.

In view of the known insolubility of deoxyribonucleoproteins in dilute salt solutions (25), one of the important points to the study of Huang and Bonner (53) was that their DNA-histone complexes were soluble. As indicated previously (page 66), Hammarsten (41) and other workers had found that the deoxyribonucleoproteins were soluble in water and in high concentrations of salt, i.e., in excess of 1 *M* NaCl. However, in the range between 0.01 and 0.5 *M* NaCl there is a very low solubility of deoxyribonucleoproteins (25, 26). Huang and Bonner (53) mixed the histones with DNA in solutions containing high concentrations of NaCl (1–2.5 *M*) and dialyzed the solutions to low ionic strengths. For the medium external to the dialysis bag, they employed a sodium citrate buffer. The deoxyribonucleohistone preparation was centrifuged, and the supernatant fraction was used as a source of the deoxyribonucleoproteins.

Huang *et al.* (53a) reported that whole thymus nucleohistone had little or no activity as a primer for RNA synthesis. Each of the histone fractions had some suppressive activity on the DNA-primed RNA synthesis in their system, but the very lysine-rich histone fraction totally blocked the activity. A slightly lysine-rich histone and two "arginine-rich" fractions decreased the activity of the system to 7.5, 25, and 66% of control activities, respectively.

*Confirmation of the Suppressive Effects of Histone on DNA as a Primer for RNA Synthesis.* Allfrey *et al.* (3) carried out experiments of a type similar to those carried out by Huang and Bonner (53), but, instead of using DNA and histones derived from different species, they utilized whole nuclei and histones obtained from calf thymus. They found (Fig. 5-2) that the lysine-rich histones were much less effective inhib-

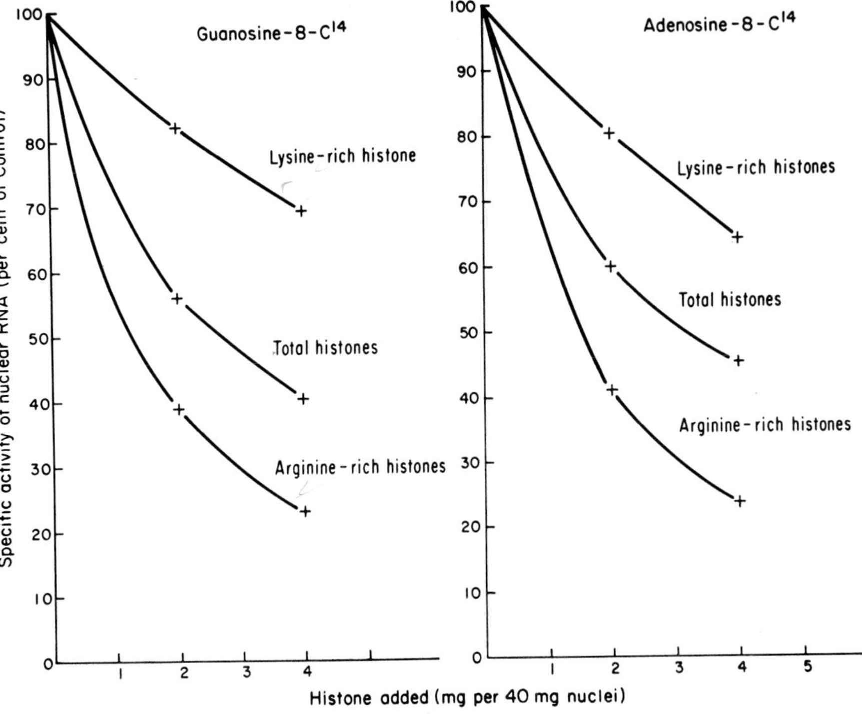


FIG. 5-2. Effects of histones on labeling of RNA with radioactive nucleosides added to calf thymus nuclear preparations. [From Allfrey *et al.* (3).]

itors of labeling of RNA than the "arginine-rich" histones. They also found that polylysine exerted a significant degree of inhibition of the uptake of guanosine or adenosine into nuclear RNA, but they did not find as great a degree of suppressive activity with either of these preparations as with the "arginine-rich" histones. As one evidence that proteins do block the activity of DNA as a primer, they noted that trypsin caused a marked increase in the activity of the isolated nucleus in labeling of RNA.

On some points, the experiments of Allfrey *et al.* (3) are open to question. The experiments were carried out on isolated nuclei and these isolated nuclei require energy-generating systems for conversion of the labeled nucleosides into the corresponding nucleoside triphosphates that are required for labeling of RNA (95). As Allfrey *et al.* (3) pointed out, there are a number of reactions that can be blocked by histones; predominant among them is nuclear ATP synthesis. It is quite possible that their inhibitory effects were due to blocks in the energy reactions of their isolated nuclei. Another problem is that the procedure employed in Mirsky's laboratory for isolation of the histones does not provide either pure or native products. They used the technique of Daly *et al.* (29, 30) in which the pH of acid extracts of thymocytes or thymus nuclei is raised to approximately 11. The precipitate is referred to as the "arginine-rich" histone fraction, and the supernatant fraction is subjected to treatment with excess ammonia to precipitate the lysine-rich histones. Since the "arginine-rich" histones are markedly aggregated above pH 4, it seems possible that this product is not a native histone fraction. The product that is precipitated by excess ammonia is not likely to be a purified histone. In the experiments on the effect of trypsin on the RNA polymerase of whole nuclei, it remains to be established whether the effects of this enzyme were primarily to hydrolyze histones, RNases, membrane proteins, or other structures.

*Subtractive Studies on Effects of Histones on RNA Biosynthesis.* The experiments of Allfrey *et al.* (3) with trypsin were designed to remove the histones from their deoxyribonucleoprotein complexes. A similar type of "subtractive" analysis was recently carried out by Hindley (45a), as illustrated in Fig. 5-3. With increasing concentrations of NaCl, Hindley extracted histone fractions (see p. 108) with a decreasing ratio of lysine to arginine. Removal of the very lysine-rich histones did not produce marked changes in the incorporation of precursors in the RNA. However, removal of the slightly lysine-rich and "arginine-rich" histones resulted in a great increase in RNA labeling.

*Other Studies on Reconstituted Nucleohistones.* Recent studies of Barr and Butler (5) and Hindley (45) have confirmed the results of Bonner and Huang (15, 53) on the inhibition of biosynthesis of RNA. The interpretation of the results differs considerably, however. Barr and Butler (5) reported that the inhibition of RNA synthesis in reconstituted nucleohistones was nonspecific. They suggested that the reconstituted material was not "native." Moreover, they found that polylysine was a very effective inhibitor of RNA synthesis in their preparations. Like Bonner and Huang (15) they found the greatest inhibition with the very lysine-rich histone fraction. Hindley (45) used unfractionated histones and lysozymes, which are also basic proteins, to form complexes with the primer. Lysozyme was a very ineffective inhibitor. Like Allfrey *et al.* (3), Hindley found that the "arginine-rich" fraction was most inhibitory but the very lysine-rich histone fraction permitted RNA labeling to proceed at about the same rate as was found with the nucleic acid-lysozyme complex. The slightly lysine-rich histones were about as effective inhibitors as were the "arginine-rich" histones.

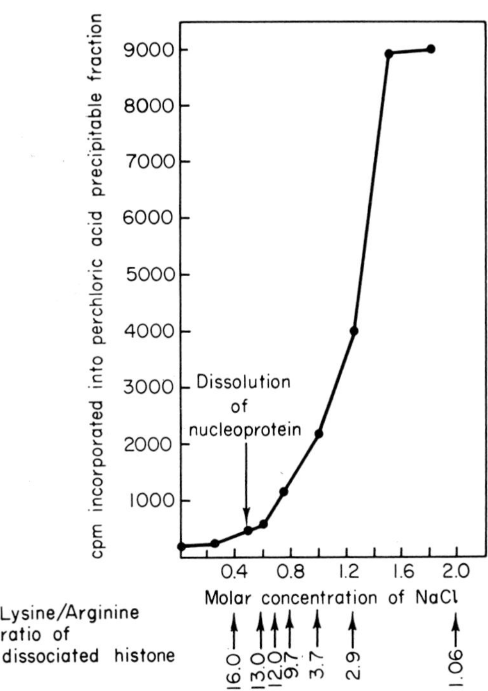


FIG. 5-3. Effects of extraction of histones from deoxyribonucleoprotein complexes on labeling of RNA with UTP-2-$C^{14}$. Removal of the very lysine-rich histones had little effect on RNA labeling as compared to extraction of the other histones. (Courtesy of Dr. John Hindley.)

***Effects of Histones on Labeling of RNA in Nucleolar Preparations.*** The evidence that has accumulated that much of the biosynthesis of RNA of tumors and other tissues (19, 64, 70a, 71, 72) occurs in the nucleolus of cells has led to experiments on the labeling of nucleolar RNA *in vitro* (80). In these studies, the system developed by Weiss (95) was also employed. It was found that purified histones isolated from calf thymus were inhibitory to the activity of the system. However, the results with histone fractions agreed more with the data obtained by Allfrey (3) than with the results obtained by Bonner and his colleagues (15, 16, 53). In this system, the inhibitory effect of the "arginine-rich" histones was greater than that of other fractions on an equal weight basis. Oddly, the very lysine-rich histones had a small stimulatory effect on the biosynthetic reactions[1] (Tables 5-II and 5-III). The

TABLE 5-II
EFFECT OF TUMOR HISTONES ON LABELING OF RNA OF ISOLATED LIVER NUCLEOLI

| Histone addition (mg) | Average S.A.[a] RNA | Per cent inhibition or stimulation |
|---|---|---|
| Control | 32,000 | — |
| F1 0.5 | 35,100 | +10 |
| 1.0 | 28,500 | —12 |
| F2a 0.5 | 22,700 | —29 |
| 1.0 | 18,400 | —42 |
| F2b 0.5 | 21,300 | —33 |
| 1.0 | 17,510 | —45 |
| F3 0.5 | 20,900 | —35 |
| 1.0 | 15,400 | —52 |

[a] Specific activity of RNA; UTP-$C^{14}$ was the precursor (80).

TABLE 5-III
EFFECT OF TUMOR HISTONES ON LABELING OF RNA OF ISOLATED TUMOR NUCLEOLI

| Histone addition (mg) | Average S.A.[a] RNA | Per cent inhibition or stimulation |
|---|---|---|
| Control | 25,800 | — |
| F1 0.25 | 32,700 | +27 |
| 0.5 | 29,900 | +17 |
| 1.0 | 29,400 | +14 |
| F2a 0.5 | 21,700 | —16 |
| 1.0 | 14,400 | —44 |
| F2b 0.25 | 22,600 | —12 |
| 0.5 | 18,200 | —29 |
| 1.0 | 13,700 | —47 |
| F3 0.25 | 28,200 | —14 |
| 0.5 | 16,800 | —35 |
| 1.0 | 15,600 | —40 |

[a] Specific activity of RNA; UTP-$C^{14}$ was the precursor (80).

slightly lysine-rich fractions had intermediate effects on the overall activity, i.e., they were not so inhibitory as the "arginine-rich" histones, but were more inhibitory than very lysine-rich histones (20a).

[1] In recent studies, Dr. J. Villalobos (unpublished results) has found that histones as well as polyamines inhibit nucleolar ribonucleases.

*Effects of the Amount of Histone Added on Suppressive Effects.* Bonner (14a) has suggested that one of the reasons for the differences in the effects of histones that have been reported from various laboratories is that the amounts of histone added have differed widely. When high concentrations of "arginine-rich" histones were added to DNA preparations, complexes were formed that were inactive in DNA synthesis. When small ratios of histones to DNA were used, i.e., 1.3:1 or less, the very lysine-rich histones were always more inhibitory than the "arginine-rich" histones.

*Effects of Histones on RNA Polymerase.* Experiments have not yet been reported on the relative effect of the histones on the enzyme and the primers. It has been assumed that DNA is combined with the histones and is unable to act as a primer. However, a direct effect of histones on the enzyme is not excluded.

*Effects of Histones on Labeling of RNA in Preparations of Chromatin.* Although the precise state of the nucleoprotein in the cell nucleus remains to be established, there is little doubt that the "gel-forming nucleoprotein fraction" described by Fredericq (34) is a closer approximation to the overall native nucleoprotein than the variety of polydisperse entities that have been isolated. When this preparation was subjected to degradation by sonication, DNase II, trypsin, or chymotrypsin, there was a decrease in rigidity and viscosity of the product as well as solubilization of DNA and histones. The proteinases produced an increase in the peptides. In view of the fact that degradation of the histones results in a loss of gel-forming properties, one possible function of the histones might be the condensation or extension of DNA strands (see Chapter IV).

Recently, Frenster *et al.* (35) reported that they could separate repressed and active chromatin from calf thymus lymphocytes. They referred to condensed chromatin as "heterochromatin" and assumed that it was inactive. The extended or "euchromatin" fraction was reported to be active in priming for RNA labeling. The relationship between coiling of chromosomes and their activity has been discussed at length by Ris (78), who also suggested that the active form was an extended form. The possibility that histones serve to enhance coiling of chromosomes, and thereby repress the activity of DNA, is inherent in some of the models in Chapter IV (see p. 111). In studies on chromosomally directed labeling of proteins, Bonner *et al.* (16) have worked out a system in which priming of RNA synthesis by chromatin derived from developing cotyledons that make pea seed globulins produced an increase in labeling and perhaps synthesis of a globulin fraction by a ribosomal system. The relationship of histone function to these syntheses was not fully defined, but Bonner *et al.* (16) suggested that the reason that globulin labeling in other plant structures that do not make globulin was not as great as in the developing cotyledons was that the specific priming segment of the genome was blocked by the histones. Removal of histones resulted in enhanced globulin labeling in systems containing chromatin from the other plant structures. This result is consistent with experimental derepression of a normally blocked genomic segment.

*Effect of Histones on Synthesis of Specific RNAs.* Skalka (85) has reported that the extent of inhibition of DNA-primed RNA synthesis by very lysine-rich histones was proportional to the AT content and size of the DNA. The histones also produced alterations in the nearest-neighbor distribution patterns of the RNA. The changes produced by lysine-rich histones and polylysine were similar, and the changes produced by "arginine-rich" histones and protamines were also similar. The greatest changes were found when AT-rich DNA such as that derived from slime mold *Dictyostelium discoideum* ($A + T/G + C = 3$) was treated with lysine-rich histones. In these studies, the amounts of histones added were sufficiently small that histones may have been bound to relatively specific affinity points in the DNA.[2]

*Effects of Acetylation and Methylation of Histones on Suppression of Nucleic Acid Synthesis.* The evidence that some histones contained acetyl and methyl groups led Allfrey *et al.* (2a) to inquire whether the presence of these groups might be related to the physiological role of the histones. They found that acetyl and methyl groups were added to the histones after the polypeptide chains were completed. Acetylation of the histones decreased their inhibitory effects on labeling of RNA in their systems despite the fact that there was no change in the binding of histones to DNA. They suggested that acetylation might be a physiological mechanism for "switching on or off" nucleic acid synthesis.

## Effects of Histones on DNA Synthesis

In studies on the effect of histones on various preparations, it is of considerable methodological significance that the components of the

[2] The inhibition of priming by AT-rich DNA is somewhat at variance with reports (see page 114) that very lysine-rich histones are associated with GC-rich components of DNA.

medium remain soluble, as Billen and Hnilica (9) have pointed out. These workers were interested in repeating the studies of Huang and Bonner (53) on the effects of histones on DNA synthesis. They noted that the activity of their DNA polymerase systems, which contained the enzyme from *E. coli* and calf thymus DNA as the primer, was also diminished on the addition of histones to the preparation. However, the inhibition induced by the histones was mainly related to the precipitation of the deoxyribonucleohistone from the preparation.

One of the points of particular interest in the study of Billen and Hnilica (9) was the differential inhibitory effect of the various histone fractions in their system. The F1 and F2a fractions completely inhibited the activity of the system, but the *N*-proline (F2b) histone fraction and fraction 3, the "arginine-rich" fraction, blocked the activity of the system by only approximately 50% at maximal levels. Assuming that their inhibitory effects were related to the precipitation alone, it is possible that the different deoxyribonucleohistones either had different dissociation constants or had different solubilities.

In recent studies on the effects of histones on DNA polymerase, Gurley *et al.* (37) have extended the hypothesis of Irvin *et al.* (54) that histones inhibit RNA synthesis at low concentrations and DNA synthesis at high concentrations. When they added unfractionated histones to a DNA polymerase system, they noted that 50% inhibition of labeling occurred when the ratio of histone to DNA was between 2 and 3 for the whole histone fraction, when the ratio was between 1 and 2 for the slightly lysine-rich fraction and the very lysine-rich fraction, and when the ratio was almost 4 for the "arginine-rich" fraction. These studies agreed with the finding of Bonner and his associates (15, 16) but are undoubtedly subject to the problem of marked precipitation of the DNA–histone complexes from solution. Such precipitation renders the primer inaccessible to the enzyme. The finding that inhibition with the whole histones occurred at a histone:DNA ratio of 2 was interpreted by these authors as evidence in favor of the idea that DNA synthesis is shut off when the concentration of histone becomes high in tissues. They noted that in regenerating liver, the ratio of histone:DNA approximated 2 shortly before mitosis and changed during and after mitosis (54). The possibility was suggested that the lysine-rich histones were particularly important in shutting off DNA synthesis (see pages 107-108).

Some interesting data have been presented by Bazill and Philpot (6) on the inhibition of DNA polymerase activity by histones. They reported that only one-fifth of the total cellular DNA polymerase activity was present in the nucleus and remained there after repeated washing of the nuclei of calf thymocytes. Only 3/1000 of a per cent (0.003%) of the DNA of these nuclei had priming ability. Histones inhibited primer activity, but neither native nor reconstituted nucleohistone had inhibitory activity. When the ratio of histone to DNA was approximately 1, the inhibition was only 50%; and when the ratio was 2, the inhibition was virtually complete. In view of the fact that the authors used cells from a tissue that is not characterized by a rapid rate of cell division the low activity of the nuclei in their system is not surprising.

*Enhancement of DNA Labeling by Histones.* Holoubek (51) reported that, following intraperitoneal injection of labeled thymidine into animals treated with histones from tumor tissues, there was an increased incorporation of the isotope into the DNA of organs of $C_3H$ mice, particularly into the spleen. The increases were in the order of 50% of control values. There were no changes when histones from nontumor tissues were injected into these animals. Histones from embryonic tissues produced some, but not very marked, stimulation. These experiments, like those from other laboratories (18) suggest that histones of tumors may have some special properties (see page 137). However, these results have not yet been verified, and tumor-specific histones have not yet been isolated.

## Numerical Relationships between the Suppressive Potentialities of Histones and Loci of DNA

The possibility of defining the precise number of loci on DNA that might be blocked by the histones is limited at present because of our limited knowledge of the molecular weights of the histones, their sites of binding to DNA, and the factors that influence their adherence to and release from DNA. There are, however, a number of interesting facts that are available, such as the number of nucleotides present in DNA in a given mammalian cell, e.g., the liver cell. Since there are 8–12 pg of DNA per nucleus (18, 72), and the average molecular weight of the nucleotides is 325, the absolute number of nucleotides present in the nucleus is about $1.5–1.9 \times 10^{10}$. Since three nucleotides are required to code for a single amino acid and double-stranded DNA codes for single-stranded messenger-RNA, the total number of coding units is $2.5–3.5 \times 10^{9}$. If one assumes that the average molecular weight of DNA in the mammalian cell is $10^7$, there would be approximately 700,000 DNA molecules each of which has about 5000 effective "codons." This would be an average number since the DNA threads may be joined in the nucleus in a sort of interconnecting syncitium and the molecular weights within the network might be very great. Nonetheless, the double-stranded DNA could code for about 3,000,000 different proteins of average molecular weight of 50,000 if there was no "nonsense" information present and also there were no "commas" (21).

The number of histone molecules in the nucleus is far greater than the number of DNA molecules inasmuch as the histones have a much smaller molecular weight and approximately the same dry weight. The total number of histone molecules would be $2.5 \times 10^8$ assuming that the average molecular weight was 20,000. Thus, there are insufficient histone molecules to combine with all the DNA "codons" if each histone were to block a single "codon." The maximum number of "codons" that could be blocked by the histones would be about 5% of the total. However, if the histones could block more than one coding unit, or if a block of a single coding unit was sufficient to prevent the DNA from priming for a sequence necessary for the formation of a messenger, there would be more than enough histones to totally suppress the action of the entire genome.

If, as seems likely, the histones could totally block the function of DNA, the situation is reminiscent of the stops on woodwinds or some reed instruments such as the saxophone. In this case there are ample stops to totally block the production of sound, and during the events that occur to produce the musical notes these stops are either removed from their blocking location or modified in their position. In the case of the overall functioning of an orchestra, it is apparent that there is a variety of types of controls exerted on the production of sounds not only by groups of individual instruments, but also by segments of the entire orchestra. In the case of the individual cell, the functional cistrons may be compared to the individual instruments and the chromosomes may be compared to the sections or types of instruments of the orchestra. The total function of the cell may be likened to the music produced by the entire orchestra, and the critical question of modern molecular biology is what constitutes the equivalent of the conductor, who not only determines the music to be played but the features of the music, such as its speed, its intensity, and its specific characteristics. If the histones play a role in this process, clearly it is not determinative of the overall function, but rather is at the cistron level.

## Histones of Specialized Tissues

If histones subserve functions related to gene expression, there should be differences in their amounts, distribution, turnover, or types in cells with varying functions. Some studies on the changes in proteins associated with DNA during various stages of ontogeny, in various species, and in various types of tissues have been fruitful in development of hypotheses of histone function.

As noted previously, Stedman and his colleagues (27, 28, 69, 86–93) claimed that the histones of various tissues of the same and different species differed in solubility, amino acid composition, electrophoretic behavior, and aggregation. On this basis, they concluded that histones were tissue- and species-specific. Their suggestion is in disagreement with that of workers in Butler's group (22, 23, 49, 61, 77) and others (94) who have used more refined techniques in recent years.

However, Neelin and Butler (73) studied the histones of a variety of tissues of the chicken by means of chromatography on IRC-50 columns and by electrophoresis and starch gel. They found 18 zones of histones in liver and spleen, and a particular zone, zone 15, which was present in erythrocytes but absent from the spleen. This zone was a slowly moving histone fraction. They showed that the testis preparation contained only seven slow-moving bands. Zone 15 was said to be characteristic of erythrocytes, but the differences between spleen and liver histones were much more subtle or perhaps did not exist. The finding of the specific histone of the chicken erythrocyte may be related to the suppression of biosynthetic reactions in the nuclei of these cells.

Relatively few studies have been made on the types and composition of histones of plants. The histones of pea seedlings have been fractionated by starch gel electrophoresis. The pattern was simpler than the pattern for the acid extractable proteins of the ribosomes which contained 16 zones (82). Johns and Butler (56) noted that wheat germ histones lacked an "arginine-rich" component. The meaning of this interesting finding cannot be yet assessed in evolutionary terms. As noted in Chapter II, an increasing effort is being made to learn more about histones of plants, molds, and yeast (66).

*Studies on Histones and Spermiogenesis.* As indicated previously in this chapter, the histones may be functional in promoting coiling of chromatin and hence in rendering the DNA unavailable for priming (35, 78). If this is the case, the ultimate in compactness should be in the cells that have the least priming activity. In the course of spermiogenesis the histones are replaced by protamines as indicated in Chapter I; perhaps the ultimate biological compactness of DNA is achieved in the deoxyribonucleoprotamine of the "head" of the sperm. Other studies have shown changes in the proteins linked to DNA in spermiogenesis in lower species than the fish. Bloch (12–14) has studied the histones of *Helix aspersa* (a snail) and *Loligo aspersa* (a squid). In the snail, the conversion of the cells from spermatocytes to sperm is associated with synthesis of histone or protamine in the early spermatid and later, a maximal synthesis in the spade and round spermatids, as measured by studies with tritiated arginine. In the initial stages of the changes in the nuclear proteins, there was a replacement of the normal histones with a protein that had no distinctive features. This histone is present until the cytoplasm is lost from the spermatid. The mature sperm contains only protamine, and the studies of Bloch (12–14) did not provide sufficient structural information for him to establish whether the histone was broken down to yield the protamine, as Kossel (58) suggested long ago, or whether there was renewed synthesis of a protein that was completely different from the histone.

Bloch (12–14) carried out starch gel electrophoresis on histones of the squid (Fig. 5-4). He noted that the sperm in a spermatophore had histones with a much higher mobility than those of the testis, which in turn had histones that had a higher mobility than those of the gill. Two of the histones from the spermatophore had electrophoretic mobilities greater than those of any proteins obtained from the testis. The two fastest bands present in the testis were absent from the somatic cells (Fig. 5-4). Of the two major and one minor fractions, only the larger of the major fractions corresponded in mobility to a fraction from the testis. From these studies Bloch (12–14) concluded that at least three transitions occurred in the histones in *Loligo*.

In these studies a histone was found in which arginine consisted of 60% of all the amino acids on a weight basis; in these proteins, there was only one-tenth as much lysine as there was arginine. The molecular weight of this protein, 8000, was twice that of the protamines in which arginine constituted 70% of the total amino acids. The histones and protamines of the spermatophore of the squid had the highest mobility of any of the samples studied. Interestingly, the histones of the unfertilized frog egg had the lowest mobility of any of the samples. Whether the histones of the various tissues of the frog were the same as those of the squid histones is not clear, but all had the same rela-

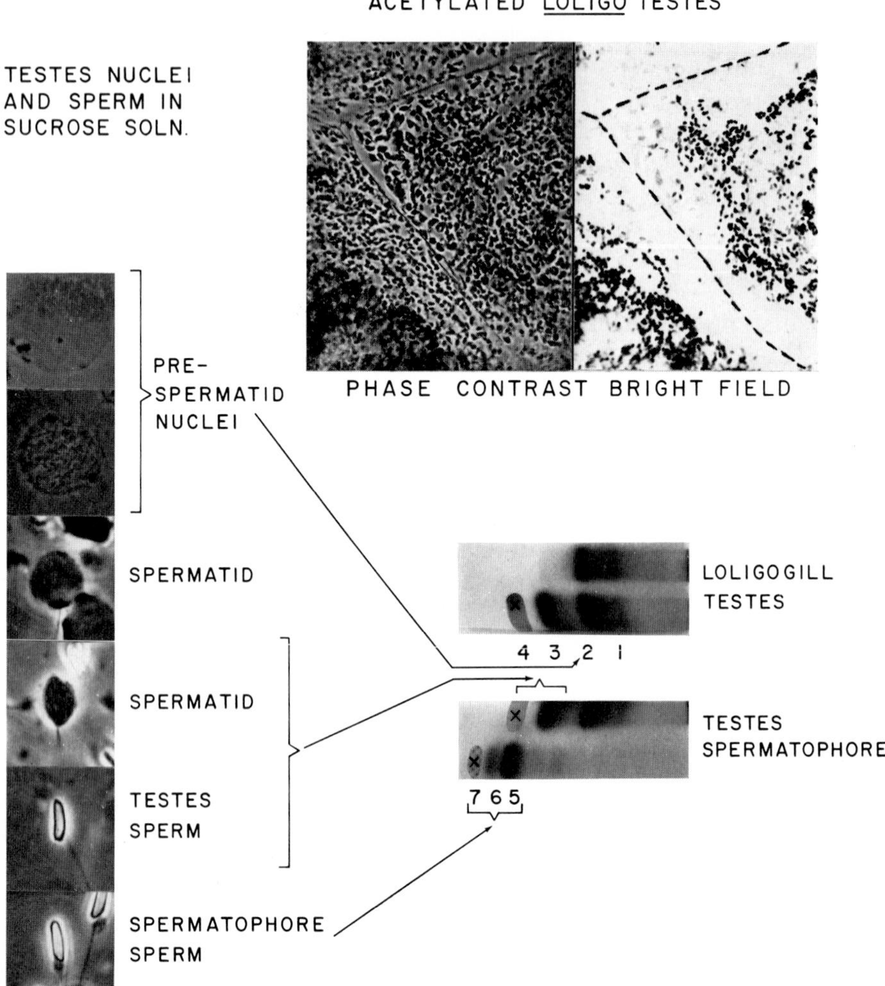


FIG. 5-4. The photographs at the upper right indicate that the spermatid and testis sperm nuclei of *Loligo* stain with acid dyes after deamination. The electrophoretic patterns (lower right) compare the mobilities of basic proteins of different organs. The zones marked with an "X" indicate components present in variable amounts. [From Bloch (13).]

tive mobilities in starch gel. The claim that such data support the concept that histones are related to the somatic expression of heredity is somewhat difficult to understand since, of the tissues studied, only the histones of the testis had marked differences in electrophoretic patterns from those of other sources.[3]

## Histones of Cancer Cells

Of all the many types of cells of higher animals it would seem that those characterized by a differentiation or "streamlining" for malignant growth would be the most likely to differ in their histones from the somatic and parenchymal cells. As indicated in Chapter VI, there are established differences in the rates of biosynthesis of histones in tumors and other tissues which may in part reflect differences in the biosynthetic requirements of dividing cells as compared to interphase cells (18, 21).

Suggestions that there were differences in content and types of histones in malignant tissues were made by Stedman and Stedman (86–93). Cruft *et al.* (27, 28) followed up these studies with the report that histones of cancer cells had a lower solubility, an anomalous pH mobility curve and greater aggregation in acid solution than was found for histones of other tissues. The insolubility of the "arginine-rich" histones of tumor cells was so great that only a few points could be measured on the electrophoretic mobility curve. Some differences were found in the "arginine-rich" histones of different tumors, and the tumors were reported to be more like one another in this respect than like other tissues. Cruft *et al.* (27, 28) suggested that there was a somatic mutation in the course of carcinogenesis. Black *et al.* (11) reported that acid-extractable nuclear proteins stained with an ammoniacal silver. In tumor cells the staining differed from that of other cells, but it was not clear whether the difference represented a different distribution of proteins or differences in the proteins. Hamer found that the amino acid compositions of the whole histone fractions of tumors were essentially the same as those derived from calf thymus (38–40). Shack and Thompsett (83) studied the viscosity, solubility, and light absorption characteristics of the nucleohistones of tumor tissues but did not report striking differences from comparable analyses for nontumor tissues.

[3] Recent studies (66a, 73a) have shown some electrophoretic differences in histones from embryonic tissues and those of adult tissues. Moreover, the amounts of histones in adult tissues varied (85a).

An interesting report of a decrease in the cellular content of "arginine-rich" histones in the Shope papilloma was presented by Rogers (80a,b) on the basis of histochemical analyses. He found that the Shope virus produced an increase in arginase in infected cells and suggested that the increase in arginase resulted in a decrease in the content of "arginine-rich" histones in these cells. The production of tumors could be related to the decreased amounts of histones in these cells.

*Chromatography of Tumor Histones.* Davison (33) showed that the elution pattern from carboxymethylcellulose was essentially the same for the histones of a variety of nontumor tissues and a mouse ascites tumor. Electrophoretic analysis of the histones of the Walker tumor did not reveal significant differences from the electrophoretic mobility of histones of the calf thymus. However, some differences were found in elution patterns for acid-soluble nuclear proteins of the Walker tumor and other tissues. When formic acid was used to elute these proteins from carboxymethylcellulose columns (32), differences were noted for the distribution of proteins labeled with lysine-U-$C^{14}$ and the overall protein content of the elution pattern (Figs. 3-3 and 5-5). The patterns of distribution of proteins and radioactivity differed for the various tissues studied, and it appeared that the pattern was quite characteristic for individual tissues. In particular, the localization of RP2-L (radioactive peak 2) of the Walker tumor was of interest because of the presence of a similar peak in other tumor tissues (Fig. 5-5) and the absence of this peak in the nontumor tissues studied (Fig. 3-3) regardless of whether the nontumor tissues were characterized by rapid or slow growth rates (24, 67).

Recently, the presence of RP2-L as a characteristic feature of proteins of the tumor has been opened to some question. Hidvegi *et al.* (43) in studying the distribution of radioactivity in acid soluble proteins of the bone marrow have found that a number of labeled peaks appeared in the region of RP2-L after prolonged incubation of marrow cells with labeled lysine. The chromatographic separation of histones has now been improved by lengthening the carboxymethylcellulose columns from 15 to 150 cm (84). When sufficient amounts of radioactivity and protein were added to columns used for fractionation of acid-soluble proteins from the liver, spleen, and Walker tumor, there were some, but not striking, differences between the elution patterns for the liver and the Walker tumor. Electrophoretic analysis of the proteins present in these peaks did not show differences between

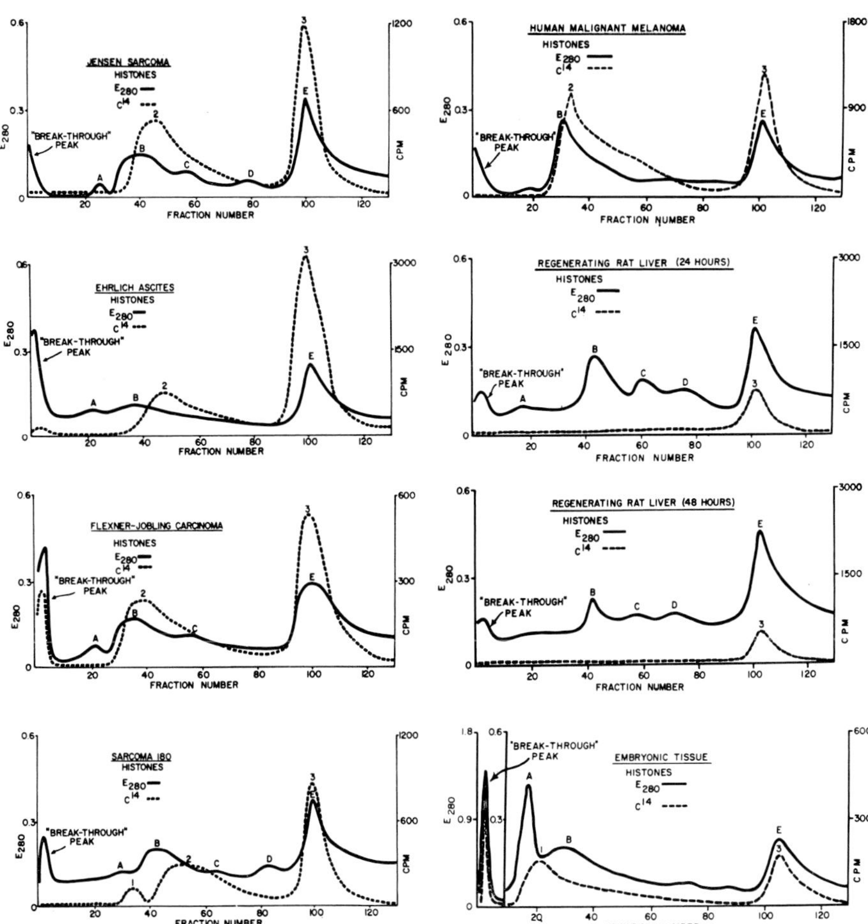


FIG. 5-5. Composite figure showing comparative chromatograms of cationic nuclear proteins of tumors and growing nontumor tissues. RP2-L (radioactive peak 2) was found in the tumors, but not in the growing nontumor tissues. [From Davis and Busch (32).]

the elution patterns of the proteins of the Walker tumor and the liver. Accordingly, it would appear possible that the earlier findings of RP2-L and differences between the tumors and the nontumor tissues may have been due to the very high labeling of the nuclear proteins of the tumors, rather than to the differences in the proteins themselves.

*Amino Acid Composition of Tumor Histones.* Butler and his colleagues (22, 23) have in general supported the concept that the histones of the tumors were essentially the same as those of other tissues. By the methods available at present they reported no significant differences in the histones of the various other tissues they have studied (22, 49, 61). The methods they employed included amino acid analysis of the whole histones and the various subfractions and starch gel electrophoresis. However, Laurence *et al.* (61) found the arginine content of the "arginine-rich" histones (fraction F3) of the Crocker tumor and a spontaneous mammary tumor was substantially lower than the arginine content of the corresponding fraction of the calf thymus.

Studies in this laboratory on purified histone fractions have in general provided support for the concept of Butler and his associates that there are few, if any, significant differences between the purified histones of a number of tumors and the calf thymus, at least insofar as the amino acid content, the $NH_2$-terminals and the "peptide maps" of the proteins are concerned (50). Claims for changes in amounts of specific amino acids in tumor histones have been made (81). In particular, a decrease was reported in aspartic acid content in histones of livers of animals treated with azo dyes. At the same time, an increase was reported in the valine content. This result suggested that a mutation occurred in these tissues in the genome coding for histone synthesis (81). However, such changes have not been reported by other workers (18).

*Sequential Analysis of Tumor Histones.* As indicated in Chapter VI, the sequences of amino acids in the histones of tumors and other tissues are just coming under experimental analysis; hence it is not yet possible to specify whether abnormal peptides exist in histones of tumors and other tissues. The evidence that there are differences between amino acids in peptides of the *N*-proline and *N*-acetylalanine histones of the Walker tumor and the calf thymus may reflect species rather than tissue differences. What is also significant is the remarkable similarity of these proteins in most respects.

*Histone Content of Leukemic Cells.* The possibility that there are differences between histones of tumors and other tissues has been widely discussed (18) and the possibility of significant alterations of genomic functions in the presence of such changes has been indicated. In relation to the work of Gurley *et al.* (37), there is evidence that the ratio of DNA to histone changes in human leukemic cells (76) such that the DNA to histone ratio falls during the G-1 phase of cell growth. This ratio returns to normalcy in nontumor cells as the cell continues into interphase. In leukemic cells, however, the DNA to histone ratio was low and there was no return to the normal ratios.

In summarizing the studies on the tissue and species differences of histones, it can only be said that at the moment the similarities of the chromatographic and electrophoretic characteristics of the histones and their amino acid compositions are much greater than the differences that have been found. In a few instances, such as spermiogenesis, there are marked changes in the types of proteins associated with DNA in a given species. However, in most instances improved techniques are required for isolation of the histones and examination of the primary amino acid sequences before it will be possible to establish whether tissue and species specificity exist.

## Histones as Ribonucleases

An elegant hypothesis for the function of histones as ribonucleases was put forward by Leslie (63), whose basis for this claim was chromatographic correspondence between protein content and ribonuclease activity of peaks of eluted histones. He utilized the system described in Chapter III for chromatography of the histones on carboxymethylcellulose. The concept that Leslie proposed (63) had considerable interest in view of the fact that it suggested that priming of RNA synthesis occurred on both strands of DNA and that two strands of RNA were produced. The RNA required for cell function would then be conserved while the other strand would be destroyed. This concept was designed to answer the question as to the mechanism by which doubly stranded DNA normally functions in the priming of RNA synthesis and yet only one strand serves as the coding entity for newly synthesized RNA. Another point of interest in Leslie's hypothesis (63) was that ribonucleases could function to define the size of RNAs released from the DNA templates. "Newly formed" RNA that is the precursor of the polysomic complexes has a very high molecular weight (96), and mechanisms involved in the precise splitting of RNA strands are still not clear (see Chapter IX).

Studies on the RNase activity of histone preparations made after the initial studies of Leslie (63) led to the conclusion that the RNase activity found in Leslie's preparations was probably fortuitously present. In a reevaluation of the question of the RNase content of the histones, Martin *et al.* (68) have reported that much lower amounts of RNase were present in the histones and that only certain of the histone peaks in the chromatogram actually contain RNase activity. In their system, 0.3 *M* NaCl, 0.7 *M* NaCl, and 0.02 *N* HCl were used to elute histones. The most active RNases were eluted with the first fraction; the second fraction was absent from ribosomal proteins. It is difficult to be certain at this time whether these results will be confirmed and, if they are, what bearing they will have on Leslie's concepts.

## Other Potential Functions of the Histones

*Inhibitory Effects of Histones on Cells.* Although the significance is not apparent, a number of workers have reported that histones and other polybasic substances inhibit the growth and function of cells *in vitro*. "Arginine-rich" calf thymus histones had an antibacterial effect on the variety of coliform bacilli and micrococci *in vitro* (46). Lethality was found when there was less than 1 μg of histone per milliliter of medium. The coliform organisms were less sensitive when cultured on solid media than when cultured in liquid media. Histones also inhibited the growth of *Escherichia coli* (10). The lysine-rich histones had no inhibitory effect but 3 μg of "arginine-rich" histones per milliliter inhibited the growth 50%. The slightly lysine-rich fraction was equally inhibitory.

Both protamines and histones inhibited the growth of ascites cells (7). The basic macromolecules combined with DNA in the nucleus and RNA in the cytoplasm. Although there were only minor effects on respiration of the cells, there was a rapid cessation of amino acid uptake into proteins.

The effects of calf thymus histone on the growth of rats bearing transplantable acute myeloid leukemias were studied with histones that were injected intravenously. The $LD_{50}$ was found to be 50 mg/kg (48). A significant number of animals treated with histones died from the histone preparations alone and no cytostatic effect was found. The average survival of the histone-treated animals was less than that of the controls.

*Interferon.* Evidence that acid-extractable proteins of tissues have both antibacterial (65) and antiviral activity (17, 60) has been obtained in recent studies that are extensions of the original findings of interferons in tissues (55). Whether the interferons are histones or contain histones has not been defined, but some of the reported properties of the interferons (44) such as molecular size and solubility certainly resemble those of the histones (Table 5-IV).

TABLE 5-IV

SUMMARY OF PROPERTIES OF PURIFIED CHICK EMBRYO INTERFERON[a]

Biochemical and biophysical properties
- Stability
  - Proteolytic enzyme sensitivity: trypsin, chymotrypsin, pepsin, papain
  - Nonproteolytic enzyme insensitivity: peptidases, $\alpha$ amylase, lipase, DNase
  - Heat sensitivity: 76°C, one hour
  - pH stability: pH 2–10, 25°C, one hour; pH 1, 4°C, one hour
  - Ultraviolet light stability: rapidly destroyed
  - Adsorbs to: glass, starch, agar, paper, cellulose acetate, pevikon
  - Eluted from glass and cellulose acetate by: Tween 80, bovine albumin
- Size
  - Nondialyzable through Visking tubing
  - Approximate molecular weight:
    - Calculated average activity sedimentation coefficient: $2.6 \times 10^{-13}$
    - Measured molecular weight (approximate): range 20,000–34,000
    - Calculated minimum molecular weight for the basic unit: 7,900 based on tyrosine–tryptophan content. Complete molecule probably consists of a multiple of this
- Composition
  - Ultraviolet extinction coefficient, 280 mμ: $E$ 1%/1cm = 8.6
- Ultraviolet absorption spectrum: characteristic of protein; max. 278 mμ, min. 253mμ
  - Slightly basic protein: isoelectric point around pH 8.0

Amino acid composition
  - Tyrosine (calculated): 2.3%
  - Tryptophan (calculated): 2.6%
  - Arginine: 7.2% (less than in lysozyme)
  - Lysine: 11.1% (more than in lysozyme)
- Other
  - Trace of carbohydrate present
  - Nucleic acid absent
  - No absorption in the visible spectrum
- Biological activities
  - Interferes with propagation of Eastern equine encephalomyelitis virus in chick embryo cell culture system
  - Unit activity in above system = 0.0017–0.0067 μg/ml
  - Prophylactically suppresses number, size, and time of appearance of virus-induced Rous tumors; ineffective therapeutically
  - Prophylactically prevents or delays death from Newcastle disease virus infection
  - Does not uncouple oxidative phosphorylation in chick liver mitochondria system
  - Does not stimulate aerobic or anaerobic glycolysis of Ehrlich ascites cell system
  - Does not affect glucose utilization or lactic acid production by chick embryo cells in culture

[a] From Lampson *et al.* (60).

Like the histones, interferon is not retained on the DEAE-cellulose, an anion exchange cellulose column. Interferon is precipitable from tissue culture media with 5% trichloroacetic acid (31) and dissolves in ethanol-HCl solutions. Although similar to albumin in some respect, interferon is not precipitated from acid-ethanol extracts by reducing the pH to 5. A molecular weight of 25,000–34,000 established for interferon by Kreuz and Levy (59) agrees well with the molecular weights of the histones.

*Oxidations.* As indicated previously in this chapter, there have been suggestions that the histones are important in the control of oxidative reactions in the mitochondria (1, 2, 42, 79), that they play a role in the transmission of ions across cell membranes and in the electrical discharges of specific components of nerve cells (70), that they may decrease liver tryptophan pyrrolase activity (57) and exert a toxohormone-like activity (74, 75), and more recently that the histones are involved in the role of ATPases that perhaps are related to ionic pumps of the cells (70, 81, 97). Also, it was recently found (81a) that in concentrations of $10^{-11}$ *M*, histones stimulated oxidation in mitochondria; at higher concentrations there was a marked suppression of oxidation in mitochondria. The importance of these possible functions of histones in cell physiology cannot be assessed at present.

## References


1. Allfrey, V. G.: Nuclear ribosomes, messenger-RNA and protein synthesis. *Exptl. Cell Res. Suppl.* **9**: 183-212 (1963).
2. Allfrey, V. G.: Studies of energy yielding reactions in isolated cell nuclei. *Exptl. Cell Res. Suppl.* **9**: 418-429 (1963).

2a. Allfrey, V. G., Faulkner, R., and Mirsky, A. E.: Acetylation and methylation of histones and their possible role in the regulation of RNA synthesis. *Proc. Natl. Acad. Sci. U.S.* **51**: 786-794 (1964).

3. Allfrey, V. G., Littau, V. C., and Mirsky, A. E.: On the role of histones in regulating ribonucleic acid synthesis in the cell nucleus. *Proc. Natl. Acad. Sci.* **49**: 414-421 (1963).
4. Avery, O. T., MacLeod, C. M., and McCarty, M.: Studies on the chemical nature of the substance inducing transformation of pneumococcal types. III. *J. Exptl. Med.* **79**: 137-157 (1944).
5. Barr, G. C., and Butler, J. A. V.: Histones and gene function. *Nature* **199**: 1170-1177 (1963).
6. Bazill, G. W., and Philpot, J. St. L.: Studies on the assay of primer DNA in the presence of histone and nucleoprotein and in isolated nuclei. *Biochim. Biophys. Acta* **76**: 223-233 (1963).
7. Becker, F. F., and Green, H.: The effects of protamines and histones on the nucleic acids of ascites tumor cells. *Exptl. Cell Res.* **19**: 361-375 (1960).

8. Bessman, M. J., Lehman, I. R., Simms, E. S., and Kornberg, A.: Enzymatic synthesis of deoxyribonucleic acid. II. General properties of the reaction. *J. Biol. Chem.* **233**: 171-177 (1958).

9. Billen, D., and Hnilica, L. S.: Inhibition of DNA synthesis by histones. *In*: "The Nucleohistones" (J. Bonner and P. Ts'o, eds.), pp. 289-297. Holden-Day, San Francisco, California, 1964.

10. Biserte, G., Tacquet, A., Leclerc, H., and Sautiere, P.: Activité de diverses histones isolées du thymus de veau sur *Escherichia coli* et les mycobactéries. *Compt. Rend. Soc. Biol.* **43**: 1790-1794 (1959).

11. Black, M. M., Speer, F. D., and Lillick, L.: Acid extractable nuclear proteins of cancer cells. I. Staining with ammoniacle silver. *J. Natl. Cancer Inst.* **25**: 967-989 (1960).

12. Bloch, D. P.: On the derivation of histone specificity. *Proc. Natl. Acad. Sci. U.S.* **48**: 324-326 (1962).

13. Bloch, D. P.: Synthetic processes in the cell nucleus. I. Histone synthesis in non-replicating chromosomes. *J. Histochem. Cytochem.* **10**: 137-143 (1962).

14. Bloch, D. P., and Hew, H. Y. C.: Changes in nuclear histones during fertilization, and early embryonic development in the pulmonate snail, *Helix aspersa*. *J. Biophys. Biochem. Cytol.* **8**: 69-81 (1960).

14a. Bonner, J.: Personal communication.

15. Bonner, J., and Huang, R. C.: Properties of chromosomal nucleohistone. *J. Mol. Biol.* **6**: 169-174 (1963).

16. Bonner, J., Huang, R. C., and Gilden, R. V.: Chromosomally directed protein synthesis. *Proc. Natl. Acad. Sci. U.S.* **50**: 893-900 (1963).

17. Burke, D. C.: The purification of interferon. *Biochem. J.* **78**: 556-564 (1963).

18. Busch, H.: "An Introduction to the Biochemistry of the Cancer Cell." Academic Press, New York, 1962.

19. Busch, H., Byvoet, P., and Smetana, K.: The nucleolus of the cancer cell: A review. *Cancer Res.* **23**: 313-339 (1963).

20. Busch, H., Davis, J. R., and Anderson, D. C.: Labeling of histones and other nuclear proteins with L-lysine-U-$C^{14}$ in tissues of tumor-bearing rats. *Cancer Res.* **18**: 916-926 (1958).

20a. Busch, H., Starbuck, W. C., Singh, E. J., and Ro, T. S.: Chromosomal proteins. *In* "Chromosomes," pp. 51-71. Symposium of the Society for Growth, Amherst, 1964.

21. Busch, H., Steele, W. J., Hnilica, L. S., Taylor, C. W., and Mavioglu, H.: Biochemistry of histones and the cell cycle. *J. Cellular Comp. Physiol.* **62**: Suppl. 1, 95-110 (1963).

22. Butler, J. A. V.: Some researches on histones. *J. Gen. Physiol.* **45**: 195-203 (1962).

23. Butler, J. A. V.: The nuclear proteins of normal and cancer cells. *Exptl. Cell Res. Suppl.* **9**: 349-358 (1963).

24. Byvoet, P., and Busch, H.: DNA-binding of RP2-L, a nuclear protein of neoplastic tissues. *Nature* **192**: 870-871 (1961).

25. Crampton, C. F., Lipshitz, R., and Chargaff, E.: Studies on nucleoproteins. I. Dissociation and reassociation of deoxyribonucleohistone of calf thymus. *J. Biol. Chem.* **206**: 499-510 (1954).

26. Crampton, C. F., Lipshitz, R., and Chargaff, E.: Studies on nucleoproteins. II. Fractionation of deoxyribonucleic acids through fractional dissociation of their complexes with basic proteins. *J. Biol. Chem.* **211**: 125-142 (1954).
27. Cruft, H. J., Mauritzen, C. M., and Stedman, E.: Abnormal properties of histones from malignant cells. *Nature* **174**: 580-585 (1954).
28. Cruft, H. J., Mauritzen, C. M., and Stedman, E.: The nature and physico-chemical properties of histones. *Phil. Trans. Roy. Soc. London Ser.* **B241**: 93-145 (1957).
29. Daly, M. M., and Mirsky, A. E.: Histones with high lysine content. *J. Gen. Physiol.* **38**: 405-413 (1954-1955).
30. Daly, M. M., Mirsky, A. E., and Ris, H.: The amino acid composition and some properties of histones. *J. Gen. Physiol.* **34**: 439-462 (1950-1951).
31. Davies, A.: The partial purification of calf interferon. *Biochem. J.* **90**: 29P (1964).
32. Davis, J. R., and Busch, H.: Chromatographic analysis of cationic nuclear proteins of a number of neoplastic tissues. *Cancer Res.* **20**: 1208-1213 (1960).
33. Davison, P. F.: Histones from normal and malignant cells. *Biochem. J.* **66**: 703-707 (1957).
34. Fredericq, E.: Enzymic degradation of thymus nucleoprotein. *Biochim. Biophys. Acta* **68**: 167-176 (1963).
35. Frenster, J. H., Allfrey, V. G., and Mirsky, A. E.: Repressed and active chromatin isolated from interphase lymphocytes. *Proc. Natl. Acad. Sci.* **50**: 1026-1032 (1963).
36. Griffith, F.: The significance of pneumococcal types. *J. Hyg.* **27**: 113-159 (1928).
37. Gurley, L. R., Irvin, J. L., and Holbrook, D. J.: Inhibition of DNA polymerase by histones. *Biochem. Biophys. Res. Commun.* **14**: 527-532 (1964).
38. Hamer, D.: Amino acid composition of thymus histone. *Nature* **167**: 40 (1951).
39. Hamer, D.: Aspects of the chemistry of the proteins in the nucleus. A short review and some experimental results. *Brit. J. Cancer* **5**: 130-139 (1951).
40. Hamer, D.: A comparison of different protein fractions obtained from thymus nuclei isolated in an aqueous medium. *Brit. J. Cancer* **7**: 151-156 (1953).
41. Hammarsten, E.: Zur Kenntnis der biologischen Bedeutung der Nucleinsäureverbindungen. *Biochem. Z.* **144**: 383-466 (1924).
42. Hanson, J. B., and Swanson, H. R.: The role of basic proteins in the declining respiration of senescing corn scutellum. *Biochem. Biophys. Res. Commun.* **9**: 442-446 (1962).
43. Hidvegi, E. J., Arky, I., Antoni, F., and Varteresz, V.: Studies on the heterogeneity and metabolic activity of histones from rabbit bone marrow cells. *Brit. J. Cancer* **17**: 377-380 (1963).
44. Hilleman, M. R.: Interferon in prospect and perspective. *J. Cellular Comp. Physiol.* **62**: 337-353 (1963).
45. Hindley, J.: The relative ability of reconstituted nucleohistones to allow DNA-dependent RNA synthesis. *Biochem. Biophys. Res. Commun.* **12**: 175-179 (1963).

45a. Hindley, J.: The role of histones in controlling DNA-dependent RNA-synthesis. *Proc. 6th Intern. Congr. Biochem. New York* 61 (1964).
46. Hirsch, J. G.: Bactericidal action of histone. *J. Exptl. Med.* **108**: 925-944 (1958).
47. Hnilica, L. S., and Busch, H.: Fractionation of the histones of the Walker 256 carcinosarcoma by combined chemical and chromatographic techniques. *J. Biol. Chem.* **238**: 918-924 (1963).
48. Hnilica, L. S., and Holoubek, V.: Effect of calf thymus histone on rats bearing transplantable acute myeloid leukemia. *Nature* **191**: 922-923 (1961).
49. Hnilica, L. S., Johns, E. W., and Butler, J. A. V.: Observations on the species and tissue specificity of histones. *Biochem. J.* **82**: 123-129 (1962).
50. Hnilica, L. S., Taylor, C. W., and Busch, H.: Analysis of peptides of the moderately lysine-rich fraction, F2b, of the Walker tumor and other tissues. *Exptl. Cell Res. Suppl.* **9**: 367-375 (1963).
51. Holoubek, V.: Stimulation of DNA synthesis with histones from tumor tissues. *Proc. Soc. Exptl. Biol. Med.* **110**: 759-761 (1962).
52. Hotchkiss, R. D.: Some evidences of molecular exchanges affecting genetic material. *Exptl. Cell Res. Suppl.* **9**: 120-123 (1963).
53. Huang, R. C., and Bonner, J.: Histone, a suppressor of chromosomal RNA synthesis. *Proc. Natl. Acad. Sci. U.S.* **48**: 1216-1222 (1962).
53a. Huang, R. C., Bonner, J., and Murray, K.: Physical and biological properties of soluble nucleohistones. *J. Mol. Biol.* **8**: 54-64 (1964).
54. Irvin, J. L., Holbrook, D. J., Jr., Evans, J. H., McAllister, H. C., and Stiles, E. P.: Possible role of histones in regulation of nucleic acid synthesis. *Exptl. Cell Res. Suppl.* **9**: 359-366 (1963).
55. Isaacs, A.: Antiviral action of interferon. *Brit. Med. J.* **ii**: 353-355 (1962).
56. Johns, E. W., and Butler, J. A. V.: Studies on histones. 4. The histones of wheat germ. *Biochem. J.* **84**: 436-439 (1962).
57. Kawachi, T., Fujii, S., Suzuki, T., Uesaki, N., and Yamamura, Y.: Effect of basic protein from tumor tissue on liver tryptophan pyrrolase activity. *Gann* **52**: 213-217 (1961).
58. Kossel, A.: "The Protamines and Histones." Longmans, Green, London, 1921.
59. Kreuz, L. E., and Levy, A. H.: Density homogeneity and estimated molecular weight interferon. *Nature* **200**: 883-884 (1963).
60. Lampson, G. P., Tytell, A. A., Nemes, M. M., and Hilleman, M. R.: Purification and characterization of chick embryo interferon. *Proc. Soc. Exptl. Biol. Med.* **112**: 468-478 (1963).
61. Laurence, D. J. R., Simson, P., and Butler, J. A. V.: Studies on histones. V. The histones of the Crocker sarcoma and spontaneous mammary tumors of mice. *Biochem. J.* **87**: 200-205 (1963).
62. Lehman, I. R., Zimmerman, S. B., Adler, J., Bessman, M. J., Simms, E. S., and Kornberg, A.: Enzymatic synthesis of deoxyribonucleic acid. V. Chemical composition of enzymatically synthesized deoxyribonucleic acid. *Proc. Natl. Acad. Sci. U.S.* **44**: 1191-1196 (1958).
63. Leslie, I.: Biochemistry of heredity. A general hypothesis. *Nature* **189**: 260-268 (1961).
64. Levy, H. B.: Effect of actinomycin D on HeLa cell nuclear RNA metabolism. *Proc. Soc. Exptl. Biol. Med.* **113**: 886-889 (1963).

65. Li, C. P., Prescott, B., Chi, L. L., and Martino, E. C.: Antiviral and antibacterial activity of thymus extracts. *Proc. Soc. Exptl. Biol. Med.* **114**: 504-509 (1963).

66. Lindegren, C. C.: Nucleoprotein layer of the yeast cell. *Nature* **198**: 1325-1326 (1963).

66a. Lindsay, D. T.: Histones from developing tissues of the chicken: heterogeneity. *Science* **144**: 420-422 (1964).

67. MacGillivray, A. J., and Greenwood, F. C.: A unique nuclear histone in leukaemic leukocytes. *Biochem. J.* **85**: 39P (1962).

68. Martin, S. J., England, H., Turkington, V., and Leslie, I.: Depolymerization of ribonucleic acid by enzymes in basic proteins from liver nuclei and ribosomes. *Biochem. J.* **89**: 327-334 (1963).

69. Mauritzen, C. M., and Stedman, E.: Cell specificity of β-histones in the domestic fowl. *Proc. Roy. Soc.* **B150**: 299-311 (1959).

70. McIlwain, H., Woodman, R. J., and Cummins, J. T.: Basic proteins and the potassium movements and phosphates of cerebral tissues. *Biochem. J.* **81**: 79-83 (1961).

70a. Muramatsu, M., and Busch, H.: Studies on nucleolar RNA of the Walker 256 carcinosarcoma and the liver of the rat. *Cancer Res.* **24**: 1028-1034 (1964).

71. Muramatsu, M., Adams, H. R., and Busch, H.: Studies on RNA of nucleoli of Walker tumor and liver. *Proc. Am. Assoc. Cancer Res.* **4**: 46 (1963).

72. Muramatsu, M., Smetana, K., and Busch, H.: Quantitative aspects of isolation of nucleoli of the Walker carcinosarcoma and liver of the rat. *Cancer Res.* **23**: 510-518 (1963).

73. Neelin, J. M., and Butler, G. C.: A comparison of histones from chicken tissues by zone electrophoresis in starch gel. *Can. J. Biochem. Physiol.* **39**: 485-491 (1961).

73a. Neidle, A., and Waelsch, H.: Histones: species and tissue specificity. *Science* **145**: 1059-1061 (1964).

74. Okamura, Y.: Biochemical studies on the liver catalase depressing factor of toxohormone. *Kyushu J. Med. Sci.* **13**: 299-311 (1962).

75. Okamura, Y., Fujii, S., Kawachi, T., Kawanami, H., Kuwano, M., and Yamamura, Y.: Effect of enzymatic hydrolysis on toxohormone activities. *Gann* **53**: 365-370 (1962).

76. Perugini, S.: The DNA and histone contents of human leukemic cells. (Cytophotometric study.) *Cancro* **15**: 172-180 (1962).

77. Phillips, D. M. P.: The histones: A review. *Progr. Biophys. Biophys. Chem.* **12**: 211-280 (1961).

78. Ris, H.: Chromosome structure. *In* "The Chemical Basis of Heredity" (W. D. McElroy and B. Glass, eds.), pp. 23-62. Johns Hopkins Press, Baltimore, Maryland, 1957.

79. Rivenbark, W. L., and Hanson, J. B.: The uncoupling of oxidative phosphorylation by basic proteins, and its reversal with potassium. *Biochem. Biophys. Res. Commun.* **7**: 318-321 (1962).

80. Ro, T. S., Muramatsu, M., and Busch, H.: Labeling of RNA of isolated nucleoli with UTP-$^{14}$C. *Biochem. Biophys. Res. Commun.* **14**: 149-155 (1964).

80a. Rogers, S.: Certain relationships between the Shope virus induced arginase, the virus and the tumor cells. *In* "The Molecular Basis of Neoplasia," pp. 483-495. Univ. of Texas Press, Austin, 1962.

80b. Rogers, S., and Moore, M.: Studies on the mechanism of action of the Shope rabbit papilloma virus. I. Concerning the nature of the induction of arginase in the infected cells. *J. Exptl. Med.* **117**: 521-542 (1963).

81. Sahasrabudhe, M. B., Apte, B. K., Aboobaker, V. S., and Jayaraman, R.: Partial deletion of aspartic acid from DNA proteins during butter yellow carcinogenesis. *Biochem. Biophys. Res. Commun.* **7**: 173-178 (1962).

81a. Schwartz, A.: Manuscript in preparation.

82. Setterfield, G., Neelin, J. M., Neelin, E. M., and Bayley, S. T.: Studies on basic proteins from ribosomes of buds of pea seedlings. *J. Mol. Biol.* **2**: 416-424 (1960).

83. Shack, J., and Thompsett, J. M.: Deoxypentose nucleic acids and nucleoproteins of malignant tissues. I. The nucleohistones of a transplantable lymphoma. *J. Natl. Cancer Inst.* **13**: 1425-1433 (1953).

84. Singh, E. J., and Busch, H.: Unpublished results.

85. Skalka, A.: The effect of histones on the enzymatic synthesis of nucleic acids from a DNA template. *Federation Proc.* **23**: 526 (1964).

85a. Sporn, M. B., and Dingman, C. W.: Histone and DNA in isolated nuclei from chicken brain, liver, and erythrocytes. *Science* **140**: 316-318 (1963).

86. Stedman, E.: The chemistry of cell nuclei. *Edinburgh Med. J.* **51**: 353-366 (1944).

87. Stedman, E., and Stedman, E.: Distribution of nucleic acid in the cell. *Nature* **152**: 503 (1943).

88. Stedman, E., and Stedman, E.: Probable function of histone as a regulator of mitosis. *Nature* **152**: 556 (1943).

89. Stedman, E., and Stedman, E.: Chromosomin, a protein constituent of chromosomes. *Nature* **152**: 267 (1943).

90. Stedman, E., and Stedman, E.: "Chromosomin" and nucleic acids. *Nature* **153**: 500-502 (1944).

91. Stedman, E., and Stedman, E.: The function of deoxyribosenucleic acid in the cell nucleus. *Symp. Soc. Exptl. Biol.* **1**: 232-251 (1947).

92. Stedman, E., and Stedman, E.: Cell specificity of histones. *Nature* **166**: 780 (1950).

93. Stedman, E., and Stedman, E.: The basic proteins of cell nuclei. *Phil. Trans. Roy. Soc. London Ser.* **B235**: 565-596 (1951).

94. Vendrely, R., Alfert, M., Matsudaira, H., and Knobloch, A.: The composition of nucleohistone from pycnotic nuclei. *Exptl. Cell Res.* **14**: 295-300 (1958).

95. Weiss, S. B.: Enzymatic incorporation of ribonucleoside triphosphate into the interpolynucleotide linkages of ribonucleic acid. *Proc. Natl. Acad. Sci. U.S.* **46**: 1020-1030 (1960).

96. Wettstein, F. O., Staehelin, T., and Noll, H.: Ribosomal aggregate engaged in protein synthesis. Characterization of the ergosome. *Nature* **197**: 430-435 (1963).

97. Wolfe, L. S., and McIlwain, H.: Migration of histones from nuclei of isolated cerebral tissues kept in cold media. *Biochem. J.* **78**: 33-40 (1961).

98. Zubay, G., and Wilkins, M. H. F.: An X-ray diffraction study of histone and protamine in isolation and in combination with DNA. *J. Mol. Biol.* **4**: 444-450 (1962).

# CHAPTER VI

# The Primary Structure of Histones



## Introduction

The current concept of the secondary structure of the histones is that these molecules largely exist as monomeric α-helices, as indicated in Chapter IV. It has also been inferred that histones are linear structures normally elongated and wound into the grooves of DNA. One of the reasons why the nature of the secondary and tertiary structures of histones is not yet defined is that information is lacking on the primary structure, i.e., the linear sequence of amino acids in the histones. Since all the theories of binding of the histones to DNA require information on the specific affinity points and binding sites of individual histones, the structures of these proteins must be determined. Such information will also aid in understanding the relative dissociation constants of the various histones and DNA. As indicated in Chapter V, it is also possible that differences in sequences of amino acids in histones may be important in functions of individual tissues.

The work of Sanger (1, 16, 17) on insulin and later studies of other groups of workers on ribonuclease (7, 8, 19), hemoglobin (11, 18), cytochrome c (12), and other proteins have all had a common set of principles. In the first stage of structural analysis, the critical feature is the purification of the protein. In the second stage, the $NH_2$-terminal amino acid is determined. In the third stage, hydrolysis of the protein is carried out both by enzymatic and chemical procedures; the peptides are analyzed for their elementary amino acid compositions. In the fourth stage, the sequences of amino acids in the peptides are determined. The fifth stage, which may be referred to as the "synthetic stage," requires the interpretation of the structure of the whole molecule on the basis of the fragmentary information provided from the smaller pieces. It is in this stage that the greatest weaknesses exist, inasmuch as there are still features of the enzymatic and chemical degradations that are not completely satisfactory or completely understood. The sixth stage is the synthesis of peptides or longer structures on the basis of the sequential information already obtained. The seventh and pharmacologically most interesting stage is the attempt to determine whether the synthesized structures have biological activity, and, if they do, whether this activity is exactly the same as the compound from which the structure was derived.

Studies on the histones have not yet reached the point of development already achieved with studies on other proteins. As noted previously, this problem was difficult to approach until at least one of the histones could be isolated by procedures that could provide one highly purified molecular species virtually completely separated from the others, i.e., the very first stage of structural analysis had to be completed. As indicated by the $NH_2$-terminal amino acid analysis, the purity of the *N*-proline histone approached the necessary requirements. Even in this case, further purification is required before a completely satisfactory sequence of amino acids can be obtained. However, some studies have been made on the available histone preparations and, despite their limitations, some inferences can be drawn about the structures and functions of the histones.

## Early Studies on Peptides of the Histones

The first studies on the structures of peptides of histones were made by Phillips and Simson (15), who were interested in the determination of linear sequences of amino acids to aid in the development of a model of deoxyribonucleohistone. It is well known that there is a very regular spacing of the phosphate groups in DNA. If the concept were correct that the histones serve simply to neutralize the phosphate groups (a phenomenon that is apparently not necessary in bacterial cells), there should be a correspondingly regular arrangement of the basic amino acids. As mentioned previously, this was not found to be the case. Even in the protamines, as noted in Chapter I, there is no precisely regular arrangement of the basic amino acids. Felix and his colleagues (6) postulated a regular alternation of tetrads of arginine with the other amino acids, but it is not clear how this arrangement of arginine residues could serve to neutralize all the phosphate groups of the associated DNA.

The fraction that Phillips and Simson (15) used was of limited value for studies on amino acid sequences because it contained several histones. As indicated in Chapter II, this "arginine-rich" fraction as obtained from calf thymus contains at least three, and perhaps more, histones. This fraction was subjected to tryptic digestion in a phosphate buffer. Within a few minutes after the incubation at 40°C was begun, a precipitate began to form. It is not clear whether the formation of the precipitate resulted from denaturation of a component, partial degradation of the protein to form insoluble peptides, or a shift in pH. In experiments in this laboratory, a precipitate was observed on hydrolysis of the proteins of histone fraction 2a, but only a cloudy suspension was noted when a pH stat was used to control the pH during the course of tryptic hydrolysis of fraction 2b. The precipitate formed from the "arginine-rich" histones (15) contained valine, serine, and tyrosine as $NH_2$-terminal amino acids as well as alanine, which was the predominant $NH_2$-terminal amino acid in the original preparation. In addition, the precipitate contained more glutamic acid, aspartic acid, alanine, and leucine or isoleucine than the original histone preparation. Since it also contained less arginine (about one-half) and less lysine than the original preparation, it seems possible that an associated acidic protein (Chapter VIII) could have been present in the original preparation because in the precipitate the ratio of basic to acidic amino acids was inverted. The soluble peptides contained arginine and lysine as $NH_2$-terminal amino acids. As might be expected on a subtractive basis, the soluble peptides also contained a substantially increased number of arginine and lysine residues so that the ratio of basic to acidic amino acids was approximately 2.0 in this fraction.

The peptides recovered (15) after "fingerprinting" of the tryptic digest of the "arginine-rich" histones are shown in Table 6-I. Among the

TABLE 6-I
PROBABLE STRUCTURES OF PEPTIDES OF ARGININE-RICH HISTONES (15)

| |
|---|
| Free arginine |
| Free lysine |
| Ala,Lys |
| Ala,Arg |
| Asp,Lys |
| Gly(Glu$_2$,Arg)-Arg |
| Gly(Gly,Ser,Thr)-Lys |
| Lys(Pro,His)Arg |

products found were free lysine and arginine; the presence of these amino acids in their hydrolyzates indicate that they were parts of peptides that contained two or more such residues in sequence. In addition, peptides containing both lysine and arginine and two arginine residues were found. These data suggest that there is steric hindrance of tryptic activity that prevents total hydrolysis of arginyl and lysyl C-terminal bonds. However, the main point is that there were peptides of different sizes in the hydrolyzate.

## Peptides of the N-Proline Histone Fraction

One of the main requirements for sequential analysis of a protein is the availability of a highly purified protein as a starting material (7, 8, 19). Unfortunately, all the chromatographic evidence pointed to a marked degree of contamination of the "arginine-rich" histone fraction selected by Phillips and Simson (15) for analysis, and hence it seems that they studied the "arginine-rich" histones, primarily to determine whether a regular order of amino acids existed in this histone fraction.

***Purity of the N-Proline Histone.*** Interest in this laboratory in the slightly lysine-rich histones came from the fact that RP2-L (p. 138), a nuclear protein fraction of tumors, contained substantial amounts of these histones (2, 4, 5). The chief component of RP2-L was the second most rapidly moving band on starch gel electrophoresis (Chapter II). As the purity of the preparation was improved (2, 9) the percentage of proline increased in the $NH_2$-terminal amino acids. Further purification of this protein from the Walker tumor was achieved by the series of extractions and chromatographic procedures delineated in Chapter III.

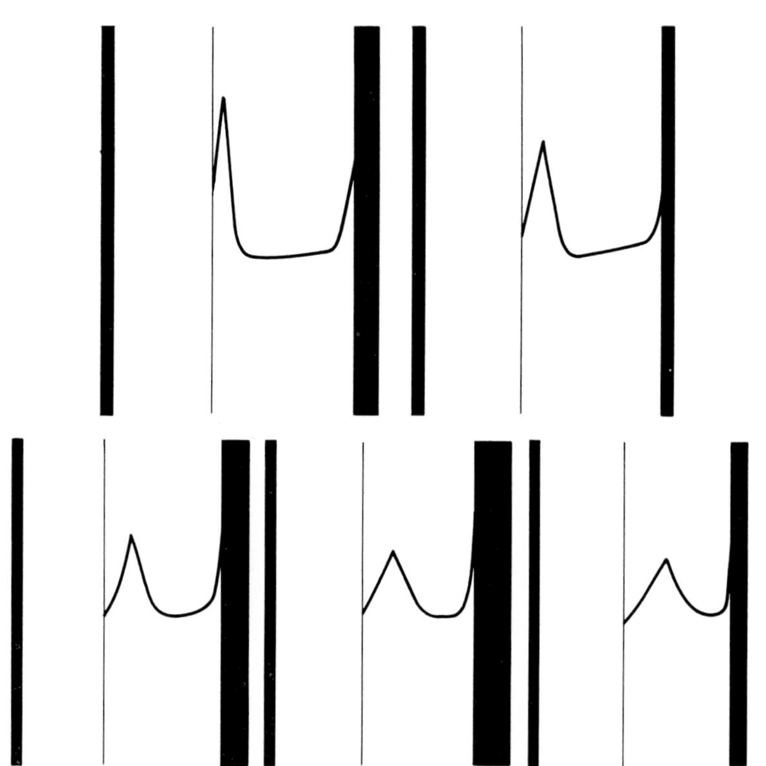

FIG. 6-1. Ultracentrifugation pattern of histone fraction 2b containing the *N*-proline histone.

Fraction 2b or the *N*-proline histone isolated as described in Chapter III, resembled RP2-L closely in amino acid composition, but was more homogeneous and somewhat more basic. In the final product, 80–95% of the total $NH_2$-terminal amino acids in the fraction were proline residues (9, 10). This index of purity would be less meaningful if other proteins in the preparation had a very high molecular weight or

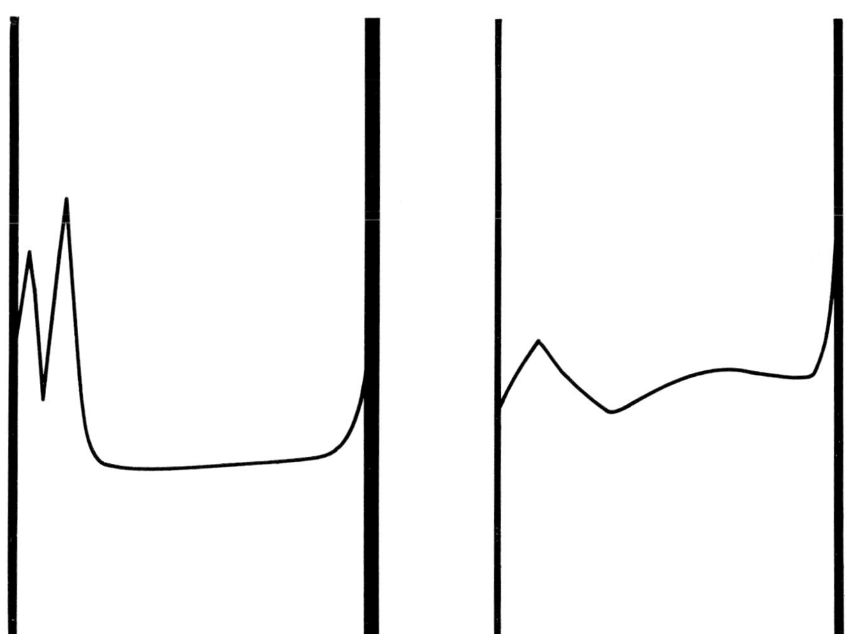

FIG. 6-2. Ultracentrifugation pattern of histone fraction 2a containing the *N*-acetylalanine histone.

blocked terminal amino acids such as are found in fraction 2a or the *N*-acetylalanine histone (14). In view of the data on ultracentrifugation, electrophoresis, and the peptide map, it would seem that the $NH_2$-terminal amino acid analysis was a reliable criterion of purity of the *N*-proline histone.

*Ultracentrifugation of the N-Proline Histone.* When the sedimentation characteristics of the *N*-proline histone were analyzed by ultracentrifugation, the resulting pattern (Fig. 6-1) had a sharp single peak (3). The fact that, over a period of 2 hours of sedimentation of the protein, no additional peaks appeared, supported the suggestion from the $NH_2$-terminal amino acid analysis that the *N*-proline histone was very highly purified by the isolation procedure employed. A striking contrast between the appearance of the ultracentrifugation pattern for this fraction and that for a cruder 2a fraction is apparent when the pattern in Fig. 6-2 is compared with that of Fig. 6-1.

FIG. 6-3A. "Fingerprint" of the tryptic hydrolyzate of the F2b histone fraction from Walker tumor, using conditions described in the text. [From Hnilica *et al.* (10).]

*Peptide Map or "Fingerprint" of the N-Proline Histone.* When peptides prepared by hydrolysis of mixtures of proteins have been subjected to the combined chromatographic and electrophoretic procedures referred to as peptide mapping or "fingerprinting," large numbers of peptides have been detected by the ninhydrin analysis or by visualization of spots with the aid of ultraviolet light. In some instances in this and other laboratories, more than one hundred spots were detected (13a). When the *N*-proline histone was "fingerprinted" in the usual solvent systems, satisfactory resolution of the spots was not achieved. When a complex mixture of solvents including *n*-butanol, secondary butanol, isoamyl alcohol, ethyl acetate acetic acid and water in a ratio of $1:1:\frac{1}{2}:\frac{1}{2}:1:1$ was used to develop the chromatogram, approximately 25

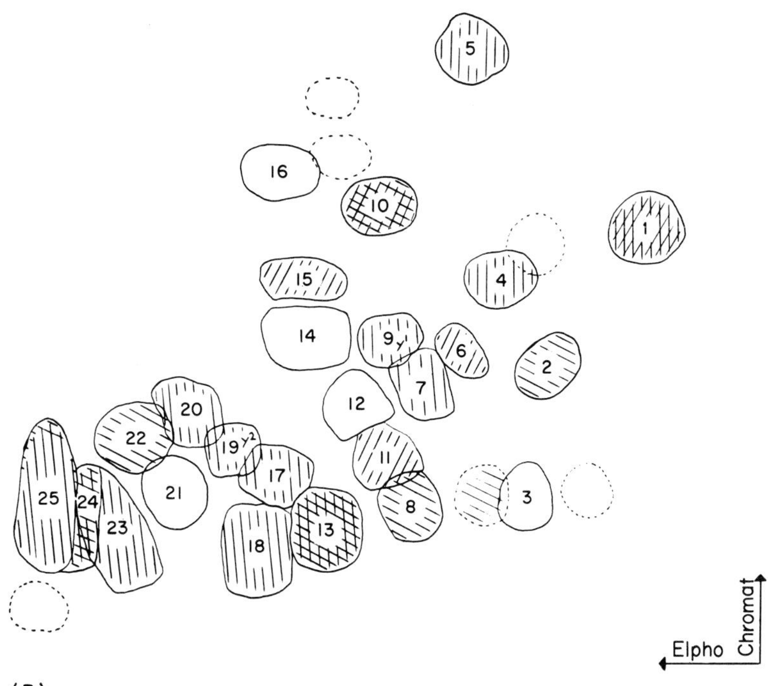


(B)

Fig. 6-3B. Distribution of arginine, histidine, and tyrosine among peptides obtained by tryptic hydrolysis of F2b histones. The spots with vertical lines were positive for arginine; those with oblique lines slanting down from top right were positive for tyrosine, and those with oblique lines slanting down from top left were positive for histidine. Circles with dashed perimeter are ninhydrin-positive spots present in some samples in trace amounts, and the solid-line circles are spots strongly positive with ninhydrin. [From Hnilica *et al.* (10).]

spots could be separated, although there was much trailing of some of the chromatographic spots. The numbering of the spots and the peptide map for the *N*-proline histone are shown in Fig. 6-3. The relatively small number of detectable spots provided further evidence for the purity of the *N*-proline histone although the number of spots was smaller than the 46 that would have been expected if hydrolysis had occurred at each arginine and lysine residue (Table 6-II). There

TABLE 6-II

Amino Acid Analysis of the *N*-Proline Histone Fraction

| Amino acid | % Total moles | % Weight | Residues/mole protein |
|---|---|---|---|
| Alanine | 10.1 | 7.1 | 20 |
| Arginine | 7.7 | 10.6 | 15 |
| Aspartic acid | 5.5 | 5.7 | 11 |
| Cysteine | — | — | — |
| Cystine | — | — | — |
| Glutamic acid | 9.4 | 10.9 | 19 |
| Glycine | 6.3 | 3.7 | 13 |
| Histidine | 2.7 | 3.3 | 5 |
| Isoleucine | 4.4 | 4.5 | 9 |
| Leucine | 5.8 | 6.0 | 12 |
| Lysine | 14.8 | 17.3 | 30 |
| Methionine | 1.5 | 1.7 | 3 |
| Phenylalanine | 1.4 | 1.8 | 3 |
| Proline | 4.7 | 4.3 | 9 |
| Serine | 8.6 | 7.1 | 17 |
| Threonine | 6.3 | 5.9 | 13 |
| Tyrosine | 2.9 | 4.1 | 6 |
| Valine | 6.6 | 6.1 | 13 |
| | | | 198 |

were no significant differences in the spots obtained when the *N*-proline fraction was isolated from rat thymus, rat spleen, calf thymus, or the Walker 256 carcinosarcoma of the rat (10).

*Column Chromatography of the Peptides of the N-Proline Histone.* When the tryptic hydrolyzate of the *N*-proline histone of the calf thymus was chromatographed on Dowex-50 (×8), the elution pattern for the peptides was that shown in Fig. 6-4. The eluting agents employed in this early study were those reported by Spackman *et al.* (20) for the optimal separation of amino acids. The use of citrate buffers in this system hampered recovery of the peptides, although they aided in the determination of peptides by the ninhydrin analysis

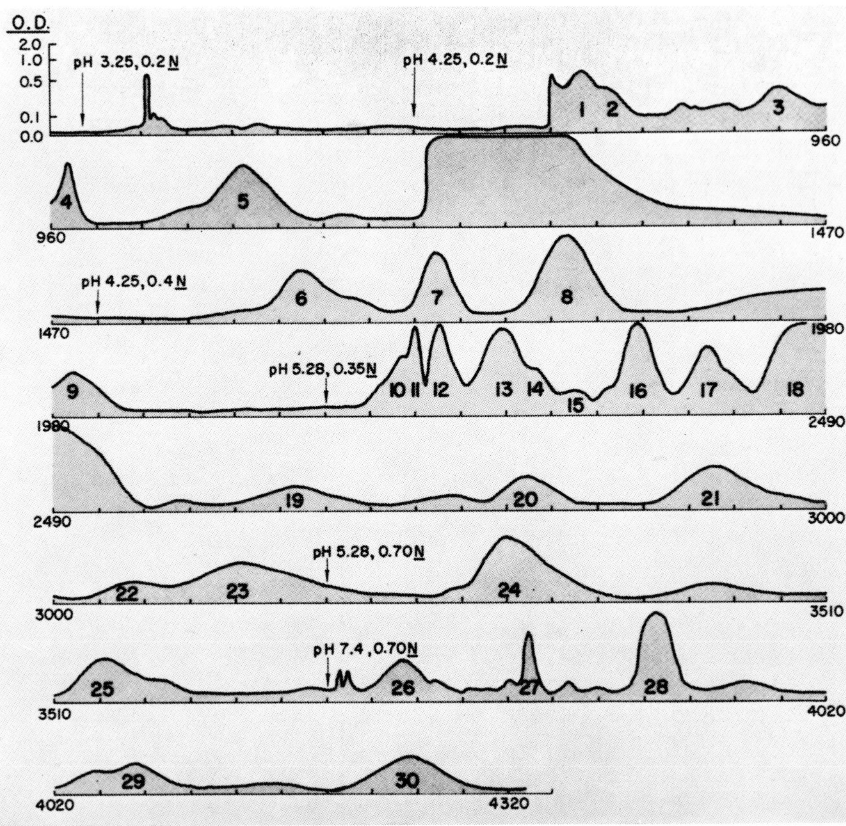


FIG. 6-4. Separation of peptides of a tryptic hydrolyzate of the *N*-proline histone on Dowex 50-X2. Sodium citrate buffers were used to elute the peptides. The column was 150 × 1.8 cm. The ordinate shows optical density at 570 mμ following the reaction with ninhydrin, and the abscissa is milliliters of effluent volume.

as carried out in the automatic amino acid analyzer. The number of peptides estimated from the "peptide map" was almost the same as that obtained by this chromatographic procedure. This result provided supporting evidence of a kind similar to that obtained by "fingerprinting" that the *N*-proline histone was a highly purified protein fraction.

## Elementary Amino Acid Analysis of Peptides of the *N*-Proline Histone Fraction

Before a specific sequence of amino acids in a given peptide could be worked out, it was essential to determine the amino acid composition of the peptides that were separated by the "fingerprinting" procedure as well as the peptides that were isolated by chromatography of the tryptic digests on the Dowex columns. To carry out such analysis on peptides obtained by peptide mapping, this procedure was carried out 5–20 times to accumulate sufficient peptide for amino acid analysis. The spots were located either by ninhydrin staining or ultraviolet (UV) light, but these procedures had serious limitations which could be resolved in part by the "imprinting" procedure. Ninhydrin staining destroys in part the $NH_2$-terminal amino acid of the peptide, and UV scanning necessitates heating of the papers with the possible formation of diketopiperazines. In addition, multiple analyses were necessary in view of the fact that virtually none of the peptides was completely pure. Contaminants were encountered that ranged in amount from 5 to 40% of individual peptides.

Table 6-III presents the estimated elementary amino acid compositions of some of the peptides of the *N*-proline histone of the Walker tumor and the calf thymus. Several tripeptides, two tetrapeptides, a hexapeptide, an octapeptide, and a dodecapeptide were found. In

TABLE 6-III
ELEMENTARY AMINO ACID ANALYSIS OF SOME PEPTIDES OF THE *N*-PROLINE HISTONE OBTAINED BY PEPTIDE MAPPING

| | Peptide source | Formula |
|---|---|---|
| 1. | Calf thymus | (Glu, Gly, $Ser_3$, Tyr, Val) Lys |
| | Walker tumor | (Glu, *Gly*?·$Ser_3$, Tyr, Val) Lys |
| 2. | Calf thymus | (Asp, Glu, Gly, His, Ileu, Pro, $Ser_2$, Thr, Val) Lys |
| | Walker tumor | (Asp, Glu, Gly, $\mathit{His}_2$, Ileu, Pro, $Ser_2$, Thr, Val) Lys |
| 3. | Calf thymus | (Asp, Gly) Lys |
| | Walker tumor | (Asp, Gly) Lys |
| 4. | Calf thymus | (Ala, Glu, Ileu, Thr, Val) Arg |
| | Walker tumor | (Ala, $\mathit{Glu}_2$, Ileu, Thr, Val) Arg |
| 5. | Calf thymus | (Ala, Glu, Gly, $\mathit{Leu}_3$, Pro) Lys |
| | Walker tumor | (Ala, Glu, Gly, $\mathit{Leu}_4$, Pro) Lys |
| 10. | Calf thymus | (Ala, Leu, *Tyr*) His |
| | Walker tumor | (Ala, Leu) His |
| 14. | Calf thymus | (Ala, Thr, Val) Lys |
| | Walker tumor | (Ala, Thr, Val) Lys |
| 15. | Calf thymus | (Tyr, Val) Lys |
| | Walker tumor | (Tyr, Val) Lys |
| 16. | Calf thymus | (Leu, Val) Lys |
| | Walker tumor | (Leu, Val) Lys |

view of the fact that 29 peptides were found for a molecule that contains approximately 176 amino acids, it would be anticipated that the peptides would contain an average of six amino acids. Of the nine peptides shown in Table 6-III, the average number of amino acid residues approximated 5–6, which is close to the overall anticipated average.

*Comparative Analysis of Peptides of Calf Thymus and the Walker Tumor.* Because of the similarity of the amino acid composition of the 2b histone fraction of calf thymus and Walker tumor, it was of interest to determine whether the elementary amino acid analyses of their peptides would be the same, particularly in view of the fact that "fingerprints" of the two proteins were quite similar. Although the similarities are much more impressive than the differences, there were quantitative differences in the composition of the peptides (Table 6-III). Glycine was present only in trace amounts in peptide 1 of the Walker tumor. There were two histidine residues in peptide 2 of the tumor as compared to one residue in the peptide of the calf thymus. In peptides 4 and 5 there were one glutamic acid and one leucine residue more in the respective peptide from the Walker tumor than the corresponding peptide from the calf thymus. Only peptide 10 differed qualitatively in amino acid composition; in this case, a tyrosine residue was present in the peptide from the calf thymus and was absent in the corresponding peptide from the Walker tumor.

These differences have been partially substantiated by studies on the peptides obtained by tryptic hydrolysis of the *N*-proline histone of the calf thymus and isolation of the peptides following chromatography on Dowex 50-X2 columns. For 4 of the 8 peptides isolated by this procedure, the elementary amino acid composition corresponded with that obtained following isolation of the peptides by peptide mapping. Since the values obtained following peptide mapping are subject to more errors, the more acceptable results are those obtained by the analytical procedures after separation of the peptides on the Dowex 50 columns. Even in this case, the similarities are much greater than the differences between the peptides from the two species.

As in the study of Phillips and Simson (15), these data emphasize the variability in the sizes of the peptides. These findings rule out the possibility of regularity of arrangement of the various segments of histones and the DNA molecule. There is no regular, ordered way to accommodate dodecapeptides, hexapeptides, octapeptides, and tripeptides. This conclusion was suggested earlier (15) and has been extended by the more recent studies.

## Sequential Analysis of Amino Acids in the *N*-Proline Histone Fraction

As noted previously, the 2b or *N*-proline histone fraction is the only histone fraction that approached the necessary purity for analysis of amino acid sequences. It was possible that contaminants were present that were high in molecular weight, a possibility that was essentially ruled out by the ultracentrifugation analysis, or had blocked terminals. However, the evidence that there were relatively few peptides, as shown by the "peptide map" (Fig. 6-3) and the elution pattern of the peptides on column chromatography (Fig. 6-4) suggested that this protein was quite pure.

Sequential analysis has been undertaken, therefore, on peptides obtained by tryptic hydrolysis. These peptides were obtained by chromatography of 300 mg of the peptides of the *N*-proline histone on Dowex 50-X2 with pyridine acetate, a completely volatile solvent, as the eluting agent (21). Interrupted gradients of pyridine acetate ranging from 0.25 *M* to 1.0 *M* with a rising pH from 3.5 to 5.50 were employed to elute the peptides. The fractions were collected through a "stream divider" system of the Spinco automatic amino acid analyzer, a device that permits most of the fraction to pass through to a fraction collector and permits a small amount to pass through the usual channels of the instrument for determination of the ninhydrin-reactive elements of the peptide. The elution pattern for the peptides is shown in Fig. 6-5. The collected fractions of individual peaks were pooled, and the solvents were evaporated. In a few instances, the purity of the peptide was in excess of 90%. In most instances, however, the purity of the peptides ranged from 75 to 90%. The results of mapping of two isolated peptides (Fig. 6-6) provide an indication of their purity. The elementary amino acid compositions of a number of peptides of the *N*-proline histone are presented in Table 6-IV. The largest peptide recovered was peptide 1, which contains 16 amino acids. The $NH_2$-terminal amino acid of this peptide is proline, and this finding suggests that this peptide may be the amino terminal peptide of the *N*-proline histone. One of the "peptides" isolated was free lysine indicated as No. 14. Thus far, amino acid sequences have been established for 5 peptides, as shown in Table 6-V. Although these

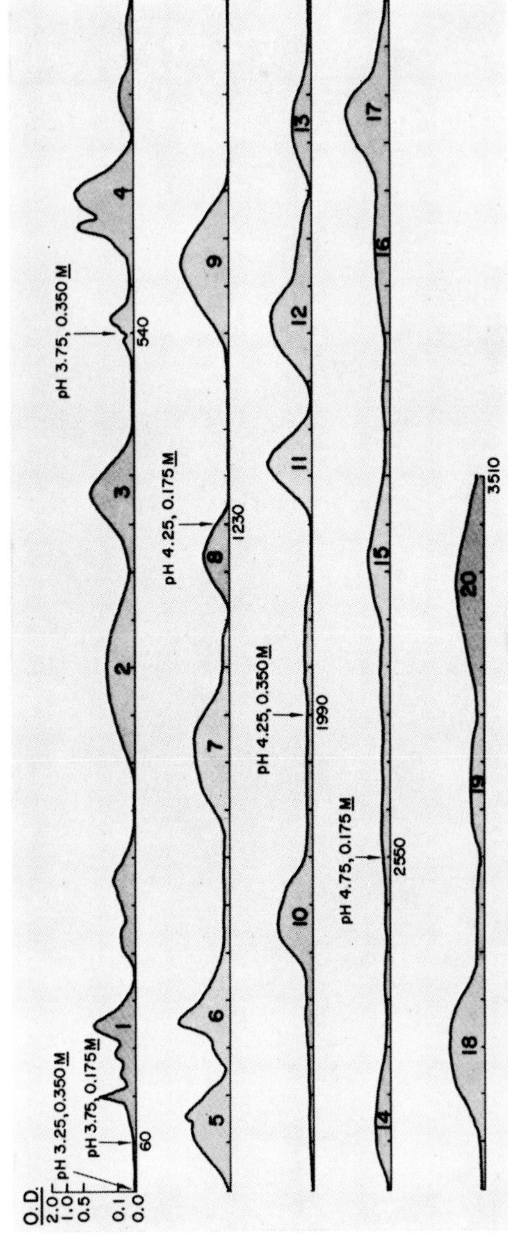


FIG. 6-5. The separation of 20 peptide peaks from a tryptic hydrolyzate of the *N*-proline histone. Pyridine acetate buffers were used to elute the peaks from a Dowex 50-X2 column 150 × 1.8 cm. The ordinate shows optical density at 570 mμ following the reaction with ninhydrin, and the abscissa represents milliliters of effluent volume.

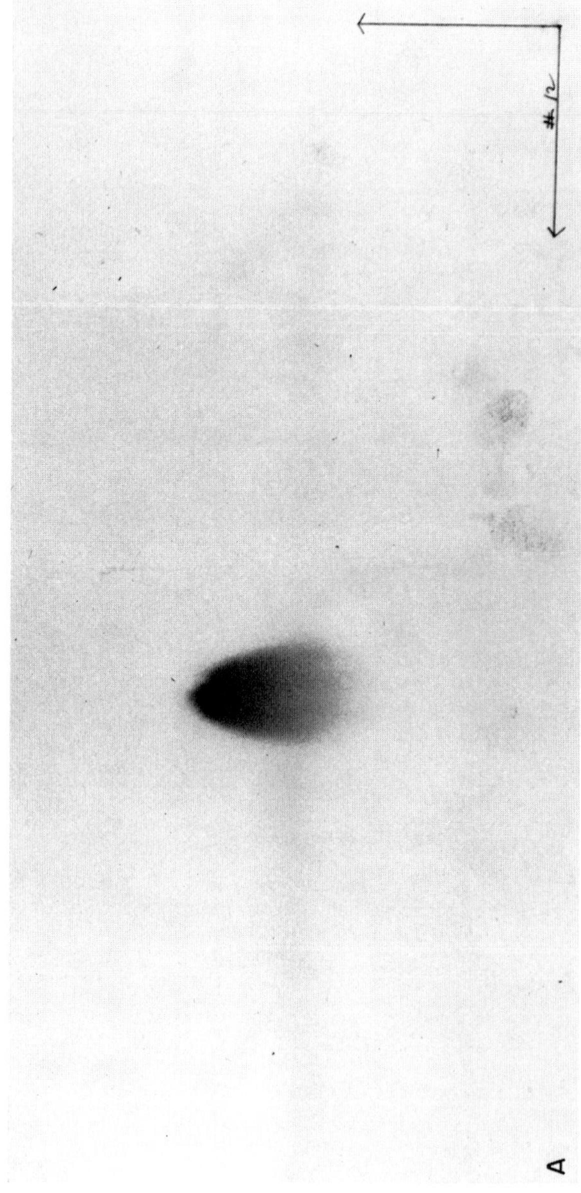
#12
A

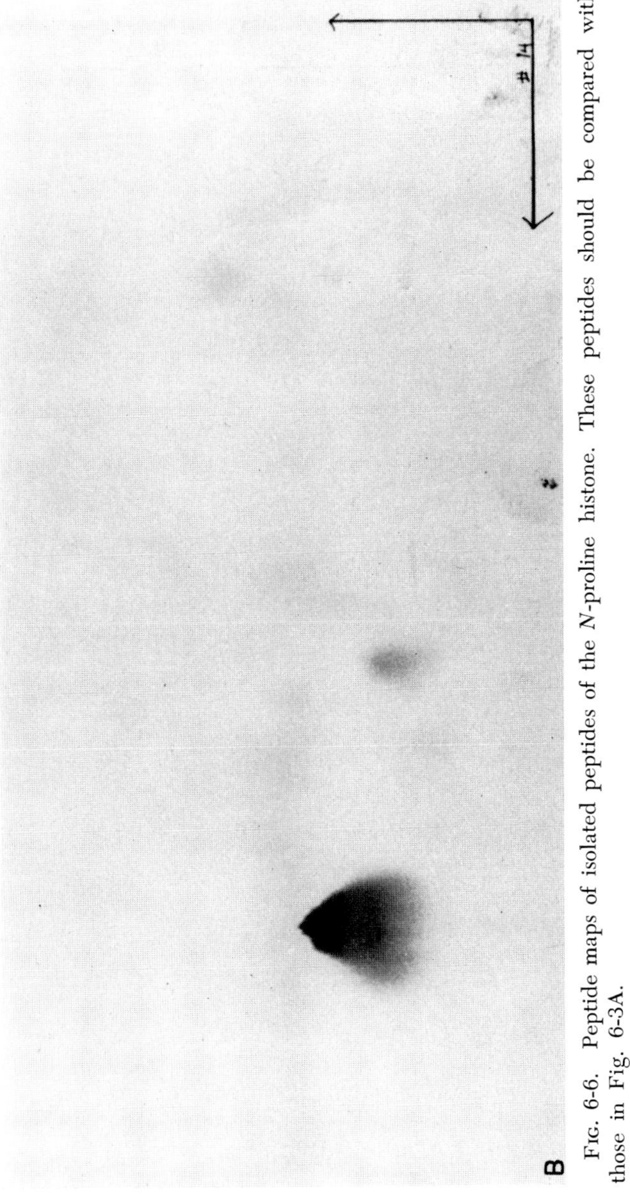


FIG. 6-6. Peptide maps of isolated peptides of the *N*-proline histone. These peptides should be compared with those in Fig. 6-3A.

TABLE 6-IV

ELEMENTARY AMINO ACID ANALYSIS OF SOME PEPTIDES OF THE *N*-PROLINE HISTONE OBTAINED BY CHROMATOGRAPHY ON DOWEX 50 COLUMNS

|  |  |
|---|---|
| 1. | $Ala_3$, $Asp_2$, $Glu_2$, $Gly_2$, $Phe_2$, Pro, Ser, Thr, Val, Lys |
| 2. | $Ala_2$, $Glu_2$, Gly, $Leu_3$, Pro, Lys |
| 3. | Ala, $Glu_2$, Gly, $Leu_3$, Pro, Lys |
| 4. | Ala, Asp, Glu, Gly, His, Ser, Lys |
| 5. | $Glu_2$, Gly, Pro, $Ser_4$, $Tyr_2$, $Val_2$, Lys |
| 6. | $Ala_2$, $Pro_2$, Ser, Lys |
| 7. | Ala, Glu, Gly, Lys |
| 8. | Asp, Gly, Ser, Thr, Lys |
| 9. | Ala, Asp, Gly, Ser, Lys |
| 10. | $Ala_2$, Glu, Gly, Ileu, Ser, Arg |
| 11. | Ileu, $Ser_2$, $Thr_2$, Arg |
| 12. | Ala, Thr, Val, Lys |
| 13. | Ala, Val, Lys |
| 14. | Lys |
| 15. | Ala, Glu, Lys |
| 16. | Ser, Thr, Tyr, Lys |
| 17. | Asp, Lys |

TABLE 6-V

AMINO ACID SEQUENCES OF SOME PEPTIDES OF THE *N*-PROLINE HISTONE

|  |  |
|---|---|
| 2. | Leu·Pro·Ala (Ala, $Glu_2$, Gly, $Leu_2$) Lys |
| 9. | Asp·Ala·Ser·Gly·Lys |
| 12. | Ala·Val·Thr·Lys |
| 13. | Ala·Val·Lys |
| 14. | Lys |
| 15. | Ala·Glu·Lys |
| 17. | Asp·Lys |

results are only a beginning of studies on the structure of the *N*-proline histone, it may be hoped that further structural information on the *N*-proline histone will be obtained in the near future (21).

## The 2a or *N*-Acetylalanine Histone Fraction

In the earlier preparations of fraction 2a or the *N*-acetylalanine histone, considerable impurity was found. However, by altering the conditions for precipitation of this fraction (13), the purity of the preparation was improved to the point that only a single peak appeared on ultracentrifugation. With this product, studies are under way similar to those described for the *N*-proline histone, although they have not advanced as far.

The peptide map or "fingerprint" of the *N*-acetylalanine histone is quite different from that of the *N*-proline histone, as might be expected from its very different amino acid composition (Chapter II). The solvent system described by Phillips and Simson (15) was satisfactory as the organic phase used for chromatography of the peptides obtained by tryptic hydrolysis of the protein of fraction 2a although different solvent systems were necessary for satisfactory "fingerprinting" of the peptides of the *N*-proline histone. Since a number of peptides were not completely separated by the "fingerprinting" procedure, it was not possible to determine the composition of all the peptides. Tables 6-VI and 6-VII present a compilation of the elementary amino

TABLE 6-VI
ELEMENTARY AMINO ACID COMPOSITION OF PEPTIDES OF FRACTION F2a WALKER TUMOR OBTAINED BY PEPTIDE MAPPING

| | |
|---|---|
| 2. | Ala, Glu, Gly, Lys, Thr |
| 3. | $Ala_2$, Gly, Lys, Pro, Ser |
| 4. | Asp, Lys |
| 5. | Arg, Glu, $Gly_3$, Lys |
| 7. | $Glu_2$, Lys, Ser |
| 8. | Ala, $Arg_2$, $Thr_2$ |
| 9. | $Gly_2$, Lys, Val |
| 10. | Glu, His, Lys, Ser, Thr |
| 11. | Gly, Lys |
| 12. | Ala, Lys |
| 13. | Ala, $Arg_2$ |
| 14. | Arg, Lys |

TABLE 6-VII
ELEMENTARY AMINO ACID COMPOSITION OF PEPTIDES OF FRACTION F2a CALF THYMUS OBTAINED BY PEPTIDE MAPPING

| | |
|---|---|
| 1. | $Ala_2$, Glu, Lys, $Thr_2$, Val |
| 2. | Ala, Arg, Glu, Gly, Thr |
| 4. | Ala, Arg, Glu, Gly, Lys, Thr |
| 5. | Arg, Glu, $Gly_2$, Lys |
| 6. | Arg, Glu, Gly |
| 7. | Arg, $Gly_3$, Lys |
| 8. | Ala, Arg, Gly |
| 9. | Ala, Arg, Gly, Leu |
| 10. | Arg, Gly, Lys |
| 11. | Arg, Gly |
| 12. | Arg, $Gly_3$, Lys |
| 13. | Ala, $Arg_2$, Lys |
| 14. | $Arg_2$, Lys |

acid compositions of peptides of 2a fractions of the Walker tumor and calf thymus. Of the thirteen peptides of the 2a fraction and the seventeen of the *N*-proline histone for which elementary amino acid analysis was established,[1] none were identical (3, 13).

These data were derived from studies in which peptides were recovered from a number of "peptide maps." As indicated previously, they are subject to a number of types of errors. Nonetheless, it is interesting that a number of quantitative and qualitative differences were found in the peptides obtained from the Walker tumor and the calf thymus.

*Comparative Analyses of Amino Acid Sequences in Histone Fractions.* The compositions of peptides derived from various histone fractions supports the impression from studies on amino acid compositions (Chapter II) that the histones differ markedly in their sequences of amino acids. This point is emphasized by the finding that none of the peptides of fraction 2a were identical to those of the *N*-proline histone. At present it is not reasonable to assume that there is regularity in the structure of histones, and along with this, it is difficult to visualize a regularity of linkage of histones to DNA. Variability of spacing of basic residues along the amino acid chain of the histones makes it unlikely that the histones serve simply to neutralize phosphate groups of the deoxyribosephosphate chain. However, a number of new questions arise, such as (i) What are the sites of linkage of DNA and the various histones? (ii) Are histones bound to DNA by multiple sites on the histone molecule, or by as few as three points, as has been suggested for many enzymes? (iii) Can a single histone link a given DNA strand at different sites on the histone molecule? (iv) What are

[1] To facilitate coding of the peptides, the amino acids were assigned the numbers recorded in the accompanying code for amino acids.

Code for Amino Acids

| | | | |
|---|---|---|---|
| Alanine | 1 | Lysine | 11 |
| Arginine | 2 | Methionine | 12 |
| Aspartic acid | 3 | Phenylalanine | 13 |
| Glutamic acid | 4 | Proline | 14 |
| Cysteine | 5 | Serine | 15 |
| Cystine | 6 | Threonine | 16 |
| Glycine | 7 | Tyrosine | 17 |
| Histidine | 8 | Tryptophan | 18 |
| Isoleucine | 9 | Valine | 19 |
| Leucine | 10 | | |

the dissociation constants for histones and artificial DNA molecules, such as the poly dA, poly dAT, poly dG, and other macromolecular entities? One may anticipate that the information emerging from studies on primary structure of histones will provide a basis for some understanding of the relationships of histones to binding sites on DNA.

## References


1. Brown, H., Sanger, F., and Kitai, R.: The structure of pig and sheep insulins. *Biochem. J.* **60**: 556-565 (1955).
2. Busch, H., Hnilica, L. S., Chien, S. C., Davis, J. R., and Taylor, C. W.: Isolation and purification of RP2-L, a nuclear protein fraction of the Walker 256 carcinosarcoma. *Cancer Res.* **22**: 637-645 (1962).
3. Busch, H., Steele, W. J., Hnilica, L. S., Taylor, C. W., and Mavioglu, H.: Biochemistry of histones and the cell cycle. *J. Cellular Comp. Physiol.* **62** (Suppl. 1): 95-110 (1963).
4. Davis, J. R., and Busch, H.: Chromatographic analysis of radioactive cationic nuclear proteins of tissues of tumor-bearing rats. *Cancer Res.* **19**: 1157-1166 (1959).
5. Davis, J. R., and Busch, H.: Chromatographic analysis of cationic nuclear proteins of a number of neoplastic tissues. *Cancer Res.* **20**: 1208-1213 (1960).
6. Felix, K., Fischer, H., and Krekels, A.: Protamines and nucleoprotamines. *Progr. Biophys. Biophys. Chem.* **6**: 1-23 (1956).
7. Hirs, C. H. W., Stein, W. H., and Moore, S.: The amino acid composition of ribonuclease. *J. Biol. Chem.* **211**: 941-950 (1954).
8. Hirs, C. H. W., Stein, W. H., and Moore, S.: Peptides obtained by chymotryptic hydrolysis of performic acid-oxidized ribonuclease. A. Partial structural formula for the oxidized protein. *J. Biol. Chem.* **221**: 151-169 (1956).
9. Hnilica, L. S., and Busch, H.: Fractionation of the histones of the Walker 256 carcinosarcoma by combined chemical and chromatographic techniques. *J. Biol. Chem.* **238**: 918-924 (1963).
10. Hnilica, L. S., Taylor, C. W., and Busch, H.: Analysis of peptides of the moderately lysine rich histone fraction, 2b, of the Walker tumor and other tissues. *Exptl. Cell Res. Suppl.* **9**: 367-375 (1963).
11. Konigsberg, W., Goldstein, J., and Hill, R. J.: The structure of human hemoglobin. VII. The digestion of the β-chain of human hemoglobin with pepsin. *J. Biol. Chem.* **238**: 2028-2033 (1963).
12. Matsubara, H., and Smith, E. L.: Human heart cytochrome c. Chymotryptic peptides, tryptic peptides and the complete amino acid sequence. *J. Biol. Chem.* **238**: 2732-2753 (1963).
13. Mavioglu, H., and Busch, H.: Unpublished data.

13a. Murray, K.: The heterogeneity of histones. In "The Nucleohistones" (J. Bonner and P. Ts'o, eds.), pp. 21-35. Holden-Day, San Francisco, California, 1964.

14. Phillips, D. M. P.: The presence of acetyl groups in histones. *Biochem. J.* **87**: 258-263 (1963).
15. Phillips, D. M. P., and Simson, P.: Identification of some peptides from an arginine-rich histone and their bearing on the structure of deoxyribonucleohistone. *Biochem. J.* **82**: 236-241 (1962).
16. Ryle, A. P., Sanger, F., Smith, L. F., and Kitai, R.: The disulphide bonds of insulin. *Biochem. J.* **60**: 541-565 (1955).
17. Sanger, F.: The free amino groups of insulin. *Biochem. J.* **39**: 507-515 (1945).
18. Schroeder, W. A., Shelton, J. R., Shelton, J. B., Cormick, J., and Jones, R. T.: The amino acid sequence of the $\gamma$-chain of human fetal hemoglobin. *Biochemistry* **2**: 992-1008 (1963).
19. Smith, D. G., Stein, W. H., and Moore, S.: The sequence of amino acid residues in bovine pancreatic ribonuclease: revisions and confirmations. *J. Biol. Chem.* **238**: 227-234 (1963).
20. Spackman, D. H., Stein, W. H., and Moore, S.: Automatic recording apparatus for use in the chromatography of amino acids. *Anal. Chem.* **30**: 1190-1205 (1958).
21. Starbuck, W. C., Taylor, C. W., Arendell, J. P., and Busch, H.: Structural studies on the N-proline histone (f2b) of calf thymus. *Federation Proc.* **23**: 370 (1964).

# CHAPTER VII

# Metabolism of Histones



## Introduction

*Site of Histone Synthesis.* The subject of the metabolism of histones includes the biosynthesis of histones and the catabolism of histones. Generally, measurements on the rates of these processes have been made by studies on the incorporation of isotope into histones and turnover rates of the histones. The direct study of the biosynthesis of histones has been difficult because systems for *in vitro* cell-free synthesis of histones have not been developed. In part, this is because the site of synthesis of most histones is not yet defined although recent studies (42a) have shown that the nucleus is the site of synthesis of lysine-rich histones. It has been suggested that in the mammalian cell the site of synthesis of histones is the nucleus since histones are not found to any significant degree in the cytoplasm (13, 14).

Recently, Reid and Cole (42a) have reported that isolated calf thymus nuclei incorporated labeled amino acids into very lysine-rich histones. The incorporation in the very lysine-rich histones by isolated nuclei was suggested to reflect actual synthesis of histones since the lysine was in peptide linkage. This is the first direct evidence for synthesis of histones in the nucleus.

In most mammalian cells, there is a very low concentration of nuclear ribosomes on which protein synthesis is believed to take place (55). The only exception to this general rule is the calf thymus, in which the nucleus is a good source of ribosomes (5, 57–59). Among the other possible nuclear sites of synthesis of histones are the chromatin, the nucleolus, and the nuclear ribonucleoprotein network. One cellular area that has been neglected in studies on biosynthesis of histones is the perinuclear ribonucleoprotein layer, which is particularly prominent in tumor cells which have a high rate of synthesis of histones (see page 60). Unfortunately, studies on histone synthesis in isolated systems have not yet been made in subfractions of such tissues as regenerating liver and thioacetamide-treated liver, in which the rate of histone synthesis is markedly accelerated (37).

*Nuclear Protein Synthesis in Nucleoli.* One of the reasons for the initiation of the studies on isolation of nucleoli in this laboratory (16, 24, 38) was the concept that if histones were to be synthesized on RNA templates, the nucleoli represented one possible place for such biosynthetic reactions. It is well known (12) that the nucleoli represent the single largest geographical concentration of RNA in the cell. However, it has not been possible to provide evidence for synthesis of histones in nucleoli either *in vivo* or *in vitro* (43), although labeling of acidic nucleolar proteins proceeds actively in the nucleolus (see Chapter VIII). The presence of ribonucleoproteins in the nucleus other than those in the nucleolus has been recognized from electron microscopic analysis (52, 53), and recently a network of ribonucleoproteins has been demonstrated that has been referred to as the nuclear ribonucleoprotein network (53). Thus far, however, direct evidence for a function of this network in synthesis of protein is not available.

The possibility that the nucleoli play a role in protein synthesis has been examined in plants by Birnstiel and Hyde (7), who provided evidence that rapid protein synthesis occurs *in vivo* and *in vitro* in nucleoli of cells of pea seedlings. These nucleoli are different from those of animal sources in a number of respects, the most important of which is that in the nucleolar preparation there are small DNA containing bodies that are referred to as "karyosomes" by Sankaranarayanan and Hyde (46). Whether these bodies or the ribonucleoprotein components of the nucleoli of plants are the sites of protein synthesis is not yet clear. It is not yet established whether the proteins produced by the plant nucleoli are histones.

*Protein Synthesis on Chromatin.* Another possibility is that histones are directly synthesized on chromatin. It is well established that the time of major histone synthesis is in the S-phase of the cell cycle at a time when DNA synthesis is either occurring or about to occur (17, 26, 31, 33, 41a). Sirlin and Knight (50) obtained autoradiographic evidence (Fig. 7-1) that there was labeling of protein with radioactive precursors, or at least uptake of labeled amino acids on the chromosomes in *Drosophila* or *Chironomus.* It is not yet clear whether these amino acids were utilized for synthesis of histones or other proteins and whether the labeling occurred directly on the chromosomes or labeled proteins were transferred to the chromosomes. In Prescott's (42) studies on synthesis of histones in *Euplotes* he noted that a wave of DNA and histone synthesis occurred simultaneously. The synthesis of both DNA and histone were closely related events. He suggested that when DNA was involved in replication it did not support RNA synthesis. Moreover, RNA apparently played no role in synthesis of either DNA or histone. These results and the experiment of Honig and Rabinowitz (32) suggest that histones may be directly synthesized on DNA. The latter workers showed that actinomycin D blocked labeling of histones in ascites cells. Under the conditions of their experiment, there was little change in the synthesis of cytoplasmic proteins and the nonhistone nuclear proteins. Such data, which suggest that histones may be synthesized on chromosomal templates or on nuclear ribonucleoproteins that turn over rapidly, are more consistent with findings of this laboratory and other laboratories that fractions corresponding to the histones are not present in any of the cytoplasmic fractions of tumor cells or other cells.

*Synthesis of Basic Proteins on Microsomes.* In a study on the release of proteins from ribosomes, Griffin *et al.* (28) reported that ribosomal proteins of Novikoff ascites cells were separable into three fractions by sedimentation, precipitation with TCA, and precipitation with TCA and tungstate. The proteins they obtained in the sedimentable fraction had a high lysine and arginine content. The fractions that were precip-

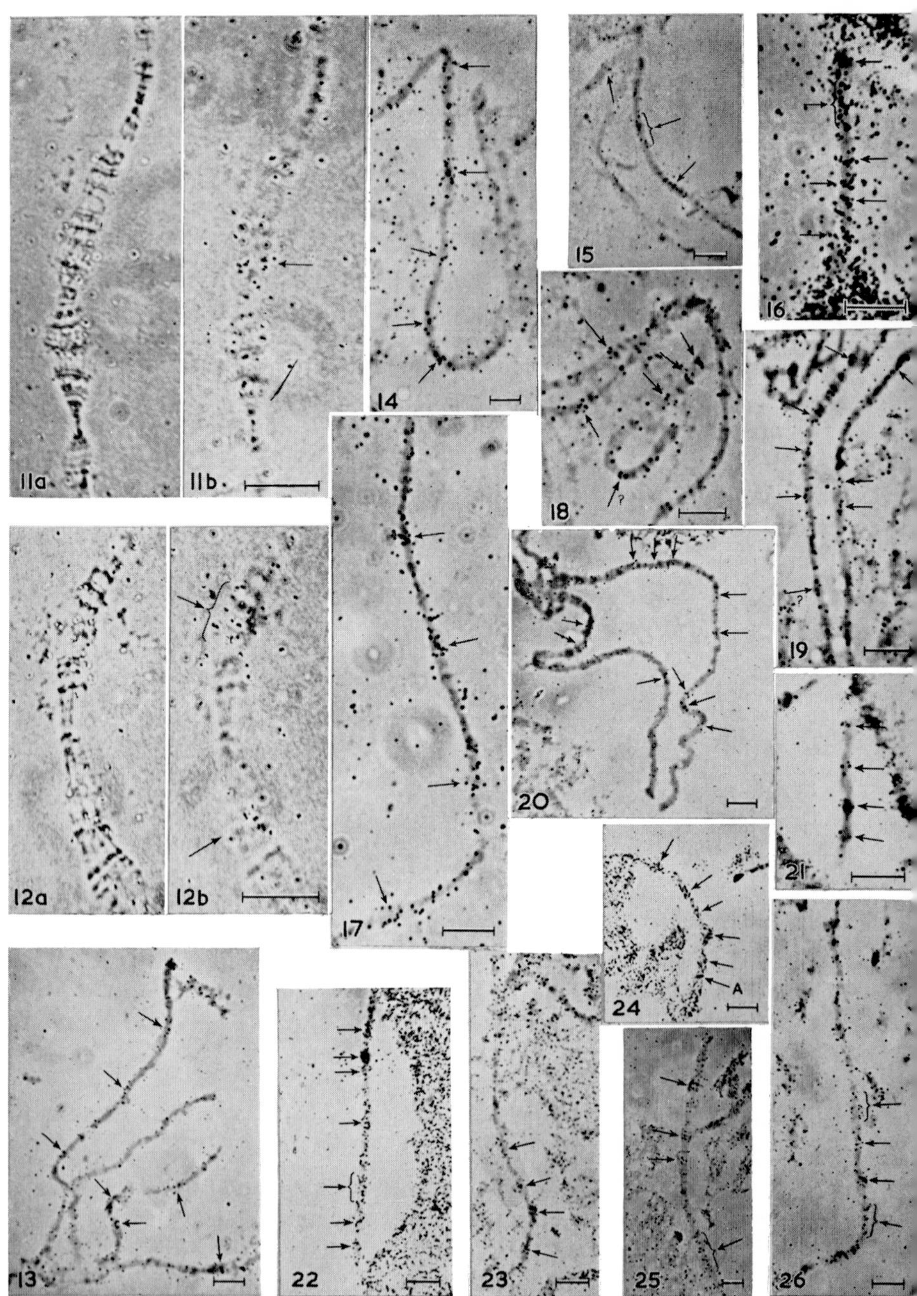


FIG. 7-1. Uptake of labeled amino acids on the chromosomes of *Drosophila*. [From Sirlin and Knight (50).]

itated had an extremely high arginine content, i.e., in these proteins, lysine accounted for 20 and 30%, respectively, of the total moles of amino acids. Although histones that correspond to these fractions are not known, this finding is a provocative one and suggests that ribosomes have a capacity for producing basic proteins. From all the studies on the various nuclear and perinuclear elements, it would seem that almost all possess the potentiality for protein synthesis. Thus far, the ones actually involved in synthesis of histones are obscure.

*Mechanism of Histone Synthesis.* The synthesis of basic nuclear proteins was reported to be blocked *in vitro* by puromycin (47). This finding suggests that the underlying mechanism of synthesis of basic proteins is the same as that for synthesis of other proteins. However, Konikova *et al.* (35) have reported that the ratios of uptake of different labeled amino acids in the histones were independent of the concentration of those amino acids in the histones. Their finding suggested that the histones differ in rates of turnover or that the mechanism of histone synthesis differs from that of synthesis of other proteins. Alternate mechanisms of synthesis were not specified.[1]

## Synthesis of Histones in Dividing Cells

Although the histones are apparently not continuous entities of the chromosomes, they are closely associated with DNA, as has been noted in previous chapters. Accordingly, it is not surprising that the most active rates of histone synthesis have been reported in cells that are actively engaged in mitosis, such as tumor cells and cells of the regenerating liver. In resting tissues such as the normal liver, the rate of synthesis of histones is low. Evidence for differences in biosynthesis of histones was provided by studies on the uptake of labeled amino acids as shown in Table 7-I (13). Values for the overall labeling of the proteins of the cell and the labeling of the mitochondrial and microsomal proteins are presented for comparison with the values for labeling of the nuclear acid-insoluble proteins and the nuclear acid-soluble proteins that include the histones. There was considerable variation in the overall labeling of the proteins from tissue to tissue. The tissues with overall high labeling of their proteins are those generally regarded as being actively involved in protein synthesis, e.g., the intestine, pancreas, liver, and the tumors. Very low uptakes of isotope were noted for the proteins of the muscle, brain, and heart.

[1] Baer (6a) has suggested a possible elementary structure of messenger RNAs for synthesis of histones.

TABLE 7-I

SPECIFIC ACTIVITY OF TISSUE PROTEINS 1 HOUR AFTER INJECTION OF L-LYSINE-U-$C^{14}$[a]

| Tissue | Whole homogenate | Mitochondria | Microsomes | Cytoplasmic sap | Nuclear HCl-insoluble | Nuclear HCl-soluble |
|---|---|---|---|---|---|---|
| Walker tumor | 532 | 431 | 442 | 653 | 574 | 671 |
| Jensen tumor | 525 | 341 | 523 | 590 | 408 | 648 |
| Brain | 74 | 44 | 76 | 134 | 46 | 61 |
| Heart | 110 | 65 | 104 | 180 | 72 | 86 |
| Intestine | 500 | 459 | 692 | 703 | 384 | 578 |
| Kidney | 225 | 227 | 288 | 288 | 143 | 171 |
| Liver | 339 | 385 | 640 | 269 | 215 | 245 |
| Lung | 197 | 247 | 392 | 220 | 78 | 140 |
| Muscle | 27 | 22 | 25 | 34 | 29 | 30 |
| Pancreas | 1620 | 1935 | 1130 | 1010 | 397 | 379 |
| Spleen | 300 | 200 | 350 | 440 | 194 | 230 |
| Testis | 152 | 165 | 220 | 200 | 80 | 140 |
| Thymus | 191 | 116 | 158 | 277 | 164 | 111 |

[a] Values are counts per minute per milligram protein. The data represent averages of four experiments with pancreas; three experiments each with Walker tumor, Jensen tumor, intestine, skeletal muscle, spleen, and thymus; two experiments each with brain, heart, kidney, liver, lung, and testis. The specific activity of the proteins of the zymogen granules of the pancreas averaged 2900.

The specific activities of the nuclear acid-soluble proteins were highest in the intestine and the tumors. Comparative studies were not made on the bone marrow, which is also a site of active synthesis of new cells, because of the difficulty of obtaining satisfactory specimens of bone marrow from the rat. Correlated with their rapid protein synthesis, the tumors had a high rate of labeling of histones *in vivo*.

Similar data were obtained from *in vitro* studies. A higher overall

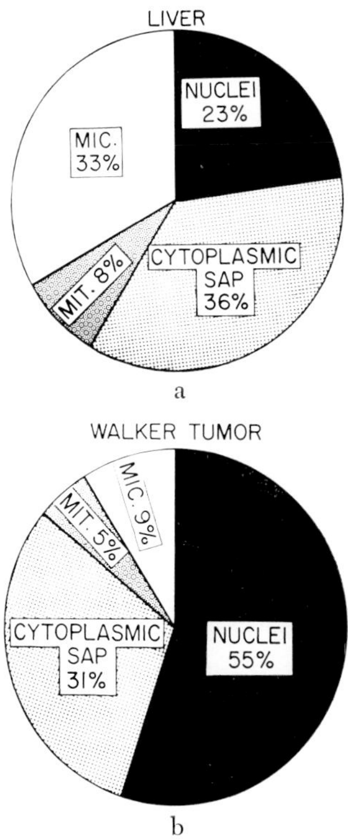


FIG. 7-2. Total isotope incorporation of L-aspartate-U-$C^{14}$ in proteins from liver and Walker 256 carcinosarcoma. Two hundred milligrams of liver or Walker tumor slices were incubated for 1 hour in Krebs-Ringer bicarbonate buffer containing 250,000 counts per minute of tracer and 20 μmoles glucose in a total volume of 3.2 ml. The gas phase was 95% $O_2$ and 5% $CO_2$. Following incubation, the slices were homogenized in 0.25 *M* sucrose and differentially fractionated. The data are expressed as percentage of the total isotope incorporated into protein of the tissue slices. The values represent averages of two experiments. Values obtained with the Walker 256 carcinosarcoma were duplicated in a single experiment with the Jensen sarcoma. The following abbreviations have been used: *MIT.*, mitochondria; *MIC.*, microsomes. [From Davis and Busch (23).]

labeling of the nuclear proteins of tumor occurred in slice systems, as shown by determination of the fraction of the total labeled amino acid incorporated into proteins that was distributed to nuclear proteins (14, 23, 54). Figure 7-2 shows that by comparison with the liver, a much higher percentage of amino acids utilized for protein synthesis went into nuclear protein in the Walker tumor. A comparison of the labeling of histones as a percentage of total incorporation of labeled alanine and lysine into proteins in slices is shown in Table 7-II (14).

TABLE 7-II
ISOTOPE IN HISTONES AS PERCENTAGE OF TOTAL ISOTOPE IN PROTEINS[a]

| Tissue | Per cent |
|---|---|
| Walker 256 carcinosarcoma | 22.0 |
| Ehrlich ascites tumor (mouse) | 24.0 |
| Rat liver | 8.0 |
| Mouse liver | 7.1 |
| Regenerating liver (rat) | 7.7 |
| Rat kidney | 7.3 |
| Rat spleen | 6.5 |
| Rat brain | 7.7 |
| Mouse pancreas | 1.0 |

[a] The values represent the percentage in the histones of the total isotope incorporated into proteins of the cell suspensions or slices *in vitro*. The values for the L-alanine-U-$C^{14}$ and L-lysine-U-$C^{14}$ were not significantly different, hence the data are pooled. Cell suspensions or slices were incubated for 1 hour in Krebs-Ringer bicarbonate buffer. [From Busch *et al.* (14).]

Although there was a marked increase in the labeling of the histones of regenerating liver, there was little change in the overall distribution of the isotope into the proteins of this tissue (14, 37). Some comparative data on labeling of various cellular proteins in slices of the regenerating and normal rat liver as well as data for tissues of the mouse are presented in Fig. 7-3. It is evident that relative labeling of histones in dividing cells is much greater than in cells with active cytoplasmic protein synthesis.

*Overall Labeling of Proteins in Tissues in Vitro.* Studies on the kinetics of labeling of histones of the various tumors and other tissues *in vitro* revealed a high rate of labeling of proteins in tumor slices in comparison to other tissues studied (Fig. 7-4) in agreement with earlier experiments of Zamecnik *et al.* (60). When uptake of isotope into microsomal proteins was compared, the rate of labeling of the tumors

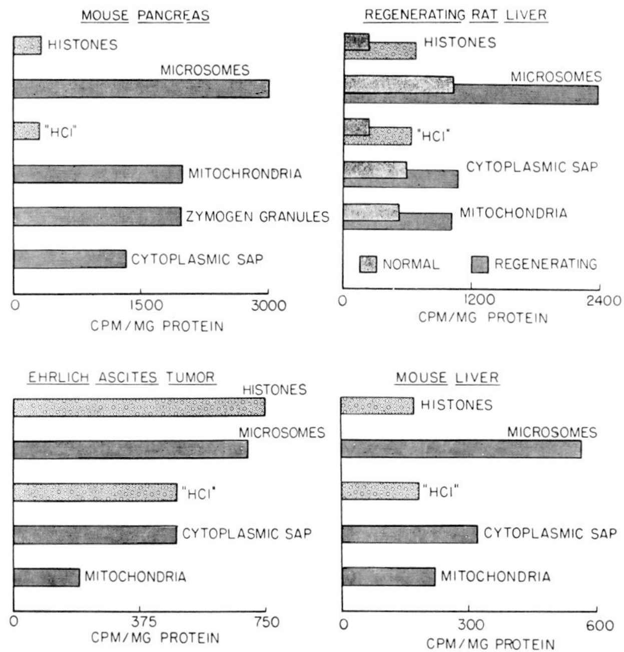


FIG. 7-3. Specific activities of intracellular proteins of mouse pancreas, mouse liver, regenerating rat liver (24 hours) and Ehrlich ascites mouse tumor after one hour of incubation with L-lysine-U-$C^{14}$. [From Busch *et al.* (14).]

was not higher than in tissues such as pancreas, spleen, and regenerating liver (Fig. 7-4). Comparison of the labeling of the histones of the tumors with those of other tissues showed a markedly greater labeling in these rapidly dividing cells (Fig. 7-4).

One problem in making comparisons between the tumors and the other tissues that have cells in division has to do with the relatively large number of dividing cells in the tumors. In regenerating liver, only a small number of cells undergo division at any time, and this is also true of the spleen and the intestine. In addition, these tissues synthesize so much protein that is not related to the process of cell division that specific activities must be interpreted carefully. With any isotope, it is now a general finding that specific activities of histones of tumors and other dividing tissues are greater than in nondividing tissues *in vitro*. Moreover, the relative labeling of histones to cytoplasmic proteins in tumors is greater than that of other tissues studied (17, 20, 21, 54).

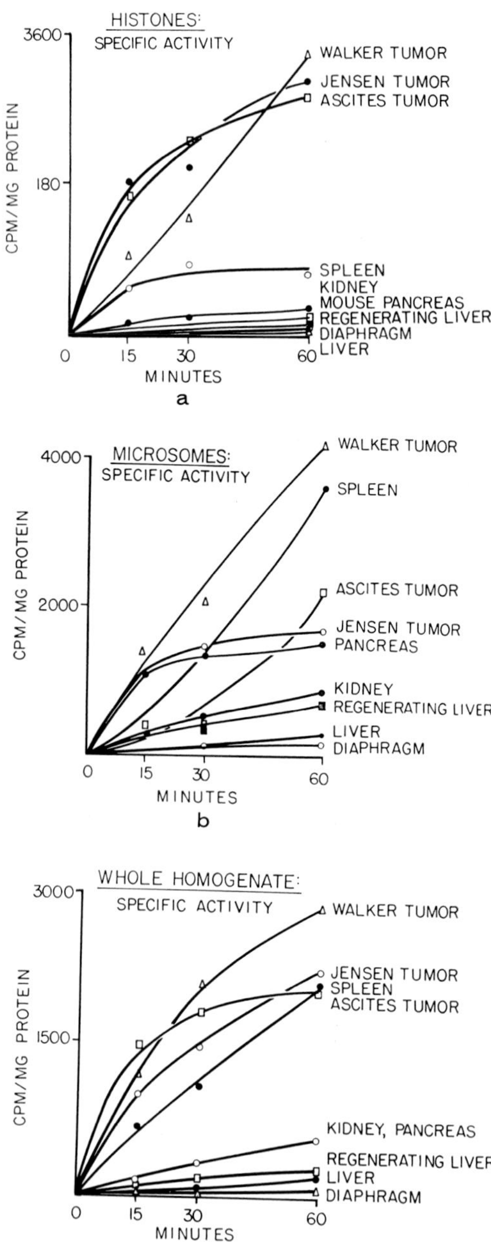


Fig. 7-4. Kinetics of labeling of proteins of tissues after incubation with L-arginine-U-$C^{14}$. [From Starbuck and Busch (54).]

Seed (48, 49) has suggested that synthesis of nuclear proteins in nontumor tissues is a discontinuous process that proceeds after a long delay following completion of telophase. On the other hand, in HeLa cells, nuclear protein synthesis was found to be continuous. He also found that RNA synthesis was continuous through the cell cycle; this finding does not agree with other studies on RNA synthesis (see page 236). The suggestion was made that deletion or alteration of a growth-controlling protein might permit continuous RNA and protein synthesis in tumor cells.

## Labeling of Histones *in Vivo*

Relatively little information has been obtained on the rates of labeling of individual histones *in vivo,* although information exists on the labeling of the acid-extractable nuclear proteins of a variety of tissues. The first studies on this subject were made by Daly *et al.* (22), who used $N^{15}$-glycine as a tracer and determined that the rate of labeling of the cytoplasmic proteins was much greater than that of the nuclear proteins in pancreas, liver, and kidney. They reported the finding, which has since been verified many times, that the acid-insoluble nuclear proteins of these nondividing tissues had a higher turnover rate than the acid-soluble nuclear proteins. Although the turnover of the latter proteins was small, it was significant. One of the critical problems of their study was the fact that they employed citric acid to purify the nuclei and, as a result, probably also extracted some of the histones. Their studies were carried out at intervals of 3–91 hours after administration of the isotope.

Because the studies of Brunish and Luck (10, 11) cast doubts on the meaningfulness of studies on the uptake of isotopically labeled amino acids into proteins, particularly histones, there was a long delay in further experiments on labeling of nuclear proteins. Actually, the studies of Brunish and Luck (10, 11) dealt primarily with the problems of adsorption of amino acids by proteins. In view of the studies of Borsook and others (8) that showed uptake of labeled amino acids into proteins of the liver within a few seconds after the tracer was administered, a number of workers set out to determine whether such labeling was due to nonenzymatic reactions. At one point the studies with release of labeled glycine from proteins by means of mercaptoethanol and other sulfhydryl reagents suggested that such labeling was indeed an artifact, although it may have reflected the formation of disulfide bonds of glutathione with sulfhydryls of proteins. Brunish and Luck (10, 11) noted that labeled glycine, phenylalanine, and alanine were adsorbed to histones. The uptake of labeled amino acid was dependent upon time, temperature, and the concentration of the tracer. The pH at which the maximal labeling of histones occurred was 8.7, and the rate of labeling was high even at 100°C. Although the adsorption was made much of by workers at that time, the total amount of isotope incorporated into the protein *in vitro* was very small, accounting for only 30 counts per minute per milligram of protein or 500 disintegrations per minute per milligram of protein. The findings of Brunish and Luck (10, 11) were verified by Konikova *et al.* (34); however, only a few per cent of the 500,000 counts added to the system were adsorbed onto the histones.

In later studies, Brunish and Luck (11) suggested that the problems of adsorption of labeled amino acids *in vitro* were minimized in studies *in vivo*. They determined the uptake of isotope of $C^{14}$-labeled alanine and phenylalanine into the histones and other nuclear proteins of rat livers at times ranging from one-half hour to 11 days after the isotope was injected. As found by others (22), the histones were the least radioactive of the proteins isolated. The acidic nuclear proteins also were found by Brunish and Luck (11) to be much more radioactive than histones. Smellie *et al.* (51) reported that the rate of labeling of the histones of the liver was very low also when $N^{15}$-glycine was injected into rats. The labeling of the other nuclear proteins approximated that of a number of cytoplasmic fractions.

## Labeling of Specific Histones *in Vivo*

***Labeling of Histone Fractions of Tumors.*** In view of the early report of Rotherham *et al.* (44) of a high rate of labeling of histones in a rat hepatoma and the reports from this laboratory of a high rate of labeling of histones in the Walker, Jensen, and Ehrlich ascites tumors (13, 15), it became of interest to compare the rates of labeling of the various histone subfractions obtained from rat liver, an example of a nondividing normal tissue and the Walker tumor, a neoplasm with a high rate of cell division. The data presented in Table 7-III indicate that in both tissues there is an inequality in the rate of labeling of the histones. Since lysine was used as a tracer in these studies (18), it is not surprising that on the basis of counts per minute per milligram of histone the rate of labeling of the F1 or very lysine-rich fraction was high in both the liver and the Walker tumor. Interestingly, the rate of labeling of lysine in protein was lowest for the very lysine-rich histones,

TABLE 7-III
SPECIFIC ACTIVITY OF VARIOUS HISTONE FRACTIONS

| | Walker tumor | | Ratio | Rat liver | | Ratio |
|---|---|---|---|---|---|---|
| Fraction | Cpm/mg | Cpm/μmole lysine | to F1 | Cpm/mg | Cpm/μmole lysine | to F1 |
| F1 | 830 | 360 | 1 | 90 | 40 | 1 |
| F2a | 400 | 540 | 1.5 | 50 | 70 | 1.8 |
| F2b | 540 | 470 | 1.3 | 80 | 70 | 1.8 |
| F3 | 460 | 700 | 2.0 | 50 | 80 | 2.0 |

[a] The data are counts per minute per milligram or per micromole 1 hour after intraperitoneal injection of 5 μc of L-lysine-U-$C^{14}$ into tumor-bearing rats (18).

which were associated previously (Chapter IV) with the lowest degrees of adherence to cation exchangers, with adherence to GC-rich DNA, and with the highest relative content of proline. On the basis of counts per minute per micromole of lysine in the protein, the highest rate of labeling was found in the "arginine-rich" fraction 3 in both the tumor and the liver. The absolute specific activity of the histones in the tumor was 7–9 times that of the histones of the liver. The ratio of specific activity of the histones of fraction 3 to the histones of the F1 group was 2 in both the tumor and the liver. The relative specific activities of the slightly lysine-rich histones of fraction 2a and 2b were quite different in the liver and the Walker tumor. In both cases, however, their rates of labeling were lower than the "arginine-rich" fraction 3.

*Comparative Labeling of Histones and Other Nuclear Proteins of Tumors.* Holbrook *et al.* (31) compared labeling of proteins in various fractions obtained from hepatomas and normal liver by a salt extraction technique (55). They found histones in each of the fractions, but noted that there was considerable cross contamination. With glycine as a tracer, they found that the specific activity of tumor histones was somewhat greater than that of the liver histones (15). However, they noted that the rate of labeling of the histones was equivalent to that of the nuclear globulins and glycoproteins in the tumors but was much less in the normal liver. Samarina (45) also showed that the specific activities of the nonhistone nuclear proteins were considerably greater in the liver than were the specific activities of the histones. In the tumors, the specific activities of both histone and nonhistone proteins were very similar.

Previous studies (13, 15) had shown that the overall uptake of lysine into the proteins of the Walker tumor was 1.5–2 times that of the liver and that the labeling of the acid-soluble nuclear proteins was about three times greater in the Walker tumor than in the liver. Recent studies (18, 55) have confirmed these earlier experiments. These data are of interest because they suggest that there is a relatively high turnover of the histones in the liver cells even though they are not dividing. Piha and Waelsch (41) have reported that the half-life of the liver histones was 18 days in mice. This was considerably less than the half-life of histones of the brain, which was estimated at 52 days. The turnover rate of histones was lower than that of any other protein fraction measured in their study.

*Synthesis of Hemoglobin in Nuclei.* Evidence for nuclear synthesis of other proteins has been provided in studies on hemoglobin. Tooze and Davies (56) found hemoglobin in chromosomal regions of the newt *Triturus*. Hammel and Bessman (29) have reported that in pigeon red cells hemoglobin synthesis is a nuclear function and, as has been pointed out in pages 10-12, globin is similar to histones in amino acid analysis. Intranuclear synthesis of hematin has also been demonstrated in chick embryo cells (46a).

## Fraction of Total Histone Turning Over in One Day

A calculation of the turnover of the histones of the liver can be made if it is assumed that the labeling of the histones is essentially linear for a period of $\frac{1}{4}$ to $\frac{1}{2}$ hour following injection of the tracer and that the incorporation of isotope reflects biosynthetic rather than exchange reactions. Evidence for the former has been obtained in both *in vivo*

TABLE 7-IV

CALCULATION OF HISTONE TURNOVER

| | |
|---|---|
| 1. Specific activity of precursor | = 10 mc/mmole lysine or<br>= 10 μc/μmole lysine<br>7,500,000 cpm/μmole lysine |
| 2. Specific activity of product | = 500 cpm/mg protein or per μmole lysine in 1 hour or<br>12,000 cpm/mg protein or μmole lysine in 24 hours |
| 3. Total specific activity: if the precursor pool was 20 times that of injected lysine, total specific activity would be 240,000 cpm/mg protein or μmole lysine | |
| 4. This value, which is approximately 3% of the specific activity of the precursor, suggests that 3% of the histones turn over per day in the normal rat liver | |

and *in vitro* studies (15, 18, 54). In the liver at 1 hour, the specific activity of histones approximates 500 cpm/mg. If the histones were labeled at a linear rate for 24 hours the specific activity would be 12,000 cpm/mg and 12,000 cpm/μmole of lysine (Table 7-IV). This would approximate a total specific activity of the lysine of 16 microcuries (μc) per mmole (1 μc = 750,000 cpm in the system employed). The actual specific activity of the lysine utilized in these experiments was 10 mc/mmole. In 24 hours, the minimal turnover of histones would be (16/10,000) × 100 or 0.16% in the liver. If the actual precursor pool was 20 times the pool of injected lysine, the turnover would approximate 3% per day, which is about the value found by Piha and Waelsch (41).

In the Walker tumor, the calculated specific activity of the histones was approximately 8 times that of the liver, and the increment in the proteins would be approximately twofold in view of the increasing mass of the tumor. From these data and estimates of a similar pool size to that of the liver it could be calculated that a minimal turnover of the histones would be 52% in the Walker tumor. Evidence that this value is low emerges from the obvious fact that the Walker tumor is doubling in size at the time of these experiments and hence the calculated value is approximately 50% too small. The low value is not surprising in view of the fact that the calculations are not based on precisely determined pool sizes for the lysine in the peritoneal cavity, blood, or individual tissue. Even with the potential errors, the data would still indicate a substantial flux in the histones of the liver, a tissue which has been shown by Brown (9, 27) and others to have a very stable DNA in the sense that there is a very low turnover of the purine bases. This turnover of histones may be related to the relatively slow rate at which the liver reacts to such biological stimuli as hepatectomy, although it may be the mechanism of adaptability to environmental change.

*Meaning of Turnover of Histones in Nondividing Cells.* The continued synthesis of histones in cells of the liver suggests that they are not part of the stable genetic machinery. Rather, the histones would appear to be temporary members of the genetic apparatus; hence they may be related to its function rather than the transmission of hereditary characteristics. If histones are biosynthesized at finite rates in the liver, it would seem logical that they would be replacing histones that are lost from the genome. If this is the case, then it is logical to postulate an equilibrium between DNA and histones that is governed by the affinity of the histones for DNA:

$$\text{DNP} \underset{k_2}{\overset{k_1}{\rightleftarrows}} (\text{histone}_x)^{+} + (\text{DNA})^{-} \qquad (1)$$

In Eq. (1), histone$_x$ is the particular histone fraction and $k_1$ and $k_2$ are the velocity constants for the dissociation and association reactions of the DNP (deoxyribonucleoprotein) complex. Evidence that these constants vary for specific histones is not available from evidence other than the rates of biosynthesis of the histones. However, the evidence that the very lysine-rich histones are different in their affinity for DNA would also serve to support this idea. Just why these histones with the apparent lowest affinity for DNA would be least rapidly biosynthesized remains unclear.

It should not be presumed that there is turnover of histones in all nondividing cells. Allfrey and Mirsky (6) reported that there was no histone synthesis in avian erythrocytes or in reticulocytes. They also found that there was no turnover of DNA as would be expected in these cells (see also page 6).

## When Are Histones Synthesized in the Cell Cycle?

The problem of ascertaining the rates of synthesis of DNA and histones has been one of considerable difficulty. Most of the methods that would be of interest are those that involve the simultaneous division of large numbers of cells or those that involve autoradiographic analysis of the rates of biosynthesis of DNA and histones. In mammalian systems, it is difficult to achieve synchrony of cell division, perhaps even more so than it is to achieve synchrony of cell division in bacteria. In addition, autoradiographic analysis of biosynthesis of histones has been difficult because of the problems associated with differentiation of synthesis of histones from synthesis of other nuclear proteins by uptake of an individual amino acid.

Holbrook *et al.* (26, 30, 31) attempted to learn more about the relationship of biosynthesis of histones to that of DNA. Their study was of particular importance because earlier experiments that simply involved cytochemical stains (1–4) led to a conclusion that the synthesis of histones proceeded simultaneously with the synthesis of DNA. There were few or no biochemical data to justify this claim and, as indicated previously, continued turnover of histones has been found in cells that are apparently not synthesizing DNA (18).

Holbrook *et al.* (26, 30) utilized the regenerating liver as a test for the timing of the biosynthesis of histones. They noted that the first peak of mitosis occurred at 32 hours after the hepatectomy and that the biosynthesis of RNA, DNA, and histones was not simultaneous. As shown in Fig. 7-5, the initial event following the hepatectomy appears to be increased biosynthesis of RNA; the data in this figure are not completely satisfactory on this point inasmuch as the biosynthesis of some proteins other than the histones apparently increased at this time. However, maximal labeling of RNA occurred at approximately 20 hours after hepatectomy. By comparison, maximal labeling of most of the histones occurred at a later time, i.e., about 22 hours. Interestingly, other nuclear proteins such as those of the globulin fraction (see Chapter VIII) were maximally labeled 19 hours after hepatectomy. In this study, little difference was found between the rates at which the biosynthesis of histones occurred, i.e., maximal labeling was found for all the histone fractions at 22 hours after hepatectomy. Although the histones were separated by Holbrook *et al.* (30, 31) into three fractions which differed in specific activity from one another at the various time points, their fractionation scheme differs from the one reported in Chapter III; hence it is difficult to establish precisely the components present in their fractions. However, each of their fractions contained a mixture of proteins.

The most interesting point of the paper of Holbrook *et al.* (30) dealt with the labeling of the DNA in comparison to the labeling of the histones. As indicated in Fig. 7-5, a sharp peak of incorporation of labeled adenine into DNA was found at 26 hours after hepatectomy. The time reported for maximal labeling of DNA (30) differed somewhat from other values reported in the literature (19), possibly because only one-third of the liver was excised. However, the chief point is that they found the maximal rate of DNA synthesis to occur after maximal rates of synthesis of RNA and histones had occurred (19).

Irvin *et al.* (33) suggested that the increased synthesis of RNA was necessary for the biosynthesis of enzymes and other proteins involved in cell division. The synthesis of the histones was related to their possible role (see Chapter V) in the suppression of synthesis of RNA. It was suggested (33) that the synthesis of histones results in the shutting off of some further synthesis of RNA in an intermediate stage of cell division. They also suggested that the increase in histones resulted

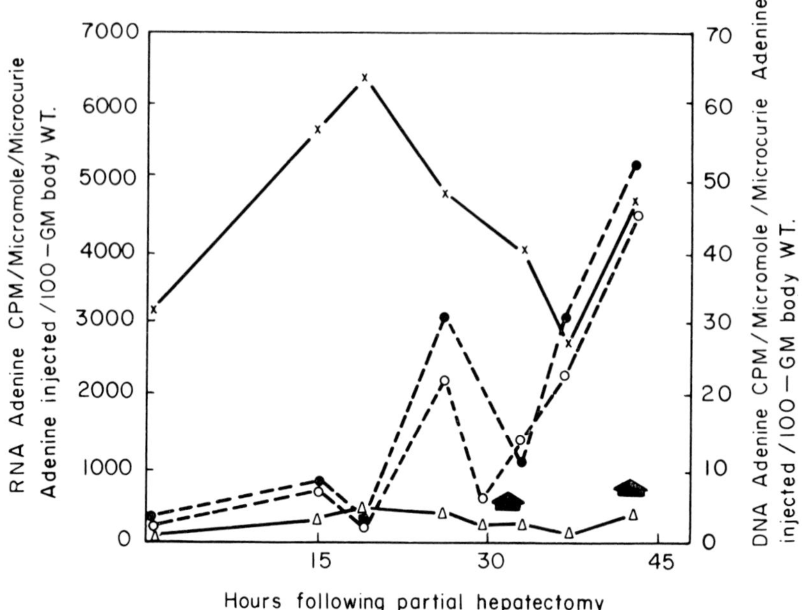


FIG. 7-5(A). Specific activities of adenine in nucleic acids at various times after partial hepatectomy. One hour before the animals were sacrificed, adenine-8-$C^{14}$ was injected intraperitoneally. △, Cytoplasmic RNA; ○, DNA II; ●, DNA III; ×, nuclear RNA. Arrows indicate time of mitotic peaks.

in an increased biosynthesis of DNA. The possibility exists that during mitosis the synthesis of histones ceases, and "extra" histone formed earlier is either degraded or modified so that after mitosis, the normal ratio of DNA to histones results.

Another possible explanation for these experimental results is that histones "lead" DNA synthesis, or that histones represent an essential component of the chromosomes that must be laid down first. Neither of the possibilities has been tested. However, the data make it quite clear that the older assumption of simultaneous synthesis of DNA and histone is no longer tenable.

Dissociation of synthesis of histones and DNA was also reported by Lindner *et al.* (36), who found that histones continued to increase in amount in tumor cells treated with 5-fluorouracil. The nuclei of these cells continued to increase in size, but the amount of DNA did not increase. In tobacco cells it was also found that histone synthesis and accumulation continued in the absence of DNA synthesis in 5-fluorodeoxyuridine-treated cells (26a).

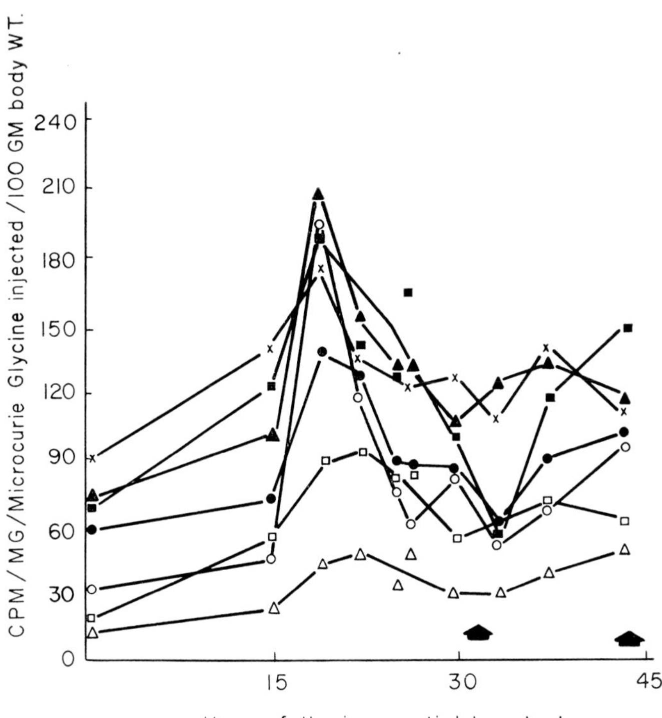


(B) Specific activities of nuclear proteins at various times after partial hepatectomy. One hour before the animals were sacrificed, glycine-1-$C^{14}$ was injected intraperitoneally. ○, Histone I; △, Histone II; □, Histone III; ●, Protein I; ▲, Protein II; ■, Protein III; ×, total cytoplasmic protein. Arrows indicate time of mitotic peaks.

## Catabolism of Histones

Studies on the sites of catabolism of histones have not been carried out as yet, possibly because the evidence that histones turn over *in vivo* was obtained only recently. However, it would appear that histones could be readily destroyed by the intranuclear proteases that are present in almost all histone preparations. Dounce and Umana (25) have analyzed the proteolytic activity of nuclei of rat liver. They found a variety of peaks of maximal activity of the proteolytic enzymes with respect to pH, although at pH 5.8 there was minimal or no proteolytic activity. Evidence that the proteolytic activity resulted in solubilization of the histones was also presented and when proteolytic activity was kept to a minimum, the amount of soluble histone was very low. In view of the activity of these proteolytic enzymes at pH 7, which is a physiologically meaningful pH, it is apparent that these enzymes could serve to hydrolyze the histones.

Phillips and Johns (39, 40) reported that histones prepared from calf thymus by acid extraction contained a proteinase that resulted in the production of an increased number of $NH_2$-terminal alanine, lysine, and glycine residues in the histones. The increase was particularly notable at pH 7–8. As was found for other proteolytic enzymes, such as trypsin and chymotrypsin, the proteinase associated with the histones was inhibited by diisopropylfluorophosphate. This contaminating proteinase has been a nuisance to workers interested in isolation of the histones, but its function in catabolism of the histones remains to be defined, as is also the case for the proteases studied by Dounce and Umana (25).

## References


1. Alfert, M.: Chemical differentiation of nuclear proteins during spermatogenesis in the salmon. *J. Biophys. Biochem. Cytol.* **2**: 109-114 (1956).
2. Alfert, M.: Some cytochemical contributions to genetic chemistry. *In* "The Chemical Basis of Heredity" (W. D. McElroy and B. Glass, eds.), pp. 186-194. Johns Hopkins Press, Baltimore, Maryland, 1957.
3. Alfert, M.: Variations in cytochemical properties of cell nuclei. *Exptl. Cell Res. Suppl.* **6**: 227-235 (1958).
4. Alfert, M., and Geschwind, I. I.: A selective staining method for the basic proteins of cell nuclei. *Proc. Natl. Acad. Sci. U.S.* **39**: 991-999 (1953).
5. Allfrey, V. G.: Nuclear ribosomes, messenger-RNA protein synthesis. *Exptl. Cell Res. Suppl.* **9**: 183-212 (1963).
6. Allfrey, V. G., and Mirsky, A. E.: The incorporation of $N^{15}$-glycine by avian erythrocytes and reticulocytes *in vitro*. *J. Gen. Physiol.* **35**: 841-846 (1951).

6a. Baer, D.: A possible mode of histone synthesis. *J. Theoret. Biol.* **6**: 282-289 (1964).

7. Birnstiel, M. L., and Hyde, B. B.: Protein synthesis by isolated pea nucleoli. *J. Cell Biol.* **18**: 41-50 (1963).
8. Borsook, H.: Peptide bond formation. *Advan. Protein Chem.* **8**: 127-174 (1953).
9. Brown, G. B., Roll, P. M., Plentl, A. A., and Cavalieri, L. F.: The utilization of adenine for nucleic acid synthesis and as a precursor of guanine. *J. Biol. Chem.* **172**: 469-484 (1948).
10. Brunish, R., and Luck, J. M.: Amino acid "incorporation" *in vitro* by deoxypentose nucleoprotein and histone. *J. Biol. Chem.* **197**: 869-882 (1952).
11. Brunish, R., and Luck, J. M.: Amino acid incorporation *in vivo* into liver fractions. *J. Biol. Chem.* **198**: 621-628 (1952).
12. Busch, H., Byvoet, P., and Smetana, K.: The nucleolus of the cancer cell: A review. *Cancer Res.* **23**: 313-339 (1963).
13. Busch, H., Davis, J. R., and Anderson, D. C.: Labeling of histones and other

nuclear proteins with L-lysine-U-$C^{14}$ in tissues of tumor-bearing rats. *Cancer Res.* **18**: 916-926 (1958).

14. Busch, H., Davis, J. R., and Anderson, D. C.: Labeling of nuclear proteins of tumors and other tissues *in vitro* with L-lysine-U-$C^{14}$ and L-alanine-U-$C^{14}$. *Acta Unio Intern. Contra Cancrum* **16**: 1125-1131 (1960).
15. Busch, H., Davis, J. R., Honig, G. R., Anderson, D. C., Nair, P. V., and Nyhan, W. L.: The uptake of a variety of amino acids into nuclear proteins of tumor and other tissues. *Cancer Res.* **19**: 1030-1039 (1959).
16. Busch, H., Muramatsu, M., Adams, H. R., Smetana, K., Steele, W. J., and Liau, M. C.: Isolation of nucleoli. *Exptl. Cell Res. Suppl.* **9**: 150-163 (1963).
17. Busch, H., and Steele, W. J.: Nuclear proteins of neoplastic cells. *Advan. Cancer Res.* **9**: 41-120 (1964).
18. Busch, H., Steele, W. J., Hnilica, L. S., Taylor, C. W., and Mavioglu, H.: Biochemistry of histones and the cell cycle. *J. Cellular Comp. Physiol.* **62**: Suppl. 1, 95-110 (1963).
19. Butler, J. A. V., and Cohn, P.: Studies on histones. 6. Observations on the biosynthesis of histones and other proteins in regenerating rat liver. *Biochem. J.* **87**: 330-334 (1963).
20. Butler, J. A. V., and Laurence, D. J. R.: Relative metabolic activities of histones in tumors and liver. *Brit. J. Cancer* **14**: 758-763 (1960).
21. Campbell, P. N., Greengard, O., and Jones, H. E. H.: The intracellular distribution of amino acid incorporation by slices of liver and liver tumors and by ascites cells. *Exptl. Cell Res.* **12**: 689-692 (1957).
22. Daly, M. M., Allfrey, V. G., and Mirsky, A. E.: Uptake of $N^{15}$-glycine by components of cell nuclei. *J. Gen. Physiol.* **36**: 173-179 (1952).
23. Davis, J. R., and Busch, H.: Rate-limiting factors in the uptake of radioactive amino acids into proteins of tumor slices. *Cancer Res.* **18**: 718-724 (1958).
24. Desjardins, R., Smetana, K., Steele, W. J., and Busch, H.: Isolation of nucleoli of the Walker carcinosarcoma and liver of the rat following nuclear disruption in a French pressure cell. *Cancer Res.* **13**: 1819-1823 (1963).
25. Dounce, A. L., and Umana, R.: The proteases of isolated cell nuclei. *Biochemistry* **1**: 811-819 (1962).
26. Evans, J. H., Holbrook, D. J., Jr., and Irvin, J. L.: Changes in content of nuclear proteins and nucleic acids in regenerating liver. *Exptl. Cell Res.* **28**: 126-132 (1962).

26a. Flamm, W. G., and Birnstiel, M. L.: Inhibition of DNA replication and its effect on histone synthesis. *Exptl. Cell Res.* **33**: 616-619 (1964).

27. Furst, S. S., Roll, P. M., and Brown, G. B.: On the renewal of the purines of the desoxypentose and pentose nucleic acids. *J. Biol. Chem.* **183**: 251-266 (1950).
28. Griffin, A. C., Ward, V. C., Wade, J., and Ward, D. N.: Synthesis and release of basic proteins or peptides by tumor ribosomes. *Biochim. Biophys. Acta* **72**: 500-503 (1963).
29. Hammel, C. L., and Bessman, S. P.: Hemoglobin synthesis in avian erythrocytes. *J. Biol. Chem.* **239**: 2228-2238 (1964).
30. Holbrook, D. J., Jr., Evans, J. H., and Irvin, J. L.: Incorporation of labeled precursors into proteins and nucleic acids of nuclei of regenerating liver. *Exptl. Cell Res.* **28**: 120-125 (1962).

31. Holbrook, D. J., Jr., Irvin, J. L., Irvin, E. M., and Rotherham, J.: Incorporation of glycine into protein and nucleic acid fractions of nuclei of liver and hepatoma. *Cancer Res.* **20**: 1329-1337 (1960).
32. Honig, G. R., and Rabinovitz, M.: Selective suppression of nuclear-histone synthesis by Actinomycin D. *Federation Proc.* **23**: 266 (1964).
33. Irvin, J. L., Holbrook, D. J., Jr., Evans, J. H., McAllister, H. C., and Stiles, E. P.: Possible role of histones in regulation of nucleic acid synthesis. *Exptl. Cell Res. Suppl.* **9**: 359-366 (1963).
34. Konikova, A. S., Kritzman, M. G., and Samarina, O. P.: The incorporation of amino acids into individual proteins and protein complexes. *Biokhimiya* **19**: 440-448 (1954).
35. Konikova, A. S., Pogosova, A. V., Rapoport, E. A., Guljamov, T. D., and Kritzman, M. G.: Independence of amounts of incorporation of amino acids into histones on the amino acid composition of these proteins. *Nature* **198**: 167-169 (1963).
36. Lindner, A., Kutkam, T., Sankaranarayanan, K., Rucker, R., and Arradondo, J.: Inhibition of Ehrlich ascites tumor with 5-fluorouracil and other agents. *Exptl. Cell Res. Suppl.* **9**: 485-508 (1963).
37. Muramatsu, M., and Busch, H.: Effects of thioacetamide on metabolism of proteins of normal and regenerating liver. *Cancer Res.* **22**: 1100-1104 (1962).
38. Muramatsu, M., Smetana, K., and Busch, H.: Quantitative aspects of isolation of nucleoli of the Walker carcinosarcoma and liver of the rat. *Cancer Res.* **23**: 510-518 (1963).
39. Phillips, D. M. P., and Johns, E. W.: The chromatography of thymus histones and the demonstration of proteinase activity in the unfractionated preparations. *Biochem. J.* **71**: 17P-18P (1959).
40. Phillips, D. M. P., and Johns, E. W.: A study of the proteinase content and the chromatography of thymus histones. *Biochem. J.* **72**: 538-544 (1959).
41. Piha, R. S., and Waelsch, H.: The turnover of histones in brain and liver. *Federation Proc.* **23**: 267 (1964).
41a. Prensky, W., and Smith, H. H.: Incorporation of $^{3}$H-arginine in chromosomes of *Vicia faba*. *Exptl. Cell Res.* **34**: 525-532 (1964).
42. Prescott, D. M.: Symposium: Synthetic processes in the cell nucleus. II. Nucleic acid and protein metabolism in the macronuclei of two ciliated protozoa. *J. Histochem. Cytochem.* **10**: 145-153 (1962).
42a. Reid, B. R., and Cole, R. D.: Biosynthesis of a lysine-rich histone in isolated calf thymus nuclei. *Proc. Natl. Acad. Sci. U.S.* **51**: 1044-1050 (1964).
43. Ro, T. S., Muramatsu, M., and Busch, H.: Labeling of RNA of isolated nucleoli with UTP-$^{14}$C. *Biochem. Biophys. Res. Commun.* **14**: 149-155 (1964).
44. Rotherham, J., Irvin, J. L., Irvin, E. M., and Holbrook, D. J., Jr.: Incorporation of glycine into protein fractions of nuclei of liver and hepatoma. *Proc. Soc. Exptl. Biol. Med.* **96**: 21-24 (1957).
45. Samarina, O. P.: Incorporation of labeled amino acids into protein fractions of nuclei of the liver and of the Ehrlich ascites carcinoma cells. *Biokhimiya* **26**: 61-69 (1961).
46. Sankaranarayanan, K., and Hyde, B. B.: Ultrastructural studies of a nuclear

body with characteristics of both chromatin and nucleoli. *J. Ultrastructural Res.* (In press.)

46a. Schjeide, O. A., Alexander, G. V., Okunewick, J. P., Carmack, C. R., Wilkens, M., Carlsen, E. N., and Hennessy, T. G.: Synthesis of cytoplasmic hematin by nuclei of erythrocytes from embryos. *Growth* **28**: 17-28 (1964).

47. Schweiger, H. G., Master, R. W. P., and Alvisatos, S. G. A.: Mechanism of basic protein (histone) biosynthesis in Ehrlich ascites tumor cells. *Federation Proc.* **23**: 382 (1964).

48. Seed, J.: The synthesis of deoxyribonucleic acid and nuclear protein in normal and tumor strain cell. *Proc. Roy. Soc.* **B156**: 41-56 (1962).

49. Seed, J.: Studies of biochemistry and physiology of normal and tumor strain cells. *Nature* **198**: 147-153 (1963).

50. Sirlin, J. L., and Knight, G. R.: Chromosomal synthesis of protein. *Exptl. Cell Res.* **19**: 210-219 (1960).

51. Smellie, R. M. S., McIndoe, W. M., and Davidson, J. N.: The incorporation of $N^{15}$, $S^{35}$, and $C^{14}$ into nucleic acids and proteins of rat liver. *Biochim. Biophys. Acta* **11**: 559-565 (1953).

52. Smetana, K., and Busch, H.: On the ultrastructure of the Walker 256 carcinosarcoma. *Cancer Res.* **23**: 1600-1603 (1963).

53. Smetana, K., Steele, W. J., and Busch, H.: A nuclear ribonucleoprotein network. *Exptl. Cell Res.* **31**: 198-202 (1963).

54. Starbuck, W. C., and Busch, H.: Kinetics of incorporation of L-arginine-U-$C^{14}$ into nuclear proteins of tumors and other tissues *in vitro. Cancer Res.* **20**: 891-896 (1960).

55. Steele, W. J., and Busch, H.: Studies on acidic nuclear proteins of the Walker tumor and liver. *Cancer Res.* **23**: 1153-1163 (1963).

56. Tooze, J., and Davies, H. G.: The occurrence and possible significance of hemoglobin in the chromosomal regions of mature erythrocyte nuclei of the newt *Triturus cristatus cristatus. J. Cell Biol.* **16**: 501-511 (1963).

57. Wang, T.-Y.: Globulin of calf thymus nuclei and the *in vitro* incorporation of $C^{14}$ adenosine triphosphate into globulin RNA. *Biochim. Biophys. Acta* **45**: 8-14 (1960).

58. Wang, T.-Y.: Metabolic activities of nuclear proteins and nucleic acids. *Biochim. Biophys. Acta* **68**: 52-61 (1963).

59. Wang, T.-Y.: Physico-chemical and metabolic properties of nuclear ribosomes. *Exptl. Cell Res. Suppl.* **9**: 213-219 (1963).

60. Zamecnik, P. C., Loftfield, R. B., Stephenson, M. L., and Steele, J. M.: Studies on the carbohydrate and protein metabolism of rat hepatoma. *Cancer Res.* **11**: 592-602 (1951).

PART II

# The Acidic Nuclear Proteins and the Nuclear Enzymes

# CHAPTER VIII

# The Acidic Nuclear Proteins



## Introduction

The presence in fractions of nuclear proteins of a group of proteins that were not histones was recognized quite early by Lilienfeld (42). However, this group of proteins was essentially unstudied until the mid-1940's, when interest developed in them both in Scotland and in New York. This large group of nuclear proteins was operationally defined as the proteins in the residues that did not dissolve when the acid-soluble proteins were extracted from any of the nuclear fractions.

There is little evidence regarding their functional role in the nucleus, partly because they are so insoluble that protein chemists have shunned the difficult task of isolating and purifying them. However, they are present in the nucleolus, deoxyribonucleoproteins, and other nuclear fractions. Moreover, the peculiar "aggregate" nature of the nucleic acid polymerases suggest that these enzymes may be members of this group of proteins. Stedman and Stedman (57–59) may have overstated the case when they suggested that the acidic proteins in "chromosomin" played a functional role in the nucleus from a genetic point of view, but this cannot be completely ruled out some twenty years later.

Despite the fact that the acidic nuclear proteins have not been characterized, two facts have been clearly established with regard to these substances. The first is that they are present in high concentrations in the nucleus, i.e., they comprise at least half of the total nuclear proteins. The second is that in resting tissues, such as the normal liver, the turnover of some of the acidic nuclear proteins is far in excess of that of the histones.

The methods for isolating groups of acidic nuclear proteins have been simplified by successive extraction of nuclear preparations with 0.15 *M* NaCl, 2 *M* NaCl, and 0.05 *N* NaOH (see page 64). This procedure is based on many studies (2, 4, 28, 52, 61, 73, 75). In essence, the nuclei are fractionated into four fractions: (i) the "nuclear sap" fraction which contains considerable ribonucleoprotein, (ii) the chromatin fractions, (iii) the acidic protein that is extractable with dilute alkali and includes much ribonucleoprotein, and (iv) a residual fraction that is not soluble in alkali and probably contains a number of denatured proteins as well as some residues contaminated by collagen that was present in the tissue and coprecipitates with the nuclei (62).

## Quantitative Studies on Acidic Nuclear Proteins

Initially, Stedman and Stedman (57–59) estimated that the "chromosomin" or the acidic nuclear proteins constituted more than 30–70% of the total dry mass of the nucleus. Later, these values were revised downward to approximately 30–50% of the dry mass. In recent studies in this laboratory (61) with the extraction scheme shown in Table 3-I, the recoveries of acidic nuclear proteins were those shown in Table 8-I. In the liver and Walker tumor, respectively, all the nuclear proteins accounted for 70 and 73% of the lipid-free dry weight of the nuclear preparations. The acidic proteins in the nuclear fractions extracted

TABLE 8-I
PERCENTAGE OF TOTAL NUCLEAR PROTEIN IN VARIOUS NUCLEAR FRACTIONS OF THE LIVER AND WALKER 256 CARCINOSARCOMA[a, b]

| Fraction | Liver | Walker tumor |
|---|---|---|
| 0.14 *M* NaCl | 16.2 | 11.4 |
| 0.10 *M* Tris (pH 7.4) | 4.3 | 10.2 |
| 2.0 *M* NaCl | 42.6 | 36.8 |
| 0.05 *N* NaOH | 5.1 | 10.5 |
| Residual fraction | 2.2 | 2.0 |
| Total recovered | 70.4 | 70.9 |

[a] From Steele and Busch (61).

[b] The values are percentages of the lipid-free dry weight of the nuclear preparations. In these experiments, the nuclei were blended in 0.15 *M* NaCl initially. This procedure has been shown to destroy high molecular weight, rapidly turning-over RNA. In more recent studies where blending was omitted and extractions were made by homogenization, only 7% of the total RNA was extracted in the Tris and dilute saline solutions.

with 2 *M* NaCl accounted for 43 and 37%, respectively, of the total protein in these "chromatin" fractions of the liver and the Walker tumor (Table 8-II). In the chromatin fractions, the ratio of histones to acidic proteins was 36:28 in the liver and 41:27 in the Walker tumor. The histone content in the other fractions was negligible. On the basis of these results, the acidic proteins comprised about two-thirds of all the nuclear proteins in both the liver and the Walker tumor. The histones represent one-third of the total protein in the nucleus, although they predominate in the "chromatin" fraction or "chromosin" as defined by Mirsky and Pollister (49, 50). The acidic proteins constitute approximately 45–50% of the lipid-free dry weight of the nucleus. This value includes all the classes of the acidic proteins.

TABLE 8-II
COMPOSITION OF DEOXYRIBONUCLEOPROTEIN FRACTION OF ISOLATED NUCLEI OF LIVER AND WALKER 256 CARCINOSARCOMA[a]

| | Recovery (% total dry weight of initial 2 *M* NaCl extract) | |
|---|---|---|
| Fraction | Liver | Walker tumor |
| Histones | 36.0 | 41.0 |
| Acid-insoluble protein | 23.0 | 24.0 |
| Phenol-insoluble protein | 5.0 | 3.0 |
| DNA | 31.0 | 27.2 |
| RNA | 5.0 | 4.8 |

[a] The values represent determinations on preparations of three to five experiments. The average deviation from the mean values presented was 12%.

Varying values have been obtained by different workers for the total weight of the acidic proteins in the nuclei of cells of various species, but the range presented by the Stedmans (57–59) of 35–50% has not been seriously challenged. Smaller values have been reported for special cells, such as the sperm heads in which the acidic nuclear proteins accounted for only 30% of the dry weight of the nuclear material. Georgiev *et al.* (30) related the low content of acidic proteins to the low biosynthetic activity of the sperm heads.

*Chromosomal Acidic Proteins.* The initial reports of the Stedmans (57–59) had established that the acidic nuclear proteins were an important part of the nuclear components. Later studies by Mirsky and Pollister (49, 50) suggested that these proteins might be the critical component of the chromosomes that define the sizes and shapes of these structures. Of course, such a role must exist for some structural component of the chromosomes which has yet to be defined. Mirsky and Pollister (49, 50) used 1–2 *M* NaCl to extract chromatin or deoxyribonucleoprotein and reported that it contained a protein that resisted extraction in acid and had a substantial amount of tryptophan. This tryptophan-containing material was referred to as Tr.Pr., or tryptophan-protein, and what was particularly interesting was the fact that this material formed a coiled thread after DNA and histone had been extracted. The tryptophan content of this protein was only 1.36% and the Tr.Pr. was only about 10% of the total deoxyribonucleoprotein mass. The possibility was proposed that Tr.Pr. was the thread around which the chromosomal structure was condensed.[1] Bernstein and Mazia (5) came to a somewhat similar conclusion following their studies on sea urchin sperm, which they found to contain a protein that comprised 40% of the dry weight and yet was not a histone. Mazia and his colleagues (47, 48) found a group of proteins to be present in the mitotic apparatus that was precipitable at pH 6. Quantitative amino acid analysis of these proteins was not reported, but the structure from which they were obtained remarkably resembled the mitotic apparatus. Mazia and his colleagues did not find DNA in this structure, but they did find RNA. Suggestions have been made by others that the acidic nuclear proteins were part of the mitotic apparatus (19, 72). High percentages of the acidic nuclear proteins were found in neoplastic cells by the Stedmans (57–59) and by Debov (22, 23), who also showed that re-

[1] A close association of acidic proteins with DNA has been confirmed in a variety of species (27a, 41a, 50a) and a possible relationship to repression and derepression has been suggested (3a).

generating liver contained substantial amounts of nuclear acidic proteins. (See also page 205.)

## Nuclear Ribonucleoproteins

It is now well recognized that a main nuclear product is ribonucleoprotein in both dividing cells and resting cells (5b, 11, 32, 33, 50c). The nuclear ribonucleoproteins that are transported across the nuclear membrane include elements of both the ribosomes and the larger polysomic mass which contains both ribosomes and linear RNA filaments with a coding function. In the ribosomes, the proteins constitute about 50% of the overall mass, although the concentration of protein is greater in the microsomal fraction of the cytoplasm that includes elements of the lining of the endoplasmic reticulum. In the nucleus, the systems forming the ribosomes and polysomes appear to include elements of both the nucleoli and the extranucleolar coding systems of the chromosomes (48a). Whether the chromatin that is not associated with the nucleoli can function so as to produce the polysomes is not yet clear (11).

Evidence for compartmentalization of the nuclear ribonucleoproteins in the nuclear sap, the nuclear ribonucleoprotein network, and the chromatin has been obtained with the aid of extraction procedures. Some of the RNA of the nucleus, i.e., that in the "nuclear sap," is extractable with a variety of salt solutions including 0.15 *M* NaCl and 0.1 *M* Tris buffer (Table 8-I). This saline extraction procedure removes the components of the nucleus that normally block the visualization of the nuclear ribonucleoprotein network (56). The fraction extractable with dilute salt solutions contains the nuclear ribosomal fraction. The ribosomes of the "nuclear sap" are sedimented by centrifugation at 105,000 *g*; the nuclear globulins and other nuclear proteins in "nuclear sap" are purified by selective precipitation. In addition, ribonucleoproteins are in the chromatin fraction that is extracted with 2 *M* NaCl. The components of the nuclear ribonucleoprotein network also resist extraction with 2 *M* NaCl and thus remain in a "residual" fraction (55).

The nuclear ribosomal fraction has been shown to be rich in particles that resemble the cytoplasmic ribosomes under the electron microscope. Another evidence of the similarity of nuclear ribosomes and the cytoplasmic ribosomes is the change in size of the particles from those sedimenting at 30 and 50 S to particles sedimenting at 80 s and 110 S (64) when the concentration of $Mg^{++}$ in the medium is increased. Purification of the nuclear ribosomal fraction by treatment with sodium deoxycholate, differential centrifugation, and centrifugation in interrupted or continuous sucrose density gradients result in the removal of lipoproteins from the ribonucleoproteins and an increased concentration of RNA in these particles.

*Nuclear Lipoproteins.* Considerable evidence that there is a high content of lipid in nuclear proteins was obtained by isolation of the nuclear ribosomal preparations. As much as 90% of the dry weight of these preparations consisted of lipids (14); some of these liporibonucleoproteins are readily extracted into 95% ethanol solutions (62a). Nuclear lipoproteins were described almost twenty-five years ago by Mayer and Gulick (46), who reported the presence of sulfur-rich nuclear proteins with an isoelectric point of about 5.3. Chargaff (18) and Carver and Thomas (17) also found proteins in the nucleus with a somewhat lower isoelectric point, e.g., about 4.7–4.8, that they reported were lipoproteins. The possible relationship between these proteins and those of the chromatin has been discussed by Engbring and Laskowski (27). Dallam (19) was able to isolate a protein from nuclei of sperm heads that was alkali-soluble and had a lipid content of 27% of the total mass. This lipid consisted of cholesterol and phospholipids. Wang *et al.* (67, 68) found that lipoproteins were present in nuclei of calf thymocytes and also contained cholesterol and phospholipids. The lipoprotein was not characterized very well but had an isoelectric point of 6.0 and a low arginine content, i.e., 5.7%. In addition, tryptophan and tyrosine were reported to comprise 2.9 and 3.2%, respectively, of the amino acids of the protein. Although the possibility has been suggested that the nuclear lipoproteins were precursors of the polysomal or ribosomal lipoproteins, Levin and Thomas (41) reported that the lipoproteins of the nuclear fraction were more similar to the mitochondrial lipoproteins than the lipoproteins of the microsomal fraction. Their data are at variance with results that were obtained in studies in this laboratory (see page 207).

*The Nuclear Globulins.* Globulins in general are a group of simple proteins, i.e., they consist of amino acids only. Their solubility is such that they are readily soluble in dilute (5%) salt solutions, about 1-2 *M* NaCl, but they are precipitated at high salt concentration. Kirkham and Thomas (38) first called attention to this group of proteins in the nucleus when they found a protein fraction that was soluble in 0.14 *M* NaCl but was precipitated by half-saturation with $(NH_4)_2SO_4$. Extensions of their studies (19, 20) showed that nuclear proteins contained an albumin fraction and an albumin-globulin fraction as well as the lipoproteins. Later, it was found that the nuclear globulin fraction contained ribonucleoproteins into which labeled ATP was incorporated (63, 65) and into which aminoacyl sRNAs transferred $C^{14}$-labeled leucine in the presence of appropriate cofactors; the rate of biosynthesis of proteins and nucleic acids was high in this fraction (66). The nuclear globulins have been reported to be precipitated by 0.33 *M* $H_2SO_4$ from solutions that were 0.2 *M* with respect to $H_2SO_4$, and in this way they differ from the histones (12, 25). Interestingly, histones may be precipitated from dilute salt solutions in complexes with the globulins (26).

At present, it is not possible to establish a relationship between the lipoproteins and the globulins and some fractions that were reported to be present in the nuclear preparations of earlier workers. Extraction of nuclei with 1 *M* NaCl is not only likely to solubilize the globulins but also to solubilize the "chromosomin" or deoxyribonucleoprotein fraction (49, 50, 70). The isoelectric point of 5–5.5 is also shared by a number of nuclear proteins described by various authors (38, 46, 48, 67, 68).

Mantiev and Belousov (44) have recently studied the nuclear globulin fractions of liver, spleen, and a variety of tumors by means of continuous curtain electrophoresis. As in many instances, one problem in dealing with the tumor nucleus was the presence of a layer of perinuclear ribonucleoprotein that may influence the results on the globulin fraction. Their "globulin fraction" comprised the whole fraction extracted with Tris buffer. Differences were found between the patterns for the pancreas and the liver as well as the patterns for the tumors. However, characterization of the proteins will be required to establish whether the differences in electrophoretic behavior represent differences in the molecular species of the tumors and nontumor tissues.

*Sulfhydryl Groups in Nuclear Proteins.* Histochemists have had much interest in the sulfhydryl groups of nuclear proteins. Albertini (1) has pointed out that there is a high perinucleolar concentration of sulfhydryl groups. Hyde (37) has shown that the ratio of disulfide to sulfhydryl groups is highest during interphase. This ratio is intermediate at metaphase and lowest at telophase. Very few disulfide bonds were present in nuclei at telophase. Hyde (37) suggested that the sulfhydryl-containing proteins are a part of the basic structure of the chromosome. Moreover, the concentration of these proteins was greater in the nucleolus than in the chromatin. Because of their interest in the possibility that sulfhydryl-containing nuclear proteins were related to mitosis, Jellum and Eldjarn (37a) subfractionated the sulfhydryl proteins on an "organomercurial polysaccharide." The nuclear proteins were separated into fractions containing 1–2, 4–5, 5–8, and 20–25 sulfhydryls per mole of proteins, assuming a molecular weight of 100,000. The proteins containing the least sulfhydryl groups contained most of the RNA. The proteins containing 5–8 sulfhydryls contained most of the DNA. The remaining fractions composed 5–10% of the total proteins. Polymerization of these proteins occurred on addition of cystamine.

Their findings may be related to those of Deakin *et al.* (21a), who found that 70% of the nuclear sulfhydryl groups were associated with the "arginine-rich" histones. They also found that X-irradiation markedly decreased the concentration of sulfhydryl groups in nuclei of large thymocytes.

## Physical and Chemical Properties of the Acidic Nuclear Proteins

It is logical to ask why most acidic nuclear proteins are grouped together if they come from a variety of types of nuclear structures which may have many different types of functions. The only common features of the acidic nuclear proteins from various nuclear components are their amino acid analyses and their solubility in dilute alkali such as 0.05 *N* NaOH. This solubility behavior is most peculiar. It is not possible to dissolve these proteins with ordinary aqueous reagents. They are not amenable to separation with the usual chromatographic or physical techniques. When the pH is lowered from 10–12 to 6, all the protein precipitates out of solution.

*Molecular Weights.* Attempts to determine the molecular weight of these proteins have not been successful when either viscosimetry, light-scattering, or ultracentrifugation has been employed. However, evidence that these proteins have high molecular weights has been obtained by studies on the $NH_2$-terminal content; these studies also show that the acidic nuclear proteins are not hydrolyzed by the alkaline extraction procedures. A completely satisfactory molecular weight cannot be obtained by the $NH_2$-terminal method because high molecular weights may result from the presence of cyclic proteins, blocked amino terminals or proteins with high molecular weights. The number of $NH_2$-terminal amino acids recovered is so low that molecular weights ranging from 300,000 to 1,000,000 have been suggested for the acidic nucleolar proteins. Values ranging from 60,000 to 400,000 have been suggested for the molecular weights of the nuclear acidic proteins (24, 61). One of the possibilities suggested by such data is that these proteins may be fibrous filaments (73, 74), reminiscent of either keratin or silk, that is the fundamental element of the nuclear ribonucleoprotein network (55).

In addition to the common solubility properties of these proteins from a variety of types of nuclear elements, they also possess common amino acid compositions and common $NH_2$-terminal analyses. Although these analytical data are certainly derived from mixtures of proteins that probably differ in both number and type in the various nuclear fractions, their similarity also justifies consideration of these proteins as a chemical class rather than as individual entities at the present time. Thus far, techniques that have been satisfactory for chromatographic separation of other acidic proteins, such as the glycoproteins (53), have not been satisfactory for fractionation of the nuclear acidic proteins.

## Subfractionation of the Acidic Nuclear Proteins

The general procedure employed for separation of nuclear components (page 64) provides fractions from which a number of subfractions were isolated. The fraction that was extracted either with 0.1 *M* Tris at pH 7.6 or with 0.14 *M* NaCl constitutes the "nuclear sap" fraction from which three groups of protein-containing components were obtained. The *nuclear ribosomes* were precipitated by centrifugation at 105,000 g for 1 hour (2, 64), and the supernatant fraction was then dialyzed against distilled water. Because the globulin fraction is soluble in dilute saline solutions, but not in water, the *globulins* were precipitated in the course of dialysis. They were then sedimented by low speed centrifugation of the sample. The proteins remaining in solution or suspension after the globulins were removed were referred to as the "*nuclear sap*" *proteins* or as the proteins that were neither sedimented by high speed centrifugation nor by dialysis.

*Separation of Chromosomal Proteins.* A number of acidic protein fractions are obtained from other fractions including the acidic proteins of the deoxyribonucleoproteins. The acidic proteins of the deoxyribonucleoprotein fraction can be separated into a number of groups on the basis of fractionation with phenol (Table 3-II). After the histones were removed from the deoxyribonucleoproteins with acid, the residue was taken up in 6% sodium *p*-aminosalicylate and treated with phenol. When the two layers separated, the aqueous phase was made to 5% with respect to trichloroacetic acid, and heated to remove the nucleic acids. The proteins represent "phenol-insoluble" proteins freed from nucleic acids. The phenol phase was treated with methanol to precipitate acid-insoluble proteins that differed some from the phenol-insoluble acidic proteins.

Most interest has centered around the "chromosomal proteins" (see page 200), the proteins associated with DNA, but it is not yet clear how closely the proteins of this acidic group are related to the chromosomes. The reason for this uncertainty is that the relative affinities of the various protein fractions for the nucleic acids has not been ascertained. Some of the problems are apparent from the fact that Zbarskii, Georgiev, and their colleagues (29–34, 70–75) refer to the "nucleolochromosomal" apparatus as a fraction containing all the nuclear components except the "nuclear sap."

Clever (18a) has found that the puffs of *Drosophila* chromosomes are largely composed of proteins that are not histones and presumably are acidic nuclear proteins. These proteins are associated with RNA in both puffs and Balbiani rings. The puffing is associated with cytoplasmic controls and is related to cell differentiation in the *Diptera*. Clever (18a) has suggested that changes in the relationships of histones to DNA may be related to the puffing phenomenon, but experimental evidence for this conclusion is required.

## Amino Acid Analysis of the Acidic Nuclear Proteins

All the acidic nuclear proteins have in common a preponderance in the concentration of the glutamic and aspartic acid residues over the basic residues, which include histidine, lysine, and arginine. On this basis, all the nuclear proteins of the tumor and liver that are soluble in 0.14 *M* NaCl are acidic proteins (Table 8-III). A similar situation prevails for the proteins of the microsomal fraction, which contains the cytoplasmic ribonucleoproteins. The ratio of acidic to basic amino acids is not so great for most of the fractions, i.e., about 1.3 for the nuclear ribosome fraction and 1.5 for the globulin fraction. For the proteins of the "nuclear sap," those that were neither precipitated by dialysis nor by centrifugation, the ratio of acidic to basic amino acids

TABLE 8-III

Amino Acid Composition of Nuclear Proteins Soluble in 0.14 *M* NaCl[a, b]

| Amino acid | Nuclear ribosomes | | | Globulins | | Nuclear sap | | Microsomes | |
|---|---|---|---|---|---|---|---|---|---|
| | Calf thymus (64) | Liver | Tumor | Liver | Tumor | Liver | Tumor | Liver | Tumor |
| Alanine | 7.4 | 7.5 | 7.9 | 7.8 | 7.9 | 9.8 | 9.1 | 8.1 | 8.0 |
| Arginine | 7.8 | 5.6 | 6.3 | 5.1 | 5.2 | 2.9 | 3.6 | 4.9 | 5.8 |
| Aspartic acid | 9.1 | 9.8 | 9.6 | 10.0 | 10.4 | 10.5 | 10.6 | 10.0 | 9.6 |
| Cystine | 0.5 | — | — | — | 0.9 | 0.8 | 0.5 | — | 0.6 |
| Glutamic acid | 10.3 | 11.2 | 11.5 | 11.9 | 12.3 | 9.2 | 10.7 | 12.1 | 11.6 |
| Glycine | 9.3 | 10.8 | 9.7 | 9.4 | 7.1 | 8.4 | 8.5 | 8.4 | 8.7 |
| Histidine | 2.5 | 2.3 | 2.2 | 2.6 | 2.9 | 4.0 | 3.6 | 2.2 | 2.4 |
| Isoleucine | 5.2 | 3.9 | 4.5 | 4.3 | 4.7 | 3.8 | 4.0 | 4.4 | 4.7 |
| Leucine | 8.7 | 7.8 | 8.5 | 8.6 | 9.0 | 9.9 | 9.0 | 9.6 | 8.8 |
| Lysine | 10.0 | 8.7 | 9.1 | 8.5 | 9.0 | 8.3 | 9.1 | 7.0 | 9.1 |
| Methionine | 2.0 | 1.4 | 1.1 | 1.1 | 1.4 | 1.3 | 1.2 | 1.9 | 1.4 |
| Phenylalanine | 3.6 | 4.3 | 3.7 | 4.0 | 3.6 | 4.4 | 3.8 | 5.1 | 3.6 |
| Proline | 4.8 | 5.5 | 5.2 | 5.2 | 5.0 | 5.5 | 5.4 | 6.0 | 5.2 |
| Serine | 4.5 | 6.7 | 6.0 | 6.3 | 6.0 | 6.2 | 6.4 | 6.7 | 5.8 |
| Threonine | 4.8 | 4.8 | 5.0 | 4.9 | 5.2 | 5.1 | 5.2 | 5.1 | 5.2 |
| Tyrosine | 3.0 | 2.5 | 2.2 | 3.4 | 2.4 | 2.2 | 2.0 | 2.9 | 2.3 |
| Valine | 6.6 | 5.1 | 6.0 | 6.7 | 7.1 | 7.6 | 7.3 | 6.5 | 7.1 |

[a] From Busch and Steele (14).

[b] The values are percentages of total moles of amino acids recovered. The tumor studied was the Walker 256 carcinosarcoma.

was about 1.4. The "nuclear sap" proteins had appreciably more histidine and less arginine than the nuclear globulins or the proteins of the nuclear ribosomes. Interestingly, the amino acid content of the proteins of the microsomal fraction was quite similar to that of the proteins of the "nuclear ribosomes" and the nuclear globulins.

What was particularly striking was the agreement between the amino acid composition of the proteins derived from the soluble fraction of the nucleus and those derived from less soluble fractions (Table 8-IV). With the exception of the "residual" fraction, which is now believed to consist primarily of collagen (62), the various fractions contained about 22–24% of the residues as aspartic and glutamic acids. The highest contents of acidic amino acids were found in the proteins of the phenol-insoluble fraction and the proteins cross-linked to nucleic acids in the nuclei of the Ehrlich ascites cells (60). The arginine content of these proteins ranged from 5 to 7% of the total residues, the lysine content ranged from 6 to 8%, and the histidine content was approximately 2%. Thus, on the average, the ratio of acidic to basic amino acids in these proteins was about 1.3–1.5.

The only comparable values for proteins from other tissues were those of the "nuclear ribosomes" of the calf thymus (63, 64), and they were remarkably similar (Table 8-III). In this case, the lysine content was exceptionally high, suggesting the possibility that some basic proteins may have been present in the extract.

***Differences in Amino Acid Composition of the Various Acidic Nuclear Proteins.*** The nuclear globulins differed from the ribosomal proteins in that the nuclear ribosomal proteins had a higher content of arginine and glycine and the globulins had a higher content of valine (Table 8-III). The globulins had virtually the same amino acid composition as the proteins of the microsomes which contained somewhat less glycine than the proteins of the nuclear ribosomes. Although there were minor differences, the compositions of the globulins, proteins of the nuclear ribosomes and proteins of the microsomes were very similar. The proteins of these fractions all differed from those of the "nuclear sap," the fraction that was not sedimented at 105,000 *g* and was not precipitated by dialysis. In these proteins, the concentrations of alanine and histidine were higher than in the other nuclear proteins that were soluble in 0.14 *M* NaCl. The concentrations of arginine and glutamic acid were lower in the proteins of the "nuclear sap" than in the other nuclear proteins soluble in 0.14 *M* NaCl.

TABLE 8-IV

AMINO ACID COMPOSITION OF VARIOUS NUCLEAR PROTEIN FRACTIONS OF LIVER AND WALKER TUMOR[a]

| | Liver | | | | | Walker tumor | | | | | Ehrlich ascites cross-linked proteins |
|---|---|---|---|---|---|---|---|---|---|---|---|
| Fraction | Tris | Acid-insoluble | Phenol-insoluble | Alkali-soluble | Residual | Tris | Acid-insoluble | Phenol-insoluble | Alkali-soluble | Residual | |
| Alanine | 7.5 | 6.7 | 6.7 | 7.4 | 9.5 | 7.6 | 7.5 | 7.4 | 7.9 | 8.4 | 7.7 |
| Arginine | 7.4 | 7.7 | 7.1 | 5.7 | 5.4 | 6.2 | 7.0 | 6.3 | 6.2 | 5.7 | 5.3 |
| Aspartic acid | 9.8 | 9.1 | 8.8 | 9.3 | 7.0 | 9.3 | 9.7 | 9.9 | 9.2 | 8.4 | 10.5 |
| ½-Cystine | — | 0.4 | — | 1.3 | 0.4 | 1.8 | 0.3 | 0.3 | 0.7 | 0.2 | — |
| Glutamic acid | 11.1 | 12.4 | 12.8 | 12.1 | 10.0 | 12.2 | 13.5 | 14.7 | 13.0 | 10.5 | 15.3 |
| Glycine | 10.9 | 9.0 | 7.3 | 8.0 | 25.7 | 6.6 | 8.1 | 7.3 | 7.4 | 23.8 | 7.0 |
| Histidine | 2.2 | 2.3 | 2.3 | 2.3 | 1.3 | 2.0 | 2.4 | 2.4 | 2.2 | 1.5 | 1.8 |
| Isoleucine | 3.6 | 4.4 | 3.7 | 4.6 | 2.8 | 4.4 | 4.8 | 4.9 | 4.6 | 3.2 | 4.4 |
| Leucine | 7.5 | 8.3 | 7.9 | 9.4 | 5.1 | 8.7 | 8.8 | 9.2 | 10.1 | 5.7 | 8.3 |
| Lysine | 8.4 | 7.3 | 7.0 | 6.3 | 4.7 | 8.1 | 7.3 | 7.6 | 6.5 | 4.5 | 7.9 |
| Methionine | 1.7 | 2.2 | 2.0 | 2.6 | 1.0 | 2.0 | 2.3 | 2.2 | 2.0 | 1.1 | 1.1 |
| Phenylalanine | 3.8 | 3.8 | 3.1 | 4.0 | 2.7 | 3.5 | 3.7 | 3.5 | 3.8 | 2.4 | 4.1 |
| Proline | 5.9 | 6.4 | 7.0 | 5.5 | 9.0 | 5.6 | 5.0 | 4.3 | 4.6 | 8.8 | 5.9 |
| Serine | 7.5 | 6.9 | 10.4 | 7.4 | 5.8 | 6.6 | 6.6 | 6.8 | 7.0 | 6.3 | 7.1 |
| Threonine | 4.7 | 5.0 | 5.1 | 5.7 | 3.7 | 5.4 | 5.6 | 5.8 | 5.7 | 4.4 | 5.2 |
| Tyrosine | 3.2 | 3.2 | 2.4 | 2.8 | 1.3 | 2.6 | 3.2 | 2.3 | 2.7 | 1.4 | 1.8 |
| Valine | 4.9 | 5.1 | 6.4 | 6.1 | 4.0 | 7.6 | 5.6 | 5.2 | 6.6 | 3.9 | 5.8 |

[a] From Busch and Steele (14).

[b] The values are percentages of total moles of amino acids recovered. See Table 3-II for extraction scheme.

The acidic protein fraction extracted with Tris (Table 8-IV) closely resembled the nuclear ribosome fraction in amino acid composition with the exception of lower glycine and higher valine content in the Tris-extracted fraction of the Walker tumor. The fraction extracted with Tris had the lowest glutamic acid content of any of the acidic nuclear protein fractions shown in Table 8-IV. The protein that was in the phenol-insoluble fraction had the highest content of glutamic acid; this value approximated that of the acidic proteins that were cross-linked to DNA in Ehrlich ascites cells exposed to nitrogen mustards. The glutamic acid content of the proteins of the various fractions was higher in the tumor than in the liver. The leucine content of the alkali-soluble fraction was higher than that of the other fractions in both the tumor and the liver (Table 8-IV). The alkali-soluble fraction also had the lowest lysine content of any of the fractions shown in Table 8-IV. With the exception of high values for serine in the phenol-insoluble fraction of the liver and the high valine content of the proteins of the Tris fraction of the Walker tumor, the remainder of the values were strikingly similar for these proteins. The values for the amino acid compositions were remarkably constant for most of the acidic nuclear protein fractions.

The amino acid compositions do not provide any clue as to the reasons for the extreme insolubility of these proteins. It has been suggested (14) that the glutamic and aspartic acid residues may be present as the amides, i.e., glutamine and asparagine, and the proteins could be very basic. This possibility does not seem too likely in view of the fact that these proteins would then be expected to be quite soluble in acids rather than in dilute alkali.

*Residual Nuclear Proteins.* The residual nuclear protein was found to contain high concentrations of glycine (Table 8-IV). Further analyses (62) showed that they contained approximately 1% of hydroxylysine and 2.5% of hydroxyproline. The presence of these amino acids in this fraction suggested that the fraction was rich in collagen. The presence of collagen was confirmed by electron microscopic studies. Although this protein fraction has been suggested to have some unusual functions, in fact it seems that it probably represents a mixture of denatured alkali-soluble nuclear proteins and collagen.

*Nucleolar Acidic Proteins.* With the development of methods for the isolation of highly purified nucleoli, it has become possible to determine the composition of the nucleolar acidic proteins (Table 8-V). In

TABLE 8-V
AMINO ACID COMPOSITION OF NUCLEOLAR ACIDIC PROTEINS (24)[a]

| Amino acid | Walker tumor | Rat liver |
|---|---|---|
| Alanine | 7.0 | 7.0 |
| Arginine | 6.0 | 5.5 |
| Aspartic acid | 10.0 | 9.7 |
| Glutamic acid | 13.8 | 13.7 |
| Glycine | 7.6 | 7.3 |
| Histidine | 2.4 | 2.5 |
| Isoleucine | 4.1 | 4.6 |
| Leucine | 8.9 | 9.3 |
| Lysine | 7.3 | 7.7 |
| Methionine | 2.1 | 2.3 |
| Phenylalanine | 3.6 | 3.7 |
| Proline | 5.3 | 6.2 |
| Serine | 7.6 | 7.2 |
| Threonine | 5.1 | 5.3 |
| Tyrosine | 2.4 | 2.2 |
| Valine | 6.0 | 5.6 |

[a] The values are percentages of total moles of amino acids in the proteins. The acid-soluble proteins were previously extracted with 0.25 *N* HCl.

essence, proteins of the basic type like the histones have not been found in the nucleolar preparations in a quantity sufficient to permit ready assay. However, there were some proteins extracted with acid that were acidic in overall composition and, like the acid-insoluble nucleolar proteins, had a composition that was quite similar to that of the microsomal proteins and the nuclear globulins (24). These proteins had a very low content of $NH_2$-terminal amino acids. When 35 mg of nucleolar acidic proteins from either the tumor or the liver were analyzed, a perceptible yellow spot was not found when the ether-soluble dinitrophenylamino acids were chromatographed on paper (24). Such data suggest that the nucleolus may "spin" a long ribonucleoprotein strand that proceeds toward the nuclear membrane through the nuclear ribonucleoprotein network (54a, 55).

The composition of the acidic or "residual" nucleolar proteins of pea seedlings has been determined by Birnstiel and Hyde (6), who found that their nucleolar proteins had virtually the same amino acid composition as the microsomal or nuclear ribosomal proteins shown in Table 8-III. They reported that asparagine rather than aspartic acid was present in large amount, but this was not chemically established. However, the presence of asparagine may be a specific difference between the amino acid composition of the plant and animal proteins. They reported that the activity of the nucleolus in the biosynthesis of these proteins was approximately twice that of the chromatin fraction obtained from the pea seedlings (see also reference 5a).

In *Vicia faba*, Mattingly (45) found that labeled lysine accumulated in the nucleolus and perinucleolar chromatin. The labeled nucleolar protein left the nucleolus very quickly and presumably proceeded to the cytoplasm as part of the polysomal complexes.

## $NH_2$-Terminal Amino Acids of the Acidic Nuclear Proteins

The results of the studies on the $NH_2$-terminal amino acids of the saline-soluble nuclear protein fractions and the other acidic nuclear proteins are presented in Tables 8-VI and 8-VII. In general, the values

TABLE 8-VI

$NH_2$-Terminal Amino Acid Analysis of Saline-Soluble Nuclear Protein Fraction of Walker Tumor[a, b]

| Amino acid | Nuclear ribosomes | Nuclear globulin | Nuclear sap | Microsomes |
|---|---|---|---|---|
| Alanine | 20.5 | 15.8 | 8.5 | 19.0 |
| Aspartic acid, Glutamic acid | 11.9 | 21.4 | 23.0 | 18.6 |
| Glycine | 28.5 | 29.6 | 25.5 | 29.4 |
| Lysine | 3.8 | 2.4 | — | 2.0 |
| Serine | 17.1 | 11.8 | 12.8 | 15.8 |
| Threonine | 6.6 | 5.1 | 5.3 | 6.1 |
| Leucine, Valine | 11.5 | 15.2 | 23.9 | 9.1 |

[a] From Steele and Busch (62).
[b] The values are percentages of total moles recovered.

for $NH_2$-terminal amino acids are subject to greater errors than the values for amino acid compositions of the proteins (61). These tables present the percentage of the amino acids comprising the total $NH_2$-terminals, but they do not indicate the absolute amounts of the $NH_2$-terminals recovered. The recovered amounts were such that the approximate molecular weights of 80,000–400,000 were obtained for the proteins. As mentioned earlier (14, 24), the low amounts of $NH_2$-terminal amino acids recovered indicate either that the proteins are cyclic, that the terminal amino acids are blocked, or that the proteins

TABLE 8-VII

$NH_2$-Terminal Amino Acids in Nuclear Protein Fractions of Liver and Walker 256 Carcinosarcoma[a, b]

| | Liver | | | | Walker tumor | | | | | |
|---|---|---|---|---|---|---|---|---|---|---|
| Fraction | Acid-insoluble | Histone | Alkali-soluble | Residual | Acid-insoluble | TCA-treated acid-insoluble | Histone | Phenol-insoluble | Alkali-soluble | Residual |
| Alanine | 17 | 35 | 18 | 20 | 18 | 11 | 35 | 9 | 17 | 24 |
| Aspartic acid | 8 | 1 | 10 | 9 | 8 | 8 | 1 | 9 | 8 | 8 |
| Glutamic acid | 7 | 1 | 9 | 6 | 8 | 6 | 1 | 4 | 7 | 8 |
| Glycine | 15 | 4 | 15 | 14 | 12 | 13 | 3 | 15 | 16 | 15 |
| Leucine | 5 | 1 | 7 | 6 | 6 | 6 | 2 | 5 | 5 | 5 |
| Lysine | 8 | 3 | 10 | 6 | 8 | 8 | 8 | 10 | 7 | 8 |
| Phenylalanine | 2 | 2 | 3 | 4 | 2 | 3 | 1 | 2 | 3 | 4 |
| Proline | 2 | 49 | 4 | — | 5 | 21 | 42 | 19 | 8 | — |
| Serine | 26 | 5 | 17 | 20 | 25 | 13 | 6 | 15 | 21 | 15 |
| Threonine | 5 | 1 | 5 | 8 | 5 | 6 | 1 | 8 | 6 | 8 |
| Valine | 3 | — | 3 | 4 | 4 | 4 | — | 5 | 3 | 5 |

[a] From Steele and Busch (61).

[b] The values are percentages of total moles recovered. See Table 3-II for extraction scheme.

are rather long filaments as was suggested by the appearance of the nuclear ribonucleoprotein network (54a, 55).

The chief amino acids found to be $NH_2$-terminal amino acids were alanine, glycine, serine, and leucine or valine. Alanine, glycine, and serine accounted for 50–65% of the $NH_2$-terminal amino acids in the proteins of the nuclear ribosomes, the nuclear globulins, the cytoplasmic microsomes, the alkali-soluble nuclear proteins, and the acid-insoluble proteins of the deoxyribonucleoprotein complex. The histones contained largely proline and alanine as the $NH_2$-terminal amino acids (Tables 8-VI, 8-VII, and 3-VI). In the residual fraction that has been shown to contain considerable collagen, the distribution of the $NH_2$-terminal amino acids was quite similar to that of the alkali-soluble nuclear proteins. This result shows that the proteins other than collagen were probably quite similar in these two fractions.

Quantitative rather than qualitative differences were found for the $NH_2$-terminal amino acids of the nuclear proteins. Larger amounts of aspartic acid and glutamic acid were found as the $NH_2$-terminal amino acids in the nuclear globulins, the alkali-soluble proteins of the liver, and the proteins of the "nuclear sap" than were found in the other nuclear protein fractions. The proteins of the cytoplasmic microsomal fraction and the nuclear proteins that were soluble in 0.14 *M* NaCl had a higher content of glycine $NH_2$-terminal amino acids than the other nuclear proteins. On the other hand, the proteins of the acid-insoluble fraction had a higher amount of serine as an $NH_2$-terminal amino acid than the other nuclear proteins. One of the remarkably similar features of the data was the high concentration of alanine, aspartic and glutamic acid, glycine, and serine as the $NH_2$-terminal amino acids in the microsomal proteins. Like the nuclear ribosomes, these proteins had a low concentration of leucine as an $NH_2$-terminal amino acid. In this respect, most of the nuclear protein fractions differed from the nuclear globulin fraction and the fraction referred to as the "nuclear sap."

One point with regard to the methods employed may be significant to the data of Table 8-VII. To remove the nucleic acids from the phenol-insoluble protein fraction and the acid-insoluble protein fraction, these fractions were extracted with hot trichloroacetic acid. The higher content of the proline $NH_2$-terminal amino acid residues may be a reflection of partial hydrolysis of these proteins or may result from differences in their protein composition from that of other fractions. In any event, the large number of types of $NH_2$-terminal amino acids in these fractions of the acidic nuclear proteins suggests that they may be quite heterogeneous.

No significant differences were found for either the amino acid composition or the $NH_2$-terminal amino acid content of the proteins of the nuclear ribosomes and the microsomal fraction. There are a number of possible explanations for this result, including the concept that ribosomes may shuttle back and forth from the nucleus to the cytoplasm, that the nuclear preparations are contaminated to a small degree with the cytoplasmic ribosomes, or that the nucleus is the site of synthesis of the ribosomes. Overwhelming evidence for this last concept is accumulating from studies on the nucleoli and their products (11).

## Cytonucleoproteins

Evidence that indicates that some proteins do indeed exchange between the nucleus and the cytoplasm was obtained by Byers *et al.* (15, 16), who transplanted labeled nuclei from amebas exposed to radioactive amino acids to amebas that were not. They noted that the label emigrated from the nucleus to the cytoplasm and that later, the label was taken up into the original unlabeled nucleus. The proteins that apparently possess the ability to move from nucleus to cytoplasm and back were called "cytonucleoproteins" by these workers, who suggested that such proteins might be involved in communication of the nucleus with the cytoplasm. Since the total isotope involved approximated 30% of the original label in protein, the amount of such proteins must be quite large. Not all of the label that left the nucleus was returned to the nucleus. Equilibrium was reached when approximately 10–40% of the total labeled protein was left in the cytoplasm.

Prescott (51) has reported a similar phenomenon in studies on mitosis. In the early phases of mitosis, the nuclear proteins apparently left the nucleus in amebas. When mitosis was completed, there was a rapid return of the proteins to the nucleus in a kind of mass immigration. These results, which did not differentiate between acidic proteins and the histones, are reminiscent of those of Horn (35, 36), who reported that in frog embryos the histones were largely localized to the cytoplasm up to the stage of the morula. After that stage, the histones were largely found in the nucleus.

Supportive evidence for the concept that cytonucleoproteins exist in a variety of species has been provided by Kroeger *et al.* (39), who transplanted chromosomes and nucleoli into the cytoplasm of receptor cells. Salivary glands from *Chironomus thummi* were incubated with tritiated lysine and then one to three chromosome sets from one cell were transplanted into the cytoplasm of an unlabeled cell. Labeled molecules were soon released from the chromosomal material into the cytoplasm and the label was incorporated almost exclusively into the nuclei. This result differed from that obtained when labeled lysine was added to the system; under these circumstances, the labeling of the nucleus was small by comparison with that of the cytoplasm. The authors concluded that there are nucleotropic proteins.

## Electrophoretic Studies

Bakay and Sorof (3) reported that they carried out a series of studies on the electrophoretic behavior of soluble nuclear proteins of the livers of normal rats and rats treated with the carcinogen, 3′-methyl-4-dimethylaminoazobenzene. The proteins were extracted from the nucleus with saline-phosphate buffers, and electrophoresis was carried out in Veronal buffers at pH 8.6. They found one positively charged and eight negatively charged classes of proteins in the nuclei of normal and dye-treated animals. In the tumors studied, there was

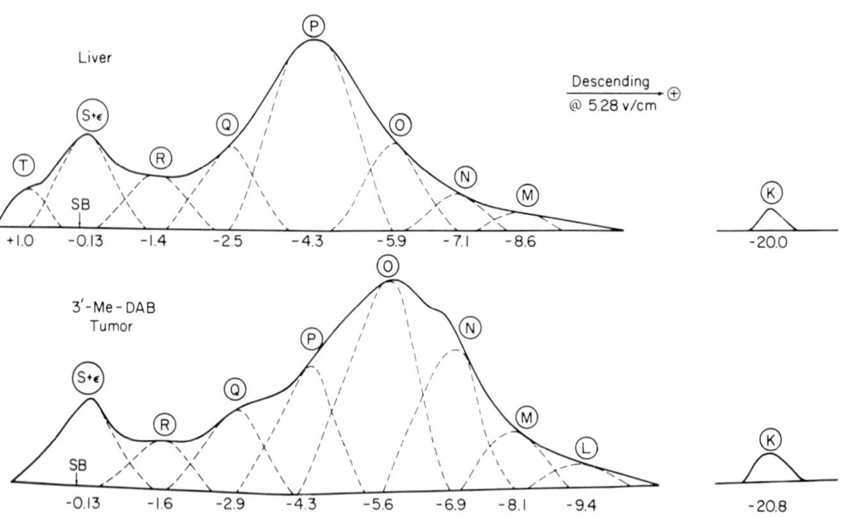


Fig. 8-1. Free boundary electrophoretic patterns of soluble nuclear macromolecules of normal liver and livers of rats treated with 3′-methyldimethylaminoazobenzene. The protein concentration was 2.7–2.9%. (Courtesy of Drs. B. Bakay and S. Sorof.)

no positively charged class, a smaller amount of the weakly negatively charged component, and more of the faster negatively charged components. In the cytoplasm, too, the tumors had less of the weakly negatively charged components which are referred to as the "h" proteins. The latter have been of interest to Sorof and his colleagues (56) since it was found that, in this class of proteins, there was a relatively selective localization of the carcinogen that was "protein bound."

As shown in Fig. 8-1, the tumor lacks the positive component T, has less of component P and more of components O, N, M, and L. The components Q, R, and S were present in similar amounts in the tumor and the normal liver. Figure 8-2 shows the ultracentrifugation patterns of these proteins. The tumor had more of the components with sedimentation constants of 2 and 4 S and less of the components with sedimentation constants of 6 and 8 S. In the preneoplastic livers, there was more of the 4 S component and less of the 8 S component than in the normal liver.

Starch gel electrophoretic analysis of the soluble nuclear proteins has also been carried out (50b). Evidence was obtained by this technique as well as by chromatography on DEAE-cellulose that there are many proteins in nuclei of calf thymocytes. Patel and Wang (50b) found that the nuclear proteins differ from those of cytoplasmic extracts in mobility and in their rates of labeling with amino acid precursors. Some fractions were rich in RNA, but the fractions differed in their uptake of RNA precursors. Immunological evidence for the presence of many nuclear ribonucleoproteins has been obtained recently (66a).

## Biosynthesis of the Acidic Nuclear Proteins

One indication of the importance of the acidic nuclear proteins aside from their high concentration in the nucleus is their rapid labeling with labeled amino acids *in vivo* (61). Daly *et al.* (21) were the first to note that, in resting tissues, the rate of labeling of the "residual proteins" of the chromosomes was higher than that of the other nuclear proteins. These proteins are in the group that are in the "nucleolochromosomal apparatus" of Zbarskii and Georgiev *et al.* (28–34, 70–75) or in the fraction containing nucleolar components and the nuclear ribonucleoprotein network. Verifications of these findings were made with similar techniques by Brunish and Luck (8, 9) and Smellie and his colleagues (54). The latter authors (54) noted that labeling of nuclear proteins that were soluble in alkali proceeded at a higher rate than labeling of proteins of cytoplasmic fractions.

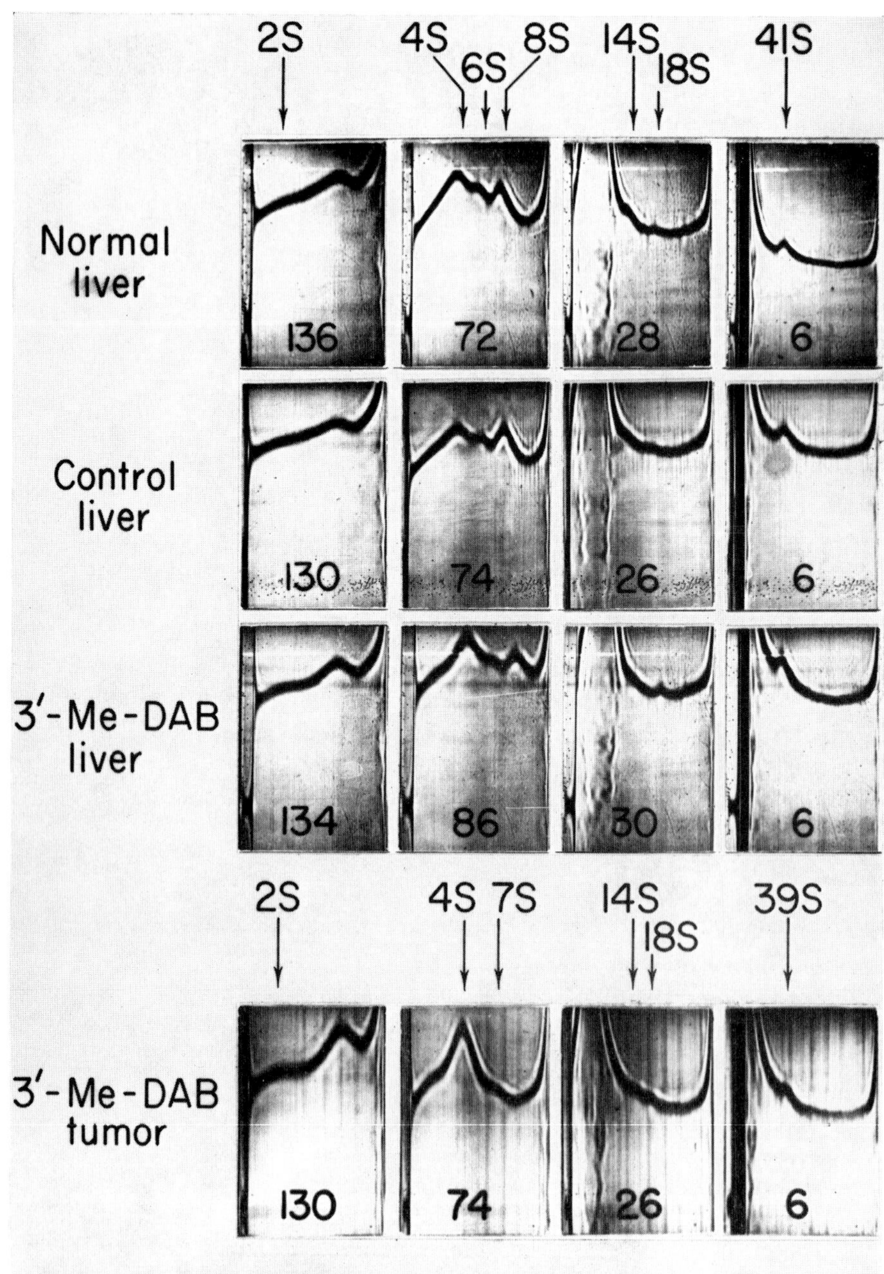
2S
4S
6S
8S
14S
18S
41S
Normal liver
136
72
28
6
Control liver
130
74
26
6
3′-Me-DAB liver
134
86
30
6
2S
4S
7S
14S
18S
39S
3′-Me-DAB tumor
130
74
26
6

Table 8-VIII presents data from this laboratory that extend the earlier findings (61). As suggested by others, the labeling of the acidic nuclear proteins of the liver was greater than that of the histones or of

TABLE 8-VIII

SPECIFIC ACTIVITIES OF VARIOUS NUCLEAR PROTEIN FRACTIONS OF LIVER AND WALKER 256 CARCINOSARCOMA[a, b]

| | Liver | | Walker tumor | |
|---|---|---|---|---|
| Fraction | Cpm/mg protein | Cpm/μmole lysine | Cpm/mg protein | Cpm/μmole lysine |
| Isolated nuclei | 210 | — | 450 | — |
| 0.14 *M* NaCl (nuclear sap) | 160 | 260 | 360 | 580 |
| Globulins | 225 | — | 509 | — |
| Ribosomes | 261 | — | 417 | — |
| Nuclear sap | 192 | — | 258 | — |
| 0.10 *M* Tris | 240 | 370 | 540 | 860 |
| 2.0 *M* NaCl | | | | |
| Acid-soluble (histones) | 220 | 180 | 680 | 640 |
| Acid-insoluble | 300 | 530 | 550 | 960 |
| Phenol-insoluble | 440 | 810 | 590 | 990 |
| 0.05 *M* NaOH | 270 | 530 | 420 | 840 |
| Residual | 130 | 320 | 160 | 410 |

[a] Data from Steele and Busch (61).

[b] One hour after administration of 5 μc lysine-U-$C^{14}$. Specific activities are corrected on the basis of the sum of the total amino acids recovered by chromatography of acid hydrolyzates.

the acid-soluble proteins of the fraction extracted with 2 *M* NaCl. In each case, labeled lysine was the radioactive precursor. This result held true when the specific activities were determined on the basis of counts per minute per milligram protein or per micromole lysine. The specific activity of the proteins of the nuclear ribosomes and the nuclear globulins was in the same range as that of the proteins of the other fractions in both the liver and the Walker tumor, but in each case the specific activities of the proteins of the nuclear sap were lower than those of the other proteins with the exception of the "residual" proteins; the latter contained much collagen, and a low turnover of the fraction would be anticipated. On the basis of counts per minute per milligram protein the specific activity of the histones was considerably

FIG. 8-2. Sedimentation patterns of soluble nuclear macromolecules of normal rat livers, livers of rats treated with 3′-methyldimethylaminoazobenzene, and tumors induced by this carcinogen. (Courtesy of Drs. B. Bakay and S. Sorof.)

higher than that of other proteins in the Walker tumor (see Chapter VII), but even in the case of the Walker tumor, the acidic nuclear proteins had a higher specific activity than the histones when the results were compared on the basis of counts per minute per micromole lysine. As others had found previously, the rate of labeling of histones in nuclear preparations of calf thymus was found to be very low by Wang (66). However, the rate of labeling of acidic proteins was considerably greater, particularly in the ribosomal fractions, in which the proteins were labeled 5–10 times more rapidly than other nuclear proteins.

The acidic proteins with the highest specific activity were found in the phenol-insoluble fraction in both the liver and the Walker tumor. The acid-insoluble proteins of the "chromosin" or chromatin fraction had a very high specific activity in the Walker tumor and in the liver. Considerably lower specific activities were found in the other fractions with the exception of the fraction extracted with Tris. In the nuclei, the protein fractions with very high specific activities were those extracted with 2 *M* NaCl and those of the residue that were extracted with 0.05 *N* NaOH (21, 28–34, 61, 70–75). These proteins are the proteins that are linked to the chromosomes and those that are part of the nucleolar fraction including the nuclear ribonucleoprotein network (NRN). Although the precise site of biosynthesis of these proteins is not clear, it would seem that some may be formed directly on the chromosomes (see page 174).

*External Stimuli and Labeling of Acidic Proteins.* The possibility that synthesis of the acidic nuclear proteins is responsive to external stimuli was suggested by the experiments of Malec *et al.* (43), who reported that phagocytosis stimulated the uptake of labeled glycine into nuclear proteins of leukocytes. The nuclear subfraction that was most stimulated in terms of labeling was the ribosomal fraction, in which a definitive increase in labeling with glycine, orotic acid, and $P^{32}$ was found. Such data could be interpreted as indicating that the rate of polysome synthesis was increased in phagocytosis of bacteria by the leukocytes.

## Effects of Antitumor Agents on the Biosynthesis of Acidic Nuclear Proteins

The biosynthesis of acidic nuclear proteins was found to be markedly suppressed in drug-sensitive tumors following the administration of alkylating agents and a variety of analog inhibitors to tumor-bearing animals. In these experiments, all the acidic proteins were studied as a group since subfractionation had not shown marked differences in either the amino acid composition or the $NH_2$-terminal analyses of the acidic proteins.

The effects of the uracil mustard (10) on the labeling of these proteins is shown in Fig. 8-3. Results similar to those obtained with this drug have also been obtained with a variety of agents including Myleran, 6-mercaptopurine, leukeran, 5-fluorouracil, and HN2 (13).

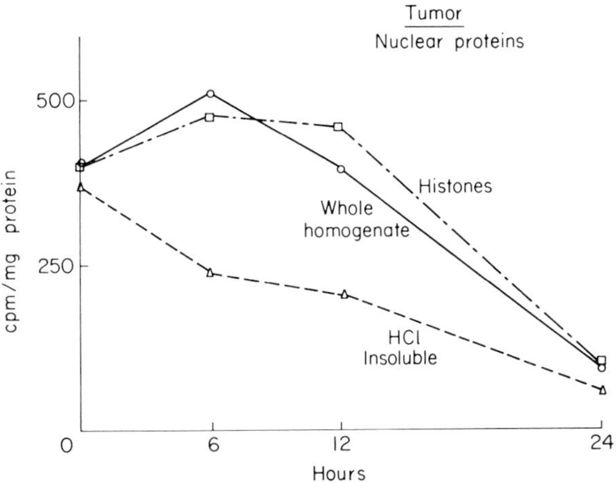


FIG. 8-3. Kinetics of the effects on amino acid incorporation into the nuclear proteins of the tumor by the aminouracil mustard. One hour prior to the designated time, 7.5 μc of L-arginine-U-$C^{14}$ were injected intraperitoneally (10).

Identical results were found when labeled lysine or arginine was used as a precursor. In some instances the suppression of biosynthesis of the acidic nuclear proteins was the chief early effect of these agents on the biosynthesis of proteins in the tumor cells. Later, suppression of biosynthesis of most cellular proteins was found as a common effect of a variety of antitumor agents.

In experiments on the action of mustards on Ehrlich ascites cells *in vitro*, Steele (60) found that acidic nuclear proteins were cross-linked to nucleic acids (Table 8-IV). It was found that the amount of protein linked to DNA was considerably increased in nuclei of cells treated with difunctional alkylating agents. No increase was found in similar fractions obtained from cells treated with monofunctional alkylating agents.

These results and those of Brookes and Lawley (7, 40) have served to suggest that a major function of the mustards is either to block replication of DNA, the priming of DNA for biosynthesis of RNA that is essential to biosynthesis of the acidic nuclear proteins, or the direct biosynthesis of protein on nucleic acids. However, evidence is now emerging that the mustards block the incorporation of purines into deoxyribonucleoside triphosphates and the incorporation of the latter into DNA. Whether these events are primary events in the remarkably widespread effects of mustards or are secondary events is still not established. From evidence of Wheeler and Alexander (69, 69a), it would appear that the general process of alkylation of DNA is not the only important effect of the mustards since cells sensitive to the mustards and resistant to the mustards were equally alkylated. It is likely that the reactive groups of the mustards affect many cell reactions, and at present it is not possible to state which affected system is rate limiting for cell growth. Inhibition of formation of acidic nuclear proteins essential for completion of ribosomes, would exert far-reaching effects on protein synthesis and other metabolic activities of mustard-treated cells.

## References

1. Albertini, de M.: Etude cytophotométrique des protéines-SH nucléolaires de la racine de Jacinthe; répartition précise de ces composes au sein du nucléole. *Compt. Rend. Acad. Sci.* **248**: 3476-3478 (1959).
2. Allfrey, V. G.: Nuclear ribosomes, messenger-RNA protein synthesis. *Exptl. Cell Res. Suppl.* **9**: 183-212 (1963).
3. Bakay, B., and Sorof, S.: Soluble nuclear proteins of liver and tumor in azo dye carcinogenesis. *Cancer Res.* **24**: 1814-1825 (1964).

3a. Balis, M. E., Salser, J. S., and Elder, A.: A suggested role of amino acids in DNA. *Nature* (1964). (In press.)

4. Bensley, R. R.: Chemical structure of cytoplasm. *Science* **96**: 389-393 (1942).
5. Bernstein, M. H., and Mazia, P.: The desoxyribonucleoprotein of sea urchin sperm. *Biochim. Biophys. Acta* **25**: 502-512 (1957).

5a. Birnstiel, M. L., Chipchase, M. I. H., and Flamm, W. G.: On the chemistry and organisation of nucleolar proteins. *Biochim. Biophys. Acta* **87**: 111-122 (1964).

5b. Birnstiel, M. L., Chipchase, M. I. H., and Hyde, B. B.: The nucleolus, a source of ribosomes. *Biochim. Biophys. Acta* **76**: 454-462 (1963).

6. Birnstiel, M. L., and Hyde, B. B.: Protein synthesis by isolated pea nucleoli. *J. Cell Biol.* **18**: 41-50 (1963).
7. Brookes, P., and Lawley, P. D.: Evidence for the action of alkylating agents on deoxyribonucleic acid. *Exptl. Cell Res. Suppl.* **9**: 521-524 (1963).
8. Brunish, R., and Luck, J. M.: Amino acid "incorporation" *in vitro* by deoxypentose nucleoprotein and histone. *J. Biol. Chem.* **197**: 869-882 (1952).

9. Brunish, R., and Luck, J. M.: Amino acid incorporation *in vivo* into liver fractions. *J. Biol. Chem.* **198**: 621-628 (1952).
10. Busch, H., Amer, S. M., and Nyhan, W. L.: Inhibition of uptake of L-arginine-U-$C^{14}$ into nuclear proteins by 5-Bis(2-chloroethyl)aminouracil. *J. Pharmacol. Exptl. Therap.* **127**: 195-199 (1959).
11. Busch, H., Byvoet, P., and Smetana, K.: The nucleolus of the cancer cell: A review. *Cancer Res.* **23**: 313-339 (1963).
12. Busch, H., and Davis, J. R.: Nuclear proteins of tumors and other tissues. *Cancer Res.* **19**: 1241-1256 (1958).
13. Busch, H., Firszt, D. C., Lipsey, A., Kohen, E., and Amer, S. M.: Inhibition by antitumor agents of labeling of nuclear proteins *in vivo* with L-arginine-U-$C^{14}$. *Biochem. Pharmacol.* **7**: 123-134 (1961).
14. Busch, H., and Steele, W. J.: Nuclear proteins of neoplastic cells. *Advan. Cancer Res.* **8**: 41-120 (1964).
15. Byers, T. J., Platt, D. B., and Goldstein, L.: The cytonucleoproteins of amoebae. I. Some chemical properties and intracellular distribution. *J. Cell Biol.* **19**: 453-466 (1963).
16. Byers, T. J., Platt, D. B., and Goldstein, L.: The cytonucleoproteins of amoebae. II. Some aspects of cytonucleoprotein behavior and synthesis. *J. Cell Biol.* **19**: 467-475 (1963).
17. Carver, M. J., and Thomas, L. E.: An electrophoretic study of lipoproteins from cellular nuclei. *Arch. Biochem. Biophys.* **40**: 342-345 (1952).
18. Chargaff, E.: Recent work on lipoproteins as cellular constituents. *Proc. Intern. Congr. Exptl. Cytol., Stockholm, 1947.* Published as *Exptl. Cell Res. Suppl.* **1**: 24-31 (1949).
18a. Clever, U.: Puffing in giant chromosomes of Diptera and the mechanism of its control. *In* "The Nucleohistones" (J. Bonner and P. Ts'o, eds.), p. 317. Holden-Day, San Francisco, California, 1964.
19. Dallam, R. D.: The chemical composition of nucleic and cytoplasmic granules. *Arch. Biochem. Biophys.* **54**: 24-37 (1955).
20. Dallam, R. D., and Thomas, L. E.: Chemical studies on mammalian sperm. *Biochim. Biophys. Acta* **11**: 79-89 (1953).
21. Daly, M. M., Allfrey, V. G., and Mirsky, A. E.: Uptake of $N^{15}$-glycine by components of cell nuclei. *J. Gen. Physiol.* **36**: 173-179 (1952).
21a. Deakin, H., Ord, M. G., and Stocken, L. A.: Glucose 6-phosphate-dehydrogenase activity and thiol content of thymus nuclei from control and X-irradiated rats. *Biochem. J.* **89**: 296-304 (1963).
22. Debov, S. S.: Amount of protein fractions in the cell nuclei of normal and malignant tissues. *Biokhimiya* **16**: 314-320 (1951).
23. Debov, S. S.: The amount of protein fractions in cell nuclei of benign tumors and of embryonic and regenerating tissues. *Vopr. Med. Khim.* **6**: 117-124 (1953).
24. Desjardins, R., and Busch, H.: Effect of uracil mustard on incorporation of L-lysine-$^{14}C$ into acidic nucleolar proteins of the Walker tumor and liver. *Texas Rept. Biol. Med.* **22**: 444-453 (1964).
25. Dounce, A. L.: The isolation of nuclei from tumor cells. *Exptl. Cell Res. Suppl.* **9**: 126-143 (1963).
26. Dounce, A. L., and Umana, R.: The proteases of isolated cell nuclei. *Biochemistry* **1**: 811-819 (1962).

27. Engbring, V. K., and Laskowski, M.: Protein components of chicken erythrocyte nuclei. *Biochim. Biophys. Acta* **11**: 244-251 (1953).

27a. Felix, K., Tabrizi, A., and Zimmermann, E.: Nachweis der "zusätzlichen Aminosäuren" Glutamin- und Asparaginsäure in Nucleoprotamin- und Desoxyribonucleinsäure-Präparaten von *Clupea harengus*. *Z. Phys. Chem.* **336**: 53-56 (1964).

28. Georgiev, G. P.: A histochemical study of nucleohistone fractions of cell nuclei. *Biokhimiya* **23**: 700-706 (1958).

29. Georgiev, G. P.: Ribonucleic acid of nucleolo-chromosomal apparatus. *Biokhimiya* **26**: 1095-1107 (1961).

30. Georgiev, G. P., Ermolaeva, L. P., and Zbarskii, I. B.: The quantitative relations between proteins and nucleoprotein fractions of various tissues. *Biokhimiya* **25**: 318-322 (1960).

31. Georgiev, G. P., and Mantieva, V. L.: The isolation of cell nuclei by a phenol method and a study of nuclei characteristics. *Biokhimiya* **25**: 143-150 (1960).

32. Georgiev, G. P., and Mantieva, V. L.: The isolation of DNA-like RNA and ribosomal RNA from the nucleolo-chromosomal apparatus of mammalian cells. *Biochim. Biophys. Acta* **61**: 153-154 (1962).

33. Georgiev, G. P., and Mantieva, V. L.: Methods of isolation and nucleotide composition of informational and ribosomal ribonucleic acids of nucleolo-chromosomal apparatus. *Biokhimiya* **27**: 949-957 (1962).

34. Georgiev, G. P., Mantieva, V. L., and Zbarskii, I. B.: RNA fractions in cell nuclei isolated by phenol and by sucroseglycophosphate. *Biochim. Biophys. Acta* **37**: 373-374 (1960).

35. Horn, E. C.: Extranuclear histone in the amphibian oocyte. *Proc. Natl. Acad. Sci. U.S.* **48**: 257-265 (1962).

36. Horn, E. C., and Ward, C. L.: The localization of basic proteins in the nuclei of larval *Drosophila* salivary glands. *Proc. Natl. Acad. Sci. U.S.* **43**: 776-779 (1957).

37. Hyde, B. B.: An evaluation of the Barnett and Seligman procedure when used to determine changes in the ratio of nuclear protein-bound disulfide to sulfhydryl groups during mitosis. *J. Histochem. Cytochem.* **9**: 640-646 (1961).

37a. Jellum, E., and Eldjarn, L.: Studies on nuclear thiol proteins by chromatography on organomercurial polysaccharide. *Biochem. J.* **92**: 7P-8P (1964).

38. Kirkham, W. R., and Thomas, L. E.: Isolation of globulins from cellular nuclei. *J. Biol. Chem.* **200**: 53-57 (1953).

39. Kroeger, H., Jacob, J., and Sirlin, J. L.: The movement of nuclear protein from the cytoplasm to the nucleus of salivary cells. *Exptl. Cell Res.* **31**: 416-423 (1963).

40. Lawley, P. D., and Brookes, P.: The action of alkylating agents on deoxyribonucleic acid in relation to biological effects of the alkylating agents. *Exptl. Cell Res. Suppl.* **9**: 512-520 (1963).

41. Levin, E., and Thomas, L. E.: Cellular lipoproteins—the insoluble lipoproteins of rat liver fractions. *Exptl. Cell Res.* **22**: 363-369 (1961).

41a. Liisberg, M. F.: Residual protein. *Acta Anat.* **53**: 240-258 (1963).

42. Lilienfeld, L.: Zur Chemie der Leukocyten. *Z. Physiol. Chem.* **18**: 472-486 (1893).

43. Malec, J., Kornacka, L., Wojnarowska, M., and Zakrzewski, K.: The activation of nuclear nucleoproteins during phagocytosis. *Exptl. Cell Res.* **25**: 457-460 (1961).

44. Mantiev, V. A., and Belousov, A. P.: Globulin fraction of nuclear proteins of cells in normal tissues and malignant tumors. *Vopr. Med. Khim.* **8**: 514-516 (1962).

45. Mattingly, A., Sr.: Nuclear protein synthesis in *Vicia faba*. *Exptl. Cell Res.* **29**: 314-326 (1963).

46. Mayer, D. T., and Gulick, A.: The nature of the proteins of cellular nuclei. *J. Biol. Chem.* **146**: 433-440 (1942).

47. Mazia, D.: The particulate organization of the chromosome. *Proc. Natl. Acad. Sci. U.S.* **40**: 521-726 (1954).

48. Mazia, D., and Dan, K.: Isolation of mitotic apparatus of sea urchin egg. *Proc. Natl. Acad. Sci. U.S.* **38**: 826-838 (1952).

48a. McConkey, E. H., and Hopkins, J. W.: The relationship of the nucleolus to the synthesis of ribosomal RNA in HeLa cells. *Proc. Natl. Acad. Sci. U.S.* **51**: 1197-1204 (1964).

49. Mirsky, A. E., and Pollister, A. W.: Nucleoproteins of cell nuclei. *Proc. Natl. Acad. Sci. U.S.* **28**: 344-352 (1942).

50. Mirsky, A. E., and Pollister, A. W.: Chromosomin, a deoxyribosenucleoprotein complex of the cell nucleus. *J. Gen. Physiol.* **30**: 117-147 (1946).

50a. Olenick, J. G., and Hahn, F. E.: Amino acids in hydrolysates of deoxyribonucleic acid of *Escherichia coli*. *Biochim. Biophys. Acta* **87**: 535-537 (1964).

50b. Patel, G., and Wang, T.-Y.: Chromatography and electrophoresis of nuclear soluble proteins. *Exptl. Cell Res.* **34**: 120-130 (1964).

50c. Pogo, A. O., Pogo, B. G. T., Littau, V. C., Allfrey, V. G., Mirsky, A. E., and Hamilton, M. G.: The purification and properties of ribosomes from the thymus nucleus. *Biochim. Biophys. Acta* **55**: 849-864 (1962).

51. Prescott, D. M., and Bender, M. A.: Synthesis and behavior of nuclear proteins during the cell life cycle. *J. Cellular Comp. Physiol.* **62**: 175-194 (1963).

52. Samarina, O. P.: Incorporation of labeled amino acids into protein fractions of nuclei of the liver and of the Ehrlich ascites carcinoma cells. *Biokhimiya* **26**: 61-69 (1961).

53. Schmid, K., MacNair, M. B., and Bürgi, A. F.: The chromatographic separation and purification of acidic proteins on carboxylated ion exchange resins. *J. Biol. Chem.* **230**: 853-864 (1958).

54. Smellie, R. M. S., McIndoe, W. M., and Davidson, J. N.: The incorporation of $N^{15}$, $S^{35}$, and $C^{14}$ into nucleic acids and proteins of rat liver. *Biochim. Biophys. Acta* **11**: 559-565 (1953).

54a. Smetana, K., and Busch, H.: On the ultrastructure of the Walker 256 carcinosarcoma. *Cancer Res.* **23**: 1600-1603 (1963).

55. Smetana, K., Steele, W. J., and Busch, H.: A nuclear ribonucleoprotein network. *Exptl. Cell Res.* **31**: 198-202 (1963).

56. Sorof, S., Young, E. M., McCue, M. M., and Fetterman, P. L.: Zonal electrophoresis of the soluble proteins of liver and tumor in azo dye carcinogenesis. *Cancer Res.* **23**: 864-882 (1963).

57. Stedman, E.: The chemistry of cell nuclei. *Edinburgh Med. J.* **51**: 353-366 (1944).

58. Stedman, E., and Stedman, E.: "Chromosomin" and nucleic acids. *Nature* **153**: 500-502 (1944).
59. Stedman, E., and Stedman, E.: The function of deoxyribosenucleic acid in the cell nucleus. *Symp. Soc. Exptl. Biol.* **1**: 232-251 (1947).
60. Steele, W. J.: Cross-linking of DNA to nuclear proteins by difunctional alkylating agents. *Proc. Am. Assoc. Cancer Res.* **3**: 364 (1962).
61. Steele, W. J., and Busch, H.: Studies on acidic nuclear proteins of the Walker tumor and liver. *Cancer Res.* **23**: 1153-1163 (1963).
62. Steele, W. J., and Busch, H.: Studies on the composition of residual proteins of isolated nuclei of liver and Walker 256 carcinosarcoma. *Exptl. Cell Res.* **33**: 68-72 (1964).
62a. Steele, W. J., Okamura, N., and Busch, H.: Prevention of loss of RNA, DNA and protein into lipid solvents. *Biochim. Biophys. Acta* **87**: 490-492 (1964).
63. Wang, T.-Y.: Globulin of calf thymus nuclei and the *in vitro* incorporation of $C^{14}$ adenosine triphosphate into globulin-RNA. *Biochim. Biophys. Acta* **45**: 8-14 (1960).
64. Wang, T.-Y.: Physicochemical and metabolic properties of nuclear ribosomes. *Exptl. Cell Res. Suppl.* **9**: 213-219 (1963).
65. Wang, T.-Y.: Incorporation of $^{14}C$ leucine into nuclear pH 5 fraction and its transfer to nuclear ribosomes. *Biochim. Biophys. Acta* **68**: 633-639 (1963).
66. Wang, T.-Y.: Metabolic activities of nuclear proteins and nucleic acids. *Biochim. Biophys. Acta* **68**: 52-61 (1963).
66a. Wang, T.-Y.: Properties of nuclear ribosomal protein from calf thymus. *Biochim. Biophys. Acta* **87**: 141-151 (1964).
67. Wang, T.-Y., Kirkham, W. R., Dallam, R. D., Mayer, D. T., and Thomas, L. E.: Acidic proteins of cellular nuclei. *Nature* **165**: 974-975 (1950).
68. Wang, T.-Y., Mayer, D. T., and Thomas, L. E.: A lipoprotein of rat liver nuclei. *Exptl. Cell Res.* **4**: 102-106 (1953).
69. Wheeler, G. P., and Alexander, J. A.: Studies with mustards. V. *In vivo* fixation of $C^{14}$ of labeled alkylating agents by bilaterally grown sensitive and resistant tumors. *Cancer Res.* **24**: 1331-1338 (1964).
69a. Wheeler, G. P., and Alexander, J. A.: Studies with mustards. VI. Effects of alkylating agents upon nucleic acid synthesis in bilaterally grown sensitive and resistant tumors. *Cancer Res.* **24**: 1338-1347 (1964).
70. Zbarskii, I. B., and Debov, S. S.: Proteins of cell nuclei. *Dokl. Akad. Nauk S.S.S.R.* **63**: 795-798 (1948).
71. Zbarskii, I. B., Dmitrieva, N. P., and Yermolayeva, L. P.: On the structure of tumor cell nuclei. *Exptl. Cell Res.* **27**: 573-576 (1962).
72. Zbarskii, I. B., and Georgiev, G. P.: Cytological characteristics of protein and nucleoprotein fractions of cell nuclei. *Biochim. Biophys. Acta* **32**: 301-302 (1959).
73. Zbarskii, I. B., and Perevoschchikova, K. A.: Contractile properties of cell nuclei proteins. *Biokhimiya* **16**: 112-124 (1951).
74. Zbarskii, I. B., and Perevoschchikova, K. A.: The nature of the contractile substance in the cell nucleus. *Biokhimiya* **16**: 347-355 (1951).
75. Zbarskii, I. B., and Samarina, O. P.: Fractionation of nuclear proteins and incorporation of glycine-$C^{14}$ into them. *Biokhimiya* **27**: 557-564 (1962).

# CHAPTER IX

# Nuclear Enzymes



## Introduction

The critical problems in the study of nuclear enzymes have been those of demonstrating that enzymes are localized in the nucleus and then of establishing the nuclear sites where they are concentrated. As indicated by Siebert and Humphrey (62a), the nuclear enzymes can now be provisionally divided into different groups on the basis of their solubility in saline solutions. The group of enzymes soluble in 0.14 *M* NaCl contains all the glycolytic enzymes as well as DNA polymerase. The second group of enzymes is soluble in 1 *M* NaCl and contains DPN synthetase or pyrophosphorylase as well as two nucleoside triphosphatases. A third group is solubilized by detergents and includes enzymes that are hydrolases usually found in microsomal or lysosomal fractions. Because of the ready solubility of the first group of enzymes in aqueous media there has been considerable question about their localization in the nucleus.

Another problem in the study of nuclear enzymes is the selection of the particular types of nuclei that should be considered as prototypes. An example of a nucleus that apparently contains many enzymes that are found in the cytoplasm in other types of cells is the nucleus of the thymus cell or thymocyte. The nucleus of this cell apparently can carry out a variety of types of metabolism including synthesis of ATP through glycolytic and oxidative systems, synthesis of protein in specialized ribosomes, and synthesis of messenger-RNA in the nucleolus (1). On the other hand, the liver cell has a nucleus which apparently lacks some of these activities although it contains enzymes of glycolysis and the citric acid cycle. The amount of nuclear ribosomes in the normal liver cell is apparently very small or at a level such that it is difficult to distinguish between the ribosomes present due to cytoplasmic contamination and those that are actually present in the nucleus.

One method that might be useful for intracellular localization of enzymes is histochemical analysis of enzyme content in tissue sections or in various cellular fractions. Alkaline phosphatase had been suggested to be an enzyme that was specifically localized to the nucleus because all the techniques employed showed that the concentration in nuclei was at least twice that of other cellular fractions. However, Novikoff (46, 47) showed that the positive staining of nuclei with the histochemical technique was unrelated to the enzyme activity, but was rather related to the adsorption by nuclei of calcium phosphate in the course of the histochemical procedure. A satisfactory biochemical proof for the presence of alkaline phosphatase in nuclei was not obtained. This type of artifact has resulted in uncertainty about the use of histochemical analysis for nuclear enzyme localization (16a).

The type of artifact represented by the studies on alkaline phosphatase is adherence of cytoplasmic components to nuclear preparations. This can come about either because soluble enzymes are adsorbed to nuclear structures or because mitochondria, lysosomes, or endoplasmic reticulum adhere to nuclear preparations (13, 29, 30, 54, 57, 58) (see also page 62).

## DPN Synthetase or Pyrophosphorylase

Out of the confusion surrounding the localization of nuclear enzymes came the finding of Hogeboom and Schneider (29, 30) that the enzyme DPN synthetase or DPN pyrophosphorylase is a nuclear enzyme. This enzyme catalyzes the reaction:

$$\text{ATP} + \text{nicotinamide mononucleotide} \rightleftharpoons \text{DPN} + \text{pyrophosphate}$$

When nuclei were obtained from liver cells in the highest purity available at the time, the enzyme was in high concentration within the nucleus and was present in low concentrations and in low amounts in the remainder of the cellular fractions obtained. Apparently, the main reason for the persistence of this enzyme in the nucleus was its very low solubility in the aqueous media of low ionic strength employed for preparation of the cytoplasmic and nuclear fractions (60, 62a). Either DPN synthetase forms an insoluble complex with a nuclear constituent or it is virtually insoluble in the aqueous systems. It is also very stable and apparently resistant to either the hydrolytic enzymes of the nucleus or the cytoplasm that may course through the nuclei in the process of their isolation.

The role of this enzyme in the nucleus is not yet clear. Although DPN is a cofactor of glycolytic and oxidative reactions and transhydrogenations, there is no evidence that it is a rate-limiting cofactor for any nuclear process. That it might be rate-limiting for cytoplasmic reactions was suggested, but there is little evidence that this is usually the case. The initial suggeston of Hogeboom and Schneider (29, 30) that this enzyme was involved in the nuclear control of cytoplasmic oxidation reactions has not been further amplified, but there seems to be little reason now to believe that either synthesis of DPN or its concentration normally controls reaction rates. Nonetheless, this enzyme has served as a kind of enzymatic standard for nuclear isolation techniques. Recently, evidence has been provided that this enzyme is closely associated with nuclear ribonucleoproteins, possibly those limited in location to the nucleolus (69a).

## Enzymes Involved in Synthesis of Nucleic Acids

*DNA Polymerase.* There is much evidence that the "duplicase" (24, 28) reactions involved in the DNA-primed synthesis of DNA occur exclusively in the nucleus. It would seem that the DNA polymerases should be present in high concentrations in the nuclei, particularly in dividing cells if they are involved in replication or "duplication" of DNA. Moreover, the biosynthesis of messenger and other RNAs is now accepted to be a nuclear function carried out by "transcriptases" (28), the DNA-primed RNA polymerases. The enzymes involved in these reactions would also be expected to be localized in the nucleus.

Because of the general interest in the enzymes of nucleic acid synthesis and their products in recent years (4, 6, 8, 23, 37, 38, 47a, 52a) it was logical to attempt to precisely define their cellular localization. The initial studies of Smellie and Eason (65) produced the very surprising finding that DNA polymerase (or DNA-nucleotidyl transferase) was primarily localized in the cytoplasm of regenerating liver cells. This result was not accepted by these investigators and led them to search for reasons why the enzyme should have been removed from the nucleus. They found that this enzyme was apparently readily extracted from the nucleus by the aqueous media employed for preparation of the nuclei such as 0.25 *M* sucrose or 0.14 *M* NaCl. The methods for preparation of nuclei have been dealt with earlier, but in this case, the methods are quite critical for evaluation of the results. In the initial procedures employed by Smellie and Eason (65) the technique for isolation of the nuclei was essentially a modification of the earlier procedures of Schneider *et al.* (29, 56) and of Chauveau *et al.* (11). In these procedures, the cells are initially dispersed in a medium that is 0.25 *M* with respect to sucrose and 0.0018–0.0033 *M* with respect to $Ca^{++}$.

The extensive studies of Siebert and his colleagues have served to show that the Behrens procedure (3) and subsequent modifications (2, 60, 63) do not interfere with the activities of a number of nuclear enzymes. Smellie and Keir (32, 33, 64, 66) and their colleagues carried forward studies on the localization of DNA polymerase (DNA-nucleotidyl transferases) in such nuclei. The largest concentration of the enzyme was found in the nucleus, not in the cytoplasm, when the nonaqueous technique was employed (Table 9-I). They, therefore, con-

TABLE 9-I
CONCENTRATION OF DNA POLYMERASE IN NUCLEAR AND CYTOPLASMIC FRACTIONS OF CALF THYMUS (66)

| Fraction | mμmole/mg[a] |
|---|---|
| Nuclear extract | 6.0 |
| Nuclear sediment | 1.5 |
| Cytoplasmic extract | 4.0 |
| Cytoplasmic sediment | 2.5 |

[a] The values are millimicromoles of $P^{32}$-TMP incorporated per milligram of protein.

cluded that the enzyme was sufficiently soluble to be extracted with the 0.25 *M* sucrose; as a result, it would be very low in amount in the nuclei isolated in this medium. This study has ramifications that are quite important from the point of view of methodology for isolation of nuclei since the suggestion naturally emerges that many nuclear constituents are leached out in the course of isolation of nuclei and their nucleoprotein products. Since the nonaqueous procedure is by no means without drawbacks, the field of isolation of nuclei and study of the components of nuclei has clearly reached a rather difficult state (13, 54, 62a) (see also page 59).

In an effort to determine whether DNA polymerase was present in the cytoplasm of living amebas, Prescott *et al.* (52) introduced exogenous DNA into living cells by means of pinocytosis. When cells exposed to DNA were simultaneously exposed to labeled thymidine, uptake of isotope into acid-insoluble cytoplasmic molecules occurred. DNase removed this radioactivity. In cells that were not exposed to DNA primer, no labeling occurred. Therefore, it seems possible that extranuclear DNA synthesis could occur although rigorous chemical proof for this has not yet been provided.

*Linear Synthesis of DNA across the Genome.* Some very important experiments have recently been carried out on the "duplicase" reactions that suggest that DNA may be duplicated simultaneously on both strands of the molecule. Kimball and Prescott (34) showed that in the macronucleus of *Euplotes,* bands of DNA synthesis moved linearly down the strandlike nucleus. When a forked tip was found in the nucleus, DNA synthesis proceeded synchronously in both prongs of the fork. Cairns (9) has shown that at least in the bacterial chromosome, which is apparently a single chromosome, the formation of DNA proceeds linearly from one end to the other. This result also means that both strands of DNA are simultaneously replicated.

Although the discovery of the reaction catalyzed by DNA polymerase has provided one mechanism for the formation of DNA, it has not completely clarified the problem of DNA synthesis. The formation of one strand of DNA by DNA polymerase proceeds by the successive addition of deoxyribonucleotides through the mechanism of pyrophosphorolysis of the terminal groups of the deoxyribonucleotide triphosphate by the 3′-hydroxyl of the terminal deoxyribose on the forming DNA chain. This reaction would provide for formation of DNA chains in the direction of left to right as shown in Fig. 9-1. If the chains of DNA were formed by two enzymes, each proceeding from the side of the oligonucleotide that contained a free 3-OH (Fig. 9-2), there would be little reason to invoke the possibility of additional enzymes for biosynthesis of DNA. However, there have been objections to this

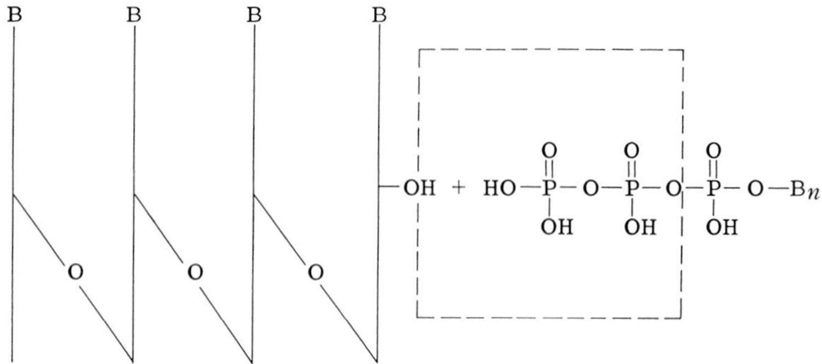


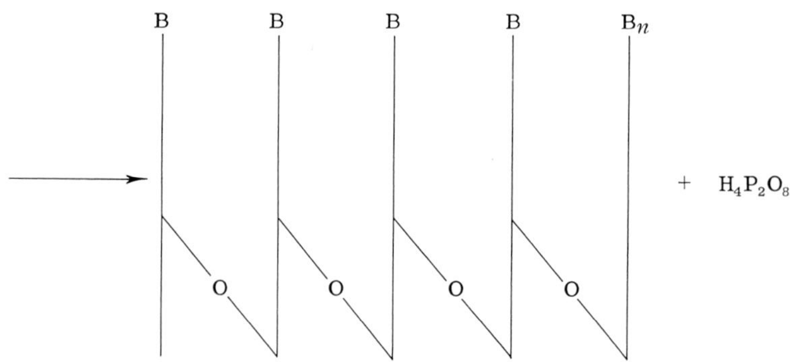


FIG. 9-1. Stepwise addition of deoxyribonucleotides to DNA by DNA polymerase.

FIG. 9-2. Directions of DNA replication on the double DNA helix if the unidirectional reaction of DNA polymerase is followed.

mechanism based on the fact that the reactions catalyzed by DNA polymerase are too slow to account for the rapid rate of synthesis of DNA in bacteria (36).

The data of Kimball and Prescott (34) and Cairns (9) showed that that scheme proposed in Fig. 9-1 cannot totally account for the synthesis of DNA. Although it is difficult to visualize that synthesis could occur in the absence of a pyrophosphorylated intermediate, the question is which intermediate could be pyrophosphorylated. Two possibilities are suggested in Figs. 9-3 and 9-4, namely, a nucleotide that

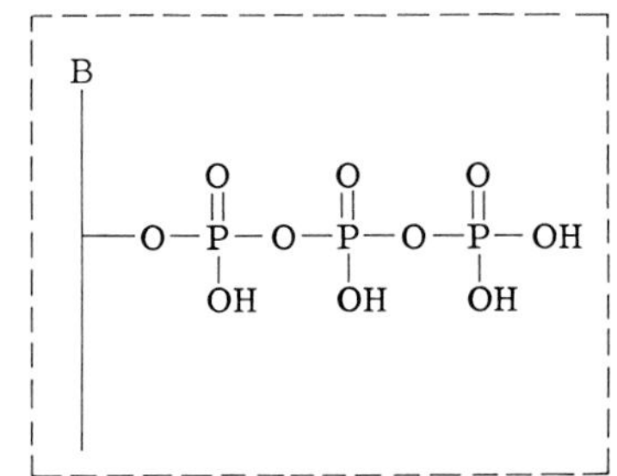


FIG. 9-3. Deoxyribonucleoside-3′-triphosphate.

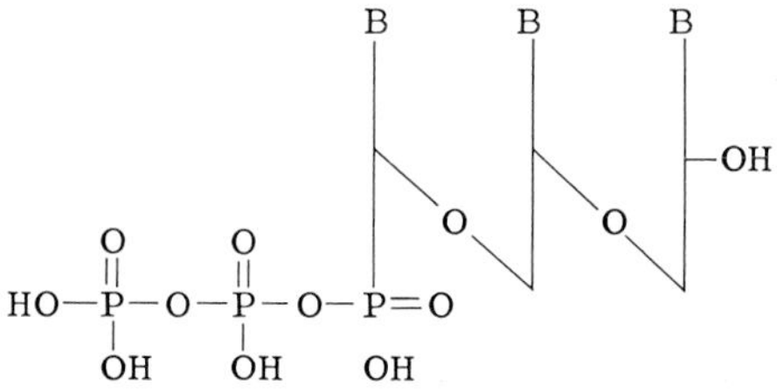

B B B
—OH
O O
O O
HO—P—O—P—O—P=O
OH OH OH

FIG. 9-4. Oligonucleotide-5′-triphosphate.

has a pyrophosphate on the 3′-hydroxyl or a triphosphate of the preformed oligodeoxyribonucleoside. Neither of these intermediates is known, and an enzyme that could convert a DNA 5′-phosphate to a DNA 5′-triphosphate has not been reported. The same holds true for the conversion of the deoxyribonucleoside to a 3′-pyrophosphate (55a).

***Factors Controlling DNA Synthesis.*** Evidence has been obtained by a number of workers (8, 23, 33, 66) that there may be enzymes that destroy the deoxyribonucleotide precursors, oligodeoxyribonucleotides and/or DNA. Grav *et al.* (23) have reported that a nuclease apparently blocks the synthesis of DNA by hydrolyzing oligodeoxyribonucleotides. Keir and Smith (33, 66) have found that oligodeoxyribonucleotides enhance DNA biosynthesis. They also found that there are inhibitors of the nucleases. The physiological significance of these inhibitors and nucleases has not been established.

## RNA Polymerase

RNA polymerase activity has been mentioned previously in connection with the studies on suppression of biosynthesis of RNA by histones (Chapter V). This enzyme is responsible for the linkage of ribonucleotides to form RNA on the DNA surface and has been referred to as a "transcriptase" by Haruna *et al.* (28) and by Gros (24). In mammalian nuclei, RNA polymerase is a part of an insoluble complex of protein and DNA and has been referred to as an "aggregate" enzyme. Other than its action, relatively little is understood about it. Evidence that it adheres to both the nucleoli and the chromatin has been obtained in studies in this and other laboratories (7, 40, 41, 53, 70). Unlike DNA polymerase, the enzyme obtained from mammalian tissues has the insolubility that characterizes DPN-synthetase. Although RNA polymerase has not been found in soluble form in mammalian systems,[1] a soluble RNA polymerase has been obtained from bacteria (10, 31).

At the present time it is not established whether this enzyme is either an acidic or basic protein and whether it is active in soluble form or functions right on the surface of the DNA. Although controversy still exists as to whether it acts on DNA that is single- or double-stranded, it is difficult to comprehend how information from both strands of DNA could be copied simultaneously, how information might be selectively copied from a single strand, and/or how unwinding of DNA could occur in the interphase cell.

Since RNA is generally assumed to be single-stranded, there is little difficulty at the moment in accepting the concept that a single enzyme simply serves to transcribe the information from DNA into internucleotide linkages. Evidence that nucleotides of RNA are linked by enzymes that have some degree of specificity for the primer was recently obtained by Haruna *et al.* (28), who reported that RNA polymerase from MS-2 virus would not catalyze RNA synthesis on RNA from TMV or TYMV virus.

In mammalian cells, the biosynthesis of RNA apparently proceeds almost entirely in the cell nucleus (7, 8, 22). Both *in vivo* (45a) and

[1] Recently, RNA polymerase has been isolated in soluble form from rat testis (2a).

*in vitro* studies (48a) have shown that substantial amounts of RNA are formed in the nucleoli, particularly in neoplastic cells. Evidence provided by Harris (25–27) suggests that some of the biosynthesis of RNA may occur in the cytoplasm, but there is very little support for the view that cytoplasmic RNA biosynthesis constitutes a significant part of overall RNA biosynthesis (22). Calculations from the data obtained with $P^{32}$ labeling of RNA (45a) have shown that virtually all the label entering the cytoplasm is lost from the nucleus. Of course, the very elegant studies of Goldstein and his associates (17–21) served to establish that the synthesis of RNA is a nuclear phenomenon in amebas. One point made by Harris (25) is that the biosynthesis of RNA is excessive for the amount that finally arrives in the cytoplasm so that in fact some RNA may be destroyed in the nucleus. It was suggested (26, 27) that a specific nuclear enzyme, a polynucleotide phosphorylase, is responsible for this intranuclear destruction of RNA.

*Mechanism of Action of RNA Polymerase.* A great deal of interest has been developed recently in the mechanism of action of RNA polymerase. When the RNA polymerase was purified from bacterial sources by Hurwitz (31) and Chamberlin and Berg (10) it became possible to study its requirements for optimal activity and its products. Chamberlin and Berg (10) found that the enzyme not only catalyzed the formation of RNA with a base composition complementary to that of single-stranded DNA, but also catalyzed the formation of RNA complementary to both strands of double-stranded DNA. This experiment was made possible by the availability of single- and double-stranded DNA from phage ΦX-174.

When only ATP was available as a substrate, the enzyme preparation catalyzed the formation of a polyadenylic acid, but none of the other ribonucleoside triphosphates were converted into the corresponding homopolymers. Addition of other ribonucleoside triphosphates to the system catalyzing the formation of the polyadenylic acid inhibited the formation of this polymer. The enzyme thus has a number of remarkable features including the ability to catalyze formation of a homopolymer of adenylic acid, the ability to catalyze the formation of phosphodiester bonds between the nucleotides of RNA in a highly specific order such that the bases are complementary to the bases of DNA and a remarkably tight adherence to DNA in the mammalian system that has prevented isolation of the enzyme.

Since the enzyme has not been purified adequately for systematic studies of its specificity and the number of its components, one cannot yet state whether it is a "four-headed" enzyme with specificity for each nucleoside triphosphate, or four enzymes each with specificity for a different nucleoside triphosphate.

A marked increase in the labeling of RNA in DNA-primed systems was found by Krakow (35) following addition of polyamines, i.e., putrescine, spermine, and spermidine (69). Although the mechanism of action of the polyamines was not established, the possibility was suggested that they might combine with newly formed RNA and stimulate its release from DNA. In addition, the possibility was suggested that the polyamines might "prepare" ribosomes for utilization of messenger RNA.

The relationship between RNA synthesis and mitosis was explored by Prescott and Bender (51) in HeLa cells and Chinese hamster cells in tissue culture. During mitosis, uridine uptake into RNA stopped completely. The synthesis of RNA stopped before disappearance of the nucleolus and disintegration of the nuclear membrane. When the nuclear membrane broke down, the nucleolus disappeared and RNA of the nucleus and nucleolus was released into the cytoplasm. Colchicine, which arrested the cells in metaphase, also blocked RNA synthesis. The enzymatic mechanisms by which RNA synthesis is suppressed before and during mitosis have not yet been elaborated.

*Nucleolar Enzymes.* As might be anticipated from the intensive biosynthesis of RNA in the nucleolus, RNA polymerase activity is readily found in nucleolar preparations (53). Following injection of thioacetamide into rats, there is marked enlargement of nucleoli in livers. This enlargement is associated with a marked increase in RNA polymerase activity (69b). Only small levels of activity of ribonuclease have been found in nucleolar preparations of normal liver. Remarkable increases, i.e., ten- to twelvefold, in ribonuclease activity have been found in nuclei and nucleoli of thioacetamide-treated animals.

*Nucleotide Synthesis.* One of the important questions regarding synthesis of the nucleic acids of mammalian cells concerns the site of synthesis of the precursors. Although the cytoplasm is rich in ATP and other ribonucleoside triphosphates, the site of synthesis of the deoxyribonucleoside triphosphates is still somewhat uncertain (57). Logically, the biosynthesis of these compounds should occur in the nucleus where DNA synthesis occurs, but to this point evidence for selective localization of either kinases or the deoxyribonucleoside phosphorylases has not been obtained.

In particular, the site of synthesis of thymidine triphosphate (TTP) would be of interest. This cofactor is the one that has been suggested by Smellie (64) to be the rate-limiting cofactor for the synthesis of DNA. It has been indicated in the discussion of the function of histones (Chapter V) that this point of view is not the only one with regard to the mechanisms of control of DNA synthesis. In the view of Smellie (64), the pathways leading to TTP are normally operative to the stage of formation of TMP. The deoxyribonucleotide, TMP, is biosynthesized through several pathways including transformylation of deoxyuridylic acid, a kinase reaction in which thymidine is directly phosphorylated, and an indirect pathway involving deamination of deoxycytidylic acid. The site and relative importance of each of these metabolic steps is far from obvious at present. The biosynthesis of TTP is markedly increased in cells that are about to divide, and such reactions as a one-step transphosphorylation or pyrophosphorylation of TMP occur with considerably greater rapidity in such tissues as the regenerating liver.

Siebert and Humphrey (62a) have found a variety of enzymes of ribonucleotide metabolism in rat liver nuclei; these include orotidylate pyrophosphorylase, UDP-glucose pyrophosphorylase, a UTP dephosphorylating enzyme, a 5′-nucleotidase, and uridine kinase.

## Nuclear Ribonucleases

The initial product of RNA synthesis in mammalian cells is a very high molecular weight material with a sedimentation constant of 45 S (55). Very soon after it is formed it is converted into RNAs of ribosomal size with sedimentation constants of 36, 28, and 16 S. Probably 4 S RNA or transfer RNA of much lower molecular weight is not formed from the high molecular weight RNA. The nature of the newly formed RNA and the reasons for its breakdown are not known, but it is logical to infer that some of the nuclear RNases are involved (22).

One enzyme that may become of increasing interest is the polynucleotide phosphorylase that has been described by Harris (25, 26) as being responsible for the breakdown of rapidly synthesized RNA. In studies on HeLa cells, Harris noted that actinomycin D inhibited labeling of RNA but did not affect the enzyme that degraded the rapidly labeled RNA. The experimental evidence for this was simply that a rapid decrease occurred in the total radioactivity in the nuclear RNA without a significant increment in the cytoplasmic RNA. Other enzymes apparently hydrolyzed the nucleoside diphosphates to the corresponding 5′-nucleotides.

Although the functions of ribonucleases are not generally regarded as being related to control of gene function, Felsenfeld *et al.* (14) have suggested that regulation of protein synthesis may result from destabilization of helical structures of nucleic acids by proteins. As an example of the selectivity which such proteins might possess, they have pointed out that pancreatic RNase has a greater affinity for AT regions than for GC regions. Evidence has been provided that this enzyme contributed to strand breakage or separation at temperatures below 60°C.

As noted previously, thioacetamide induced a marked increase in the latent ribonuclease activity in cell nuclei. Conceivably, this ribonuclease serves to hydrolyze extranucleolar RNA. The mechanism of the response of the cell to this hydrolysis is not clear, but apparently it is correlated with the great enlargement of the nucleoli in the liver cells.

## Oxidative Enzymes in the Nucleus

Most of the studies on the presence of glycolytic enzymes and enzymes of the citric acid cycle in nuclei have been carried out with nuclei prepared by the modifications of the Behrens procedure that were introduced by Allfrey *et al.* (2). Siebert (59, 60) has reviewed the kinds of enzymes that are present in nuclei of a variety of cells; among the glycolytic enzymes that have been reported to be present are hexokinase, phosphofructokinase, aldolase, 6-phosphogluconate dehydrogenase, glucose-6-phosphate dehydrogenase, triosephosphate dehydrogenase, triosephosphate isomerase, enolase, pyruvic kinase, and lactic dehydrogenase. Other related enzymes that are present in nuclei include $\alpha$-glycerol phosphate dehydrogenase and phosphoglycerate kinase. Penniall *et al.* (48) have also shown that nuclei have activity in conversion of inorganic to organic phosphate, presumably as a result of phosphorylation of ribonucleotides (5).

The overall glycolytic activity of nuclei has been determined; it was found to be approximately the same in nuclei of normal and of regenerating liver and in tumors (61). One of the important characteristics of the glycolytic enzymes is their ready solubility in aqueous media; hence, it is difficult to determine their concentration in nuclei when isolation techniques are employed that utilize aqueous solvents. When nuclei were isolated by the nonaqueous procedures, the specific activities of the enzymes of glycolysis were essentially the same in nuclei and in the cytoplasmic fractions (60). The same holds true for the relative activities of the enzymes of the varying fractions.

One question that has been discussed is whether the amount of glycolytic activity of the nuclear fraction is large compared to that of the cytoplasm. Approximately 10% of the total glycolytic potential of the liver cell was found in the nucleus (57, 60), and this is approximately the same percentage of the total cell volume that is comprised by the nucleus. Thus, the nucleus is not a major site of the glycolytic activity of the cell, but on the other hand the glycolytic reactions in the nucleus may be important to nuclear function (57, 60).

Schneider (57) has pointed out that improvement is necessary in techniques for the study of nuclear enzymes, particularly with regard to the possibility of contamination of the nuclei with cytoplasm. One of the points that Schneider (57) has made is that the content of glycolytic and hydrolytic enzymes in nuclear preparations diminished as the nuclear preparations were purified, as indicated by the increased concentration of DNA. Moreover, enzymes such as acid phosphatase and β-glucuronidase, which are concentrated in the lysosomes (12), and glucose-6-phosphatase, which is concentrated in microsomes, were also reported to be present in nuclei. Such data suggested to Schneider (57) that the organic solvents used in the nonaqueous technique permit coprecipitation of cytoplasmic structures with nuclei and hence that the nuclei only apparently contain these enzymes. Accordingly, there are still some reservations about the data that suggest that glycolytic and oxidative enzymes are present in the nucleus.

***Differences of Nuclear and Cytoplasmic Lactic Dehydrogenases.*** One kind of evidence that the nuclear enzymes differ from those of the cytoplasm is that provided recently by Siebert and Hannover (62). In their studies, paper electrophoresis, heat denaturation, reduction of α-ketobutyrate, reduction of DPN, and inhibition of the reaction by sulfite were used as comparative analyses for the nuclear and cytoplasmic lactic dehydrogenases. By these means, significant differences were not found between the nuclear and cytoplasmic lactic dehydrogenases. However, differences were found between these lactic dehydrogenases when studies were made on the rates of reduction of DPN analogs, temperature-dependent changes of kinetic properties, and pH-dependent binding of pyruvate as determined by substrate inhibition. This finding is one that needs to be extended to other enzymes and requires both confirmation and explanation. It suggests that nuclear enzymes may be linked to molecules that are not present in the cytoplasm but the possibility also exists that the identity of the proteins is different in the cytoplasm from that in the nucleus.

*Citric Acid Cycle Enzymes.* Evidence has also been obtained that there are enzymes involved in oxidation of substrates of the citric acid cycle in the nuclei. Stern *et al.* (67, 68) initially reported that malic and isocitric dehydrogenases were present in nuclei of thymocytes. In addition, they found that α-ketoglutaric acid was present in these nuclei. Siebert (59, 60) found that glutamic dehydrogenase was present in nuclei of liver cells as well as malic and isocitric dehydrogenase. He has not found either α-ketoglutaric oxidase or succinic dehydrogenase in the nuclear preparations. Since most of these enzymes are found in mitochondria, it would seem that either mitochondrial precursors are formed in nuclei or that there is adherence of cytoplasmic fractions to nuclei.

McEwen *et al.* (43–45) have indicated that the nuclear preparations from calf thymus carry out synthesis of RNA and protein with energy derived from ATP synthesis in nuclei. Unlike mitochondrial ATP synthesis, nuclear ATP synthesis was insensitive to $Co^{++}$, $Ca^{++}$, and methylene blue. Histones blocked mitochondrial ATP synthesis, but nuclear ATP synthesis was uninhibited. Moreover, DNase blocked nuclear ATP synthesis. A variety of enzymes of glycolysis and the citric acid cycle was found in their nuclear preparations. They also found the flavin coenzyme of succinic dehydrogenase and pyruvic, lactic, α-ketoglutaric, succinic, and malic acids in their preparations. Inhibitors of glycolysis and the citric acid cycle such as iodoacetic acid and fluoroacetic acid blocked nuclear respiration and decreased nuclear ATP levels.

## Enzymes of Protein Synthesis

Most of the studies on uptake of amino acids into proteins of isolated nuclei have been carried out with calf thymus nuclei in systems in which uptake of amino acids was measured by labeling of protein with radioactive amino acids. For the most part these studies have not attempted to show that the labeling was internal in the proteins or that the amino acids were bound in peptide linkages, and it is important to establish that the labeling was not simply due to terminal addition of the amino acids (see page 18). Allfrey *et al.* (1) have shown that the nuclei can rapidly synthesize the ATP required for labeling of proteins with radioactive amino acids. In some respects, these synthetic reactions for ATP were found to differ from those that are reported to occur in mitochondria. In addition, evidence has been presented for a substantial activity of the amino acid activating enzymes in the nuclei as well as the amino acid transferases (15, 16, 63). One important property that has been reported for the activity of the nuclear systems is the requirement for $Na^+$ (1). In this respect, the nuclear systems differ from those of the cytoplasm, which require $K^+$. Recently, it was found that nuclear enzymes of the liver convert L-glutamic acid to pyrrolidonecarboxylic acid; this reaction is an energy-requiring reaction (45b).

## Hydrolytic Enzymes of Nuclei

Stern *et al.* (67) reported that a variety of hydrolytic enzymes were present in nuclei including arginase, uricase, catalase, alkaline phosphatase, β-glucuronidase, esterases, and a nucleoside phosphorylase. They divided the nuclear enzymes into several groups: Those present in low concentrations were alkaline phosphatases, nucleotide phosphatases and β-glucuronidase. Esterases were present in varying concentrations. Nucleoside phosphorylase and guanase were present in high concentrations, as was adenine deaminase.

Siebert and his colleagues (60-63) reported the presence in nuclei of β-glucuronidase, acid phosphatase, glucose-6-phosphatase, triphosphatases, esterases, 5′-nucleotidases, phosphatases, and other enzymes, some of which are probably representative of lysosomal contamination of nuclear preparations (12). The presence of ribonucleases in nuclear preparations, and even in isolated histones has been reported by Leslie (39, 42) (cf. Chapter V). In addition, the presence of proteolytic enzymes in histone preparations has been reported by Phillips and Johns (49, 50). Other reports have appeared of catheptic activity in nuclear preparations. The presence in nuclei of polynucleotide phosphorylase has been reported. Somewhat surprisingly, cholinesterase has also been found in nuclei (6).

Siebert has also reported that some rather specific hydrolytic enzymes could be found in nuclei, such as guanosine triphosphatase, which is apparently completely specific for GTP. This enzyme has been extensively purified (60). Other enzymes that hydrolyze nucleoside and deoxyribonucleoside pyrophosphates have been found in the nuclei of liver cells (60). ATPases from kidney cortex of the pig referred to as ATPase A and B have been found to have different specificity for deoxy-ATP and ATP. ATPase A has a relatively higher activity in hydrolysis of deoxy-ATP and ITP than does ATPase B. The activity of these enzymes in hydrolysis of GTP, UTP, and CTP was similar to their activity in hydrolysis of the other triphosphates studied. Marked increases were found in the activities of these ATPases following hepatectomy, adrenalectomy, and treatment of rats with 3′-methyl-4-dimethylaminoazobenzene. Apparently, there was a greater increase in the pyrophosphorolytic activity for CTP in ATPase B and for UTP in ATPase A than in the activity for other substrates.

Although there is little doubt that there are hydrolytic enzymes in the nuclear preparations obtained by Siebert (60), one question is how they get into nuclei. Although they may be synthesized in the nucleus, another possibility is that there is simple diffusion of the soluble enzymes from cytoplasm to nucleus and back to the cytoplasm. The other possibility mentioned is that the enzymes from the cytoplasm simply adhere to the nucleus either as the whole molecules or as parts of organelles such as the lysosomes (12) that are simply not removed from the nucleus. The essence of the argument of Schneider (57) is that the latter is the case. However, Siebert (60) takes the position that it is not yet established whether lysosomes do contaminate nuclear preparations despite the fact that acid phosphatase and β-glucuronidase are present in his nuclear preparations. In fact, the specific activities of the β-glucuronidase and the acid phosphatase were between 40 and 100% of those of the whole tissue, and this finding diminishes the possibility that there is contamination of the nucleus with the lysosomes. He points out that the lysosomes are not in close proximity to the nucleus. The possibility has not been ruled out that the nuclei are the source of lysosomal enzymes.

*The role of the hydrolytic enzymes in the nucleus* is not clear, but it seems possible that they may either serve as a means for destruction of either cytoplasmic or nuclear macromolecules that are not required for nuclear reactions. In addition, these enzymes may serve as parts of controlling mechanisms that are related to either genetic function or the biosynthesis of specific proteins or ribonucleic acids by controlling the concentrations of precursors. Finally, they may be simple anachronisms that are remnants from evolutionary development. No specific role for a nuclear hydrolytic enzyme has been described, but the evidence for formation of ribosomal and messenger-RNAs from large precursors (55) suggests that specific cleavage enzymes cause formation of particles of defined sizes.

## Other Nuclear Enzymes

There is another group of enzymes that has been found in the nuclei for which a function has not been defined. These include such enzymes as adenosine deaminase, catalase, leucine aminopeptidase, peroxidase, tyrosinase, urocaninase, and verdoperoxidase. Some of these enzymes are potentially oxidative in function and some serve to destroy small molecules. Since none of the nuclear enzymes have been isolated in a form sufficiently satisfactory to permit analysis of their protein structure, it is not possible to answer the intriguing question of whether they are the same enzymes as those present in the cytoplasm. The lack of clarity of a nuclear function for such enzymes as catalase, peroxidase, and others is, of course, part of the overall uncertainty with regard to the role of these enzymes in the cell.

### References


1. Allfrey, V. G.: Studies of energy-yielding reactions in isolated cell nuclei. *Exptl. Cell Res. Suppl.* **9**: 418-429 (1963).
2. Allfrey, V. G., Stern, H., Mirsky, A. E., and Saetren, H.: The isolation of cell nuclei in non-aqueous media. *J. Gen. Physiol.* **35**: 529-554 (1951).

2a. Ballard, P., and Williams-Ashman, H. G.: Isolation of a soluble RNA polymerase from rat testis. *Nature* **203**: 150-151 (1964).

3. Behrens, M.: Untersuchungen an isolierten Zell- und Gewebs-bestandteilen. I. Mitteilung: Isolierung von Zellkernen des Kalbshertzmuskels. *Z. Physiol. Chem.* **209**: 59-74 (1932).
4. Bessman, M. J., Lehman, I. R., Simms, E. S., and Kornberg, A.: Enzymatic synthesis of deoxyribonucleic acid. II. General properties of the reaction. *J. Biol. Chem.* **233**: 171-177 (1958).
5. Betel, I., and Klouwen, H. M.: Adenosine triphosphate synthesis in isolated rat-thymus nuclei. *Biochim. Biophys. Acta* **76**: 327-329 (1963).
6. Busch, H.: "An Introduction to the Biochemistry of the Cancer Cell." Academic Press, New York, 1962.
7. Busch, H., Byvoet, P., and Smetana, K.: The nucleolus of the cancer cell: A review. *Cancer Res.* **23**: 313-339 (1963).
8. Busch, H., and Starbuck, W. C.: Biochemistry of cancer. *Ann. Rev. Biochem.* **33**: 519-570 (1964).
9. Cairns, J.: The bacterial chromosome and its manner of replication as seen by radioautography. *J. Mol. Biol.* **6**: 208-213 (1963).
10. Chamberlin, M., and Berg, P.: Deoxyribonucleic acid-directed synthesis of ribonucleic acid by an enzyme from *Escherichia coli*. *Proc. Natl. Acad. Sci. U.S.* **48**: 81-94 (1962).

10a. Chamberlin, M., and Berg, P.: Mechanism of RNA polymerase action: Formation of DNA-RNA hybrids with single-stranded templates. *J. Mol. Biol.* **8**: 297-313 (1964).

11. Chauveau, J., Moulé, Y., and Rouiller, C.: Isolation of pure and unaltered

liver nuclei, morphology and biochemical composition. *Exptl. Cell Res.* **11**: 317-321 (1956).

12. de Duve, C.: The lysosome concept. *In* "Lysosomes," *Ciba Found. Symp.* (A. V. S. Reuck and M. P. Cameron, eds.), pp. 1-34. Little, Brown, Boston, 1963.
13. Dounce, A. L.: The isolation of nuclei from tumor cells. *Exptl. Cell Res. Suppl.* **9**: 126-143 (1963).
14. Felsenfeld, G., Sandeen, G., and von Hippel, P. H.: The destabilizing effect of ribonuclease on the helical DNA structure. *Proc. Natl. Acad. Sci. U.S.* **50**: 644-651 (1963).
15. Frenster, J. H.: Constraints on isolation of mammalian chromosomes. *Exptl. Cell Res. Suppl.* **9**: 235-238 (1963).
16. Frenster, J. H., Allfrey, V. G., and Mirsky, A. E.: Metabolism and morphology of ribonucleoprotein particles from the cell nucleus of lymphocytes. *Proc. Natl. Acad. Sci. U.S.* **46**: 432-444 (1960).

16a. Goldfischer, S., Essner, E., and Novikoff, A. B.: The localization of phosphatase activities at the level of ultrastructure. *J. Histochem. Cytochem.* **12**: 72-95 (1964).

17. Goldstein, L., Cailleau, R., and Crocker, T. T.: Nuclear-cytoplasmic relationships in human cells in tissue culture. II. The microscopic behavior of enucleate human cell fragments. *Exptl. Cell Res.* **19**: 332-342 (1960).
18. Goldstein, L., and Micou, J.: Nuclear-cytoplasmic relationships in human cells in tissue culture. III. Autoradiographic study of interrelation of nuclear and cytoplasmic ribonucleic acid. *J. Biophys. Biochem. Cytol.* **6**: 1-6 (1959).
19. Goldstein, L., and Micou, J.: On the primary site of nuclear RNA synthesis. *J. Biophys. Biochem. Cytol.* **6**: 301-304 (1959).
20. Goldstein, L., Micou, J., and Crocker, T. T.: Nuclear-cytoplasmic relationships in human cells in tissue culture. IV. A study of some aspects of nucleic acid and protein metabolism in enucleate cells. *Biochim. Biophys. Acta* **45**: 82-86 (1960).
21. Goldstein, L., and Plaut, W.: Direct evidence for nuclear synthesis of cytoplasmic ribose nucleic acid. *Proc. Natl. Acad. Sci. U.S.* **41**: 874-880 (1955).
22. Graham, A. F., and Rake, A. V.: RNA synthesis and turnover in mammalian cells propagated *in vitro*. *Ann. Rev. Microbiol.* **17**: 139-166 (1963).
23. Grav, E. D., Weissman, S. M., Richards, J., Bell, D., Keir, H. M., Smellie, R. M. S., and Davidson, J. N.: Studies on the biosynthesis of deoxyribonucleic acid by extracts of mammalian cells. V. Factors interfering with biosynthesis. *Biochim. Biophys. Acta* **45**: 111-120 (1960).
24. Gros, F.: Regulation of messenger-ribonucleic acid synthesis. *Biochem. J.* **90**: 21P (1964).
25. Harris, H.: Rapidly labelled ribonucleic acid in the cell nucleus. *Nature* **198**: 184-185 (1963).
26. Harris, H.: The breakdown of ribonucleic acid in the cell nucleus. *Proc. Roy. Soc.* **B158**: 79-87 (1963).
27. Harris, H., and Watts, J. W.: The relationship between nuclear and cytoplasmic ribonucleic acid. *Proc. Roy. Soc.* **B156**: 109-121 (1962).

28. Haruna, I., Nozu, K., Ohtaka, Y., and Spiegelman, S.: An RNA "replicase" induced by and selective for a viral RNA: Isolation and properties. *Proc. Natl. Acad. Sci. U.S.* **50**: 905-911 (1963).

29. Hogeboom, G. H., Schneider, W. C., and Striebich, M. J.: Cytochemical studies. V. On the isolation and biochemical properties of liver cell nuclei. *J. Biol. Chem.* **196**: 111-120 (1952).

30. Hogeboom, G. H., Schneider, W. C., and Striebich, M. J.: Localization and integration of cellular function. *Cancer Res.* **13**: 617-632 (1953).

31. Hurwitz, J.: RNA polymerase. *Methods Enzymol.* **6**: 23-27 (1963).

31a. Keir, H. M.: Stimulation and inhibition of deoxyribonucleic acid nucleotidyltransferase by oligodeoxyribonucleotides. *Biochem. J.* **85**: 265-276 (1962).

32. Keir, H. M., Smellie, R. M. S., and Siebert, G.: Intracellular location of DNA nucleotidyltransferase. *Nature* **196**: 752-754 (1962).

33. Keir, H. M., and Smith, M. J.: Characteristics of the DNA nucleotidyltransferase activity in non-aqueous type calfthymus nuclei. *Biochim. Biophys. Acta* **68**: 589-598 (1963).

34. Kimball, R. F., and Prescott, D. M.: Deoxyribonucleic acid synthesis and distribution during growth and amitosis of the macronucleus of *Euplotes. J. Protozool.* **9**: 88-92 (1962).

35. Krakow, J. S.: Ribonucleic acid polymerase of *Azobacter vinelandii*. III. Effect of polyamines. *Biochim. Biophys. Acta* **72**: 566-571 (1963).

36. Kuempel, P. L., and Pardee, A. B.: The cycle of bacterial duplication. *J. Cellular Comp. Physiol.* **62**, Suppl. 1: 15-30 (1963).

37. Lehman, I. R., Bessman, M. J., Simms, E. S., and Kornberg, A.: Enzymatic synthesis of deoxyribonucleic acid. I. Preparation of substrates and partial purification of an enzyme from *Escherichia coli. J. Biol. Chem.* **233**: 163-170 (1958).

38. Lehman, I. R., Zimmerman, S. B., Adler, J., Bessman, M. J., Simms, E. S., and Kornberg, A.: Enzymatic synthesis of deoxyribonucleic acid. V. Chemical composition of enzymatically synthesized deoxyribonucleic acid. *Proc. Natl. Acad. Sci. U.S.* **44**: 1191-1196 (1958).

39. Leslie, I.: Biochemistry of heredity. A general hypothesis. *Nature* **189**: 260-268 (1961).

40. Maggio, R., Siekevitz, P., and Palade, G. E.: Studies on isolated nuclei. I. Isolation and chemical characterization of a nuclear fraction from guinea pig liver. *J. Cell Biol.* **18**: 267-293 (1963).

41. Maggio, R., Siekevitz, P., and Palade, G. E.: Studies on isolated nuclei. II. Isolation and chemical characterization of nucleolar and nucleoplasmic subfractions. *J. Cell Biol.* **18**: 293-313 (1963).

42. Martin, S. J., England, H., Turkington, V., and Leslie, I.: Depolymerization of ribonucleic acid by enzymes in basic proteins from liver nuclei and ribosomes. *Biochem. J.* **89**: 327-334 (1963).

43. McEwen, B. S., Allfrey, V. G., and Mirsky, A. E.: Studies of energy-yielding reactions in thymus nuclei. I. Comparison of nuclear and mitochondrial phosphorylation. *J. Biol. Chem.* **238**: 758-766 (1963).

44. McEwen, B. S., Allfrey, V. G., and Mirsky, A. E.: Studies on energy-yielding

reactions in thymus nuclei. II. Pathways of aerobic carbohydrate catabolism. *J. Biol. Chem.* **238**: 2571-2578 (1963).

45. McEwen, B. S., Allfrey, V. G., and Mirsky, A. E.: Studies on energy-yielding reactions in thymus nuclei. III. Participation of glycolysis and the citric acid cycle in nuclear adenosine triphosphate synthesis. *J. Biol. Chem.* **238**: 2579-2586 (1963).

45a. Muramatsu, M., and Busch, H.: Studies on nucleolar RNA of the Walker 256 carcinosarcoma and the liver of the rat. *Cancer Res.* **24**: 1028-1034 (1964).

45b. Niwaguchi, T., and Strecker, H. J.: Energy production and pyrrolidonecarboxylic acid formation in rat liver nuclei. *Biochem. Biophys. Res. Commun.* **16**: 535-540 (1964).

46. Novikoff, A. B.: The validity of histochemical phosphatase methods on the intracellular level. *Science* **113**: 320-325 (1951).

47. Novikoff, A. B.: Histochemical demonstration of nuclear enzymes. *Exptl. Cell Res. Suppl.* **2**: 123-143 (1952).

47a. Okazaki, T., and Kornberg, A.: Enzymatic synthesis of deoxyribonucleic acid. XV. Purification and properties of a polymerase from *B. subtilis*. *J. Biol. Chem.* **239**: 259-268 (1964).

48. Penniall, R., Liu, S.-M., and Saunders, J. P.: Studies of phosphorus metabolism by isolated nuclei. I. *Biochim. Biophys. Acta* **76**: 170-172 (1963).

48a. Perry, R. P.: Role of the nucleolus in ribonucleic acid metabolism and other similar processes. *J. Natl. Cancer Inst. Monograph* **14**: 73-92 (1964).

49 Phillips, D. M. P., and Johns, E. W.: The chromatography of thymus histones and the demonstration of proteinase activity in the unfractionated preparations. *Biochem. J.* **71**: 17P-18P (1959).

50. Phillips, D. M. P., and Johns, E. W.: A study of the proteinase content and the chromatography of thymus histones. *Biochem. J.* **72**: 538-544 (1959).

51. Prescott, D. M., and Bender, M. A.: Synthesis of RNA and protein during mitosis in mammalian tissue culture cells. *Exptl. Cell Res.* **26**: 260-268 (1962).

52. Prescott, D. M., Bollum, F. J., and Kluss, B. C.: Is DNA polymerase a cytoplasmic enzyme? *J. Cell Biol.* **13**: 172-174 (1962).

52a. Richardson, C. C., Schildkraut, C. L., Aposhian, H. V., and Kornberg, A.: Enzymatic synthesis of deoxyribonucleic acid. XIV. Further purification and properties of deoxyribonucleic acid polymerase of *E. coli*. *J. Biol. Chem.* **239**: 222-232 (1964).

53. Ro, T. S., Muramatsu, M., and Busch, H.: Labeling of RNA of isolated nucleoli with UTP-$^{14}$C. *Biochem. Biophys. Res. Commun.* **14**: 149-155 (1964).

54. Roodyn, D. B.: A comparative account of methods for the isolation of nuclei. *In* "Methods of Separation of Subcellular Structural Components" (C. de Duve and J. K. Grant, eds.), pp. 20-36. Cambridge Univ. Press, London and New York, 1963.

55. Scherrer, K., and Darnell, J. E.: Sedimentation characteristics of rapidly labelled RNA from HeLa cells. *Biochem. Biophys. Res. Commun.* **7**: 486-489 (1962).

55a. Schildkraut, C. L., Richardson, C. C., and Kornberg, A.: Enzymic synthesis of deoxyribonucleic acid. XVII. Some unusual physical properties of the product primed by native DNA templates. *J. Mol. Biol.* **9**: 24-45 (1964).

56. Schneider, W. C.: Intracellular distributions of enzymes. III. Oxidation of octanoid acid by rat liver fractions. *J. Biol. Chem.* **176**: 259-266 (1948).

57. Schneider, W. C.: Enzymes of cancer nuclei. *Exptl. Cell Res. Suppl.* **9**: 430-434 (1963).

58. Schneider, W. C., and Hogeboom, G. H.: Biochemistry of cellular particles. *Ann. Rev. Biochem.* **25**: 201-224 (1956).

59. Siebert, G.: Enzyme and substrates of glycolysis in isolated cell nuclei. *Biochem.* **334**: 369-387 (1961).

60. Siebert, G.: Enzymes of cancer nuclei. *Exptl. Cell Res. Suppl.* **9**: 389-417 (1963).

61. Siebert, G., Bassler, K. H., Hannover, R., Adloff, E., and Beyer, R.: Enzymatic activity in isolated nuclei in the presence of mitotic activity. *Biochem. Z.* **334**: 388-400 (1961).

62. Siebert, G., and Hannover, R.: Lactate dehydrogenase studies on isolated cell nuclei. *Biochem. Z.* **339**: 162-174 (1963).

62a. Siebert, G., and Humphrey, G. B.: Enzymology of the nucleus. *Advan. Enzymol.* in press (1965).

63. Siebert, G., Lang, K., Muller, L., Lucius, S., Muller, E., and Kuhle, E.: Metabolic processes in isolated cell nuclei. VII. Enzymes of amino acid and peptide metabolism in nuclei. *Biochem. Z.* **323**: 532-545 (1953).

64. Smellie, R. M. S.: Some studies on the enzymes of DNA biosynthesis. *Exptl. Cell Res. Suppl.* **9**: 245-258 (1963).

65. Smellie, R. M. S., and Eason, R.: Studies on the intracellular location of deoxyribonucleic acid "polymerase." *Biochem. J.* **80**: 39P (1961).

66. Smith, M. J., and Keir, H. M.: DNA nucleotidyltransferase in nuclei and cytoplasm prepared from thymus tissue in nonaqueous media. *Biochim. Biophys. Acta* **68**: 578-588 (1963).

67. Stern, H., Allfrey, V., Mirsky, A. E., and Saetren, H.: Some enzymes of isolated nuclei. *J. Gen. Physiol.* **35**: 559-578 (1951).

68. Stern, H., and Mirsky, A. E.: Soluble enzymes of nuclei isolated in sucrose and non-aqueous media. *J. Gen. Physiol.* **37**: 177-187 (1953).

69. Tabor, H., and Tabor, C. W.: Spermidine, spermine and related amines. *Pharm. Rev.* **16**: 245-300 (1964).

69a. Traub, A., Kaufmann, E., and Ginzburg-Tietz, Y.: Studies on nuclear ribosomes. I. Association of DPN-Pyrophosphorylase with nuclear ribosomes in normal and neoplastic tissues. *Exptl. Cell Res.* **34**: 371-383 (1964).

69b. Villalobos, J. G., Steele, W. J., and Busch, H.: Effects of thioacetamide on labeling of RNA of isolated nucleoli *in vitro*. *Biochim. Biophys. Acta* **91**: 233-238 (1964).

70. Weiss, S. B.: Enzymatic incorporation of ribonucleoside triphosphate into the interpolynucleotide linkages of ribonucleic acid. *Proc. Natl. Acad. Sci. U.S.* **46**: 1020-1030 (1960).

# Author Index

Numbers in parentheses are reference numbers and indicate that an author's work is referred to although his name is not cited in the text. Numbers in italic show the page on which the complete reference is listed.

## A



## B

## C



## D

## N



## O

## P



## R

## S

## T

## U



## V



## W

# Subject Index

## F



## G



## H